W9-CSU-003

CARPENTRY FOR BUILDING CONSTRUCTION

BY

U.S. DEPARTMENT
OF THE ARMY

DOVER PUBLICATIONS, INC., New York

Published in Canada by General Publishing Company, Ltd., 30 Lesmill Road, Don Mills, Toronto, Ontario.

Published in the United Kingdom by Constable and Company, Ltd., 10 Orange Street, London WC2H 7EG.

This Dover edition, first published in 1989, is an unabridged, unaltered republication of Technical Manual (TM) No. 5-551B, *Carpenter,* originally published at the U.S. Government Printing Office, Washington, D.C., on July 19, 1971, for Headquarters, Department of the Army. A consecutive pagination, enclosed in parentheses, has been added to the original serial pagination.

Manufactured in the United States of America
Dover Publications, Inc., 31 East 2nd Street, Mineola, N.Y. 11501

Library of Congress Cataloging-in-Publication Data

Carpenter.
    Carpentry for building construction / by U.S. Department of the Army.
        p.   cm.
    Reprint. Originally published: Carpenter. Washington, D.C. : U.S. G.P.O., 1971. Originally published in series: Technical manual /Department of the Army ; TM5-551B.
    Bibliography: p.
    Includes index.
    ISBN 0-486-26071-2
    1. Carpentry. I. United States. Dept. of the Army. II. Title.
TH5606.C37 1989
624.1'84—dc20   89-34046
                                                                              CIP

CONTENTS

CHAPTER 1

INTRODUCTION

1–1. Purpose and Scope

This manual provides guidance and reference data needed in the training of the carpenter in his military occupational specialty (MOS) 51B, a part of MOS career group 51. It covers only the technical phases of that skill. It assumes that he is generally familiar with the tools used by the construction and utilities worker (MOS 51A), also a part of career group 51. This manual provides information on construction print reading, construction techniques, the preparation and use of bills of materials, building layout, forming for concrete, frame and finish carpentry, and bridge and wharf building, and the materials used in their construction. The entire pattern for soldiers in MOS career group 51 is described in AR 611–201.

1–2. Comments

Users of this manual are encouraged to submit recommended changes to improve the manual. Comments should be keyed to the specific paragraph in which the change is recommended. Reasons will be provided for each comment to insure complete evaluation. Comments should be prepared using DA Form 2028 (Recommended Changes to Publications) and forwarded directly to the Commandant, US Army Engineer School, Fort Belvoir, Va., 22060.

CHAPTER 2

CONSTRUCTION PRINT READING

Section I. WORKING DRAWINGS

2-1. Introduction

a. Working drawings plus specifications are the main sources of information for supervisors and technicians responsible for the actual work of construction. The construction working drawing gives a complete graphic description of the structure to be erected, the construction site, the materials to be used, and the construction method to be followed. Most construction drawings consist of orthographic views (right angles and perpendicular lines). A set of working drawings includes both general and detail drawings. General drawings consist of plans and elevations, while detail drawings consist of sections and detail views.

b. Site plans, elevations, floor plans, sections, and details are described in this section together with the most common architectural symbols and material conventions in military use.

2-2. Architectural Symbols and Material Conventions

a. Architectural Symbols. Architectural symbols on construction plans show the type and location of doors, windows, and other features. They have the same general shape as the feature itself and show any motion that is supposed to occur. Figure 2-1 shows several of these symbols.

b. Material Conventions. Material conventions are symbols that show the type of material used in the structure. Appendix B illustrates those for the more common types of materials. The symbol selected normally represents the material in some way where possible. For example, the symbol for wood shows the grains in the wood. It is not always possible to use a common characteristic of the material for the symbol. The carpenter should know all these symbols for materials to help him read a construction print. A symbol should always be checked if there is any doubt about its meaning.

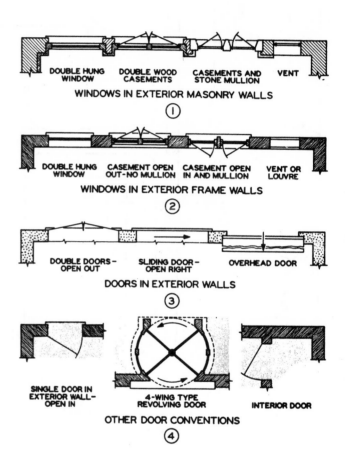

Figure 2-1. Window, door, and wall symbols.

2-3. Site Plans

a. A site plan (also called plot plan) shows all necessary property lines and locations, contours and profiles, building lines, location of structures to be constructed, existing structures, approaches, finished grades, existing and new utilities such as sewer, water, gas, and the like. Figure 2-2 shows a typical site plan. Appropriate outlines show the location of the new facility. The site plan has a north-pointing arrow to indicate site north (not magnetic north). Each facility has a number (or code letter) to identify it in the schedule

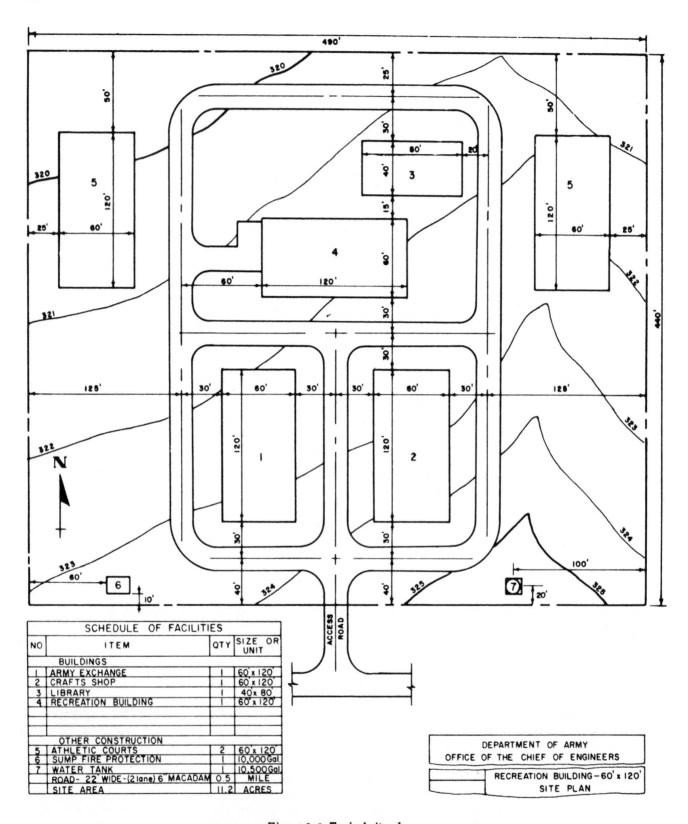

Figure 2-2. Typical site plan.

SCHEDULE OF FACILITIES

NO	ITEM	QTY	SIZE OR UNIT
	BUILDINGS		
1	ARMY EXCHANGE	1	60'x120'
2	CRAFTS SHOP	1	60'x120'
3	LIBRARY	1	40'x80'
4	RECREATION BUILDING	1	60'x120'
	OTHER CONSTRUCTION		
5	ATHLETIC COURTS	2	60'x120'
6	SUMP FIRE PROTECTION	1	10,000 Gal.
7	WATER TANK	1	10,500 Gal
	ROAD-22' WIDE-(2 lane) 6" MACADAM	0.5	MILE
	SITE AREA	11.2	ACRES

DEPARTMENT OF ARMY
OFFICE OF THE CHIEF OF ENGINEERS

RECREATION BUILDING-60'x120'
SITE PLAN

of facilities. The contour lines show the elevation of the earth surfaces; all points on a contour have the same elevation. Distances are given between principal details and reference lines. (The coordinate reference lines on figure 2-2 are centerlines of the roads surrounding the area.) All distances in a plan view simply give the horizontal measurement between two points and do not show terrain irregularities. The sizes of proposed facilities are given in the schedule of facilities.

b. Examine the site plan shown in figure 2–2 to see what information can be obtained from it. For example, the contour lines show that the ground surface of the site area slopes. The plan locates and identifies each facility. Most of the facilities are spaced at least 60 feet apart, while the library (facility No. 3) and the recreation building (facility No. 4) must be only 15 feet apart. Besides being the smallest of the four buildings, the library is closest to the road; that is, the east wall of the library is 20 feet from the centerline of the road, while the other buildings are 30 or 60 feet from the centerline.

2–4. Elevations

a. Elevations are drawings that show the front, rear, or side view of a building or structure. Sample elevation views are given in figure 2–3.

Construction materials may be shown on the elevation. It may also show the ground level surrounding the structure, called the grade. When more than one view is shown on a drawing sheet, each view is given a title. If any view has a scale different from that shown in the title block, the scale is given beneath the title of that view.

b. The centerline symbol of alternate long and short dashes in an elevation shows finished floor lines. Foundations below the grade line are shown by the hidden line symbol of short, evenly spaced dashes. Note in figure 2–3 that the footings are shown below grade.

c. Elevations show the locations and kind of doors and windows. Each different type window shown in the elevations is marked (in figure 2–3, the three types of windows are marked W–1, W–2, and W–3). These identifying marks refer to a particular size window whose dimensions are given in a table known as the window schedule. In some cases, the rough opening dimensions of

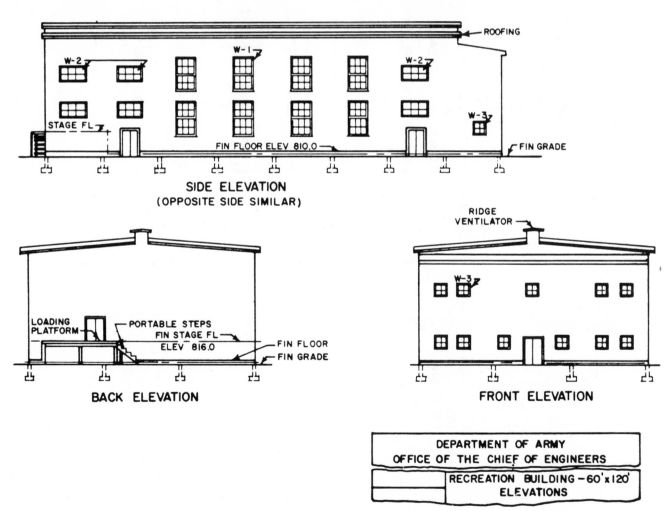

Figure 2–3. Elevation views.

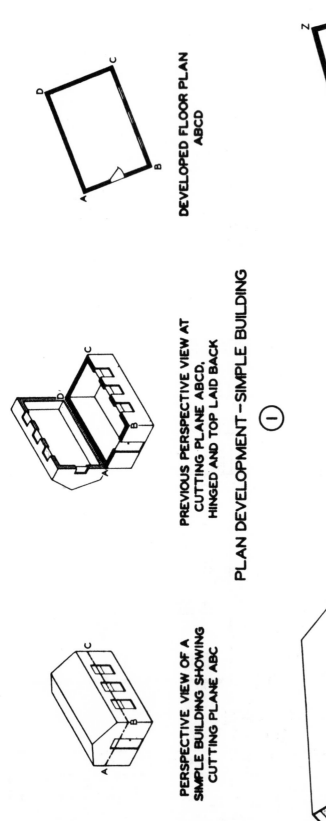

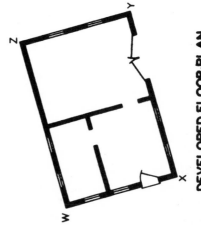

DEVELOPED FLOOR PLAN
ABCD

DEVELOPED FLOOR-PLAN
WXYZ

PREVIOUS PERSPECTIVE VIEW AT
CUTTING PLANE ABCD,
HINGED AND TOP LAID BACK

PREVIOUS PERSPECTIVE VIEW AT
CUTTING PLANE WXYZ,
TOP REMOVED

PLAN DEVELOPMENT–SIMPLE BUILDING

①

PLAN DEVELOPMENT–TYPICAL T.O. BUILDING

②

PERSPECTIVE VIEW OF A
SIMPLE BUILDING SHOWING
CUTTING PLANE ABC

PERSPECTIVE VIEW OF A
TYPICAL T/O BUILDING SHOWING
CUTTING PLANE WXY

Figure 2–4. Floor plan development.

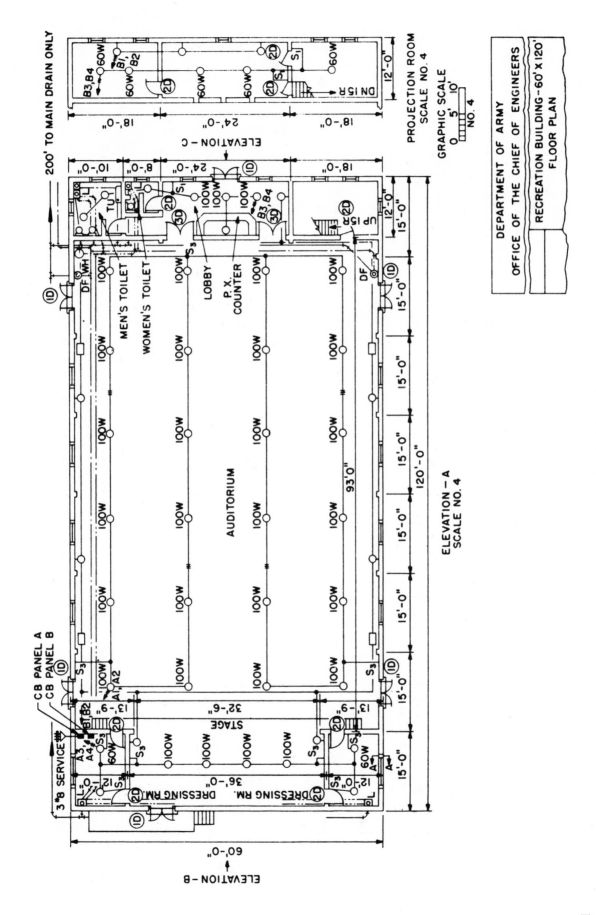

Figure 2-5. Typical floor plan.

windows are given on the drawing. Note that the recreation building shown in figure 2–3 has two double doors on each side and a double door at each end. The elevation also shows that at the end of the building with loading platform, the door is at the level of the stage floor and all the other doors are at grade level.

2–5. Floor Plans

a. A floor plan is a cross-sectional view of a building. The horizontal cut crosses all openings regardless of their height from the floor. The development of a floor plan is shown in figure 2–4. Note that a floor plan shows the outside shape of the building; the arrangement, size, and shape of the rooms; the type of materials; and the length, thickness, and character of the building walls at a particular floor. A floor plan also includes the type, width, and location of the doors and windows; the types and locations of utility installations; and the location of stairways. A typical floor plan is shown in figure 2–5.

b. Read the floor plan shown in figure 2–5 and note the features of the recreation building.

Basically, the lines with small circles show wiring for electrical outlets; appropriate symbols show the plumbing fixtures. These features are important to the carpenter from the standpoint of coordination. He may have to make special provisions, at various stages of construction, for the placement of electrical or plumbing fixtures. These provisions should be studied on the floor plan and coordinated with the electrician, plumber, and foreman.

c. Figure 2–6 shows how a stairway is drawn in a plan and how riser-tread information is given. The symbol shows the direction of the stairs from the floor shown in the plan and the amount of risers in the run. For example, 17 DN followed by an arrow means that there are 17 risers in the run of stairs going from the floor shown on the plan to the floor below in the direction indicated by the arrow. The riser-tread diagram provides height and width information. The standard for the riser, or height from step-to-step, is from 6 1/2 to 7 1/2 inches. The tread width is usually such that the sum of riser and tread is about 18 inches (a 7-inch riser and 11-

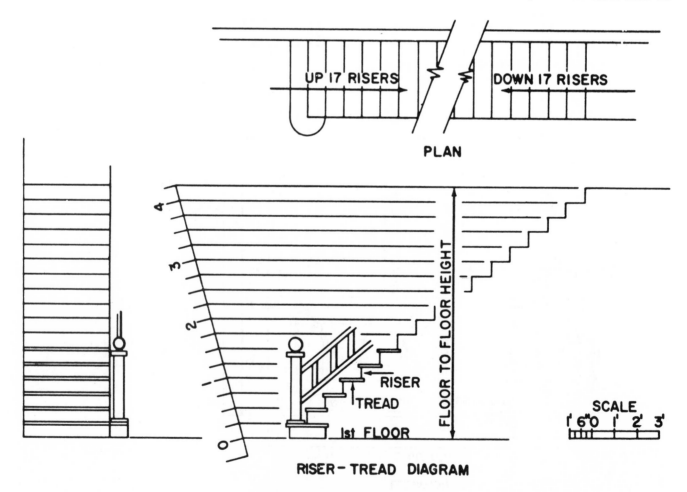

Figure 2–6. Stairway and steps.

inch tread is standard). On the plan, the distance between the riser lines is the width of the tread.

d. By examining the floor plan (fig. 2–5) it is seen that the interior of the building will consist of an auditorium, a lobby with a P.X. counter, a men's toilet, a women's toilet, a projection room on a second level above the lobby, two dressing rooms, and a stage. The stage may not be apparent but, by noting the steps adjacent to each dressing room, it can be seen that there is a change in elevation. The elevation view, as in figure 2–3, will show the stage and its elevation. The plan gives the dimensions of the areas specified. Note that all building entrances and/or exit doors are the same type (1D) and that all windows are the double-hung type. All interior single doors (2D) are the same and two double doors (3D) open into the lobby from the auditorium. The projection room will be reached via a 15-riser stairway located in a 12- by 18-foot room. Entrances to this room will be from the auditorium through a single door opening into the room. At the top of the stairway, a single door opens into the projection room. The wall of the projection room that faces the stage (inside wall) has three openings. Note that no windows are shown for the sides of the building where the projection room is located, but are shown at the main level.

e. The symbols shown in figure 2–7 are typical representations of exterior and interior walls. Note how the material conventions are used in the makeup of the symbols for masonry, brick, and concrete walls. The carpenter should become familiar with these symbols, which can be found in appendix B.

2–6. Sections
   a. A section shows how a structure looks when

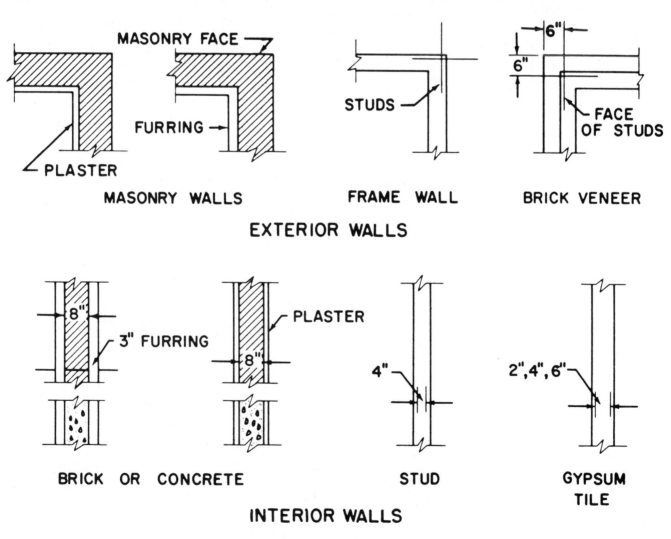

Figure 2–7. Typical wall symbols.

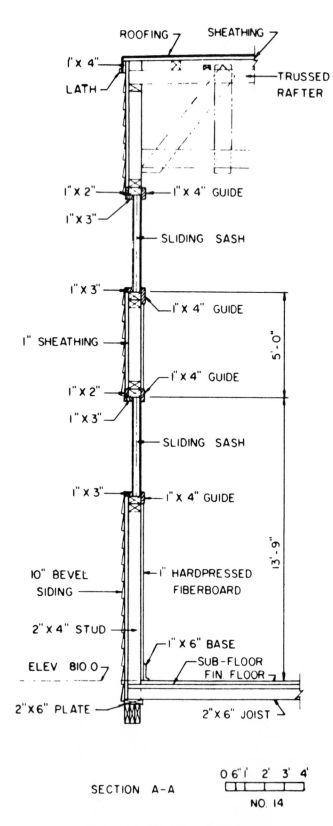

SECTION A-A

NO. 14

Figure 2-8. Typical wall section.

EXTERIOR DOOR DETAILS

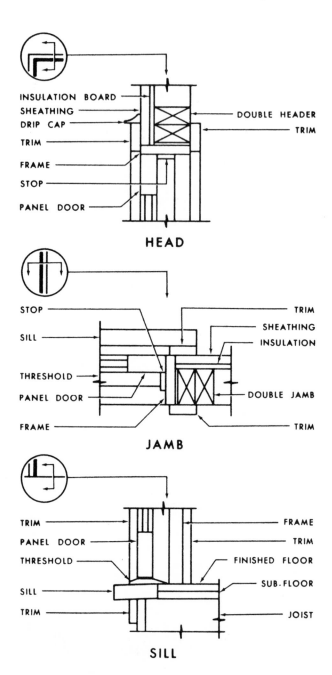

Figure 2-9. Typical door details.

cut vertically by a cutting plane. It is drawn to a large scale showing details of a particular construction feature that cannot be given in the general drawing. The section provides information on height, materials, fastening and support systems, and concealed features.

b. Of primary importance to construction supervisors and to the craftsmen who do the actual building are the wall sections. These show the construction of the wall as well as the way in which structural members and other features are joined to it. Wall sections extend vertically from the foundation bed to the roof. A typical wall

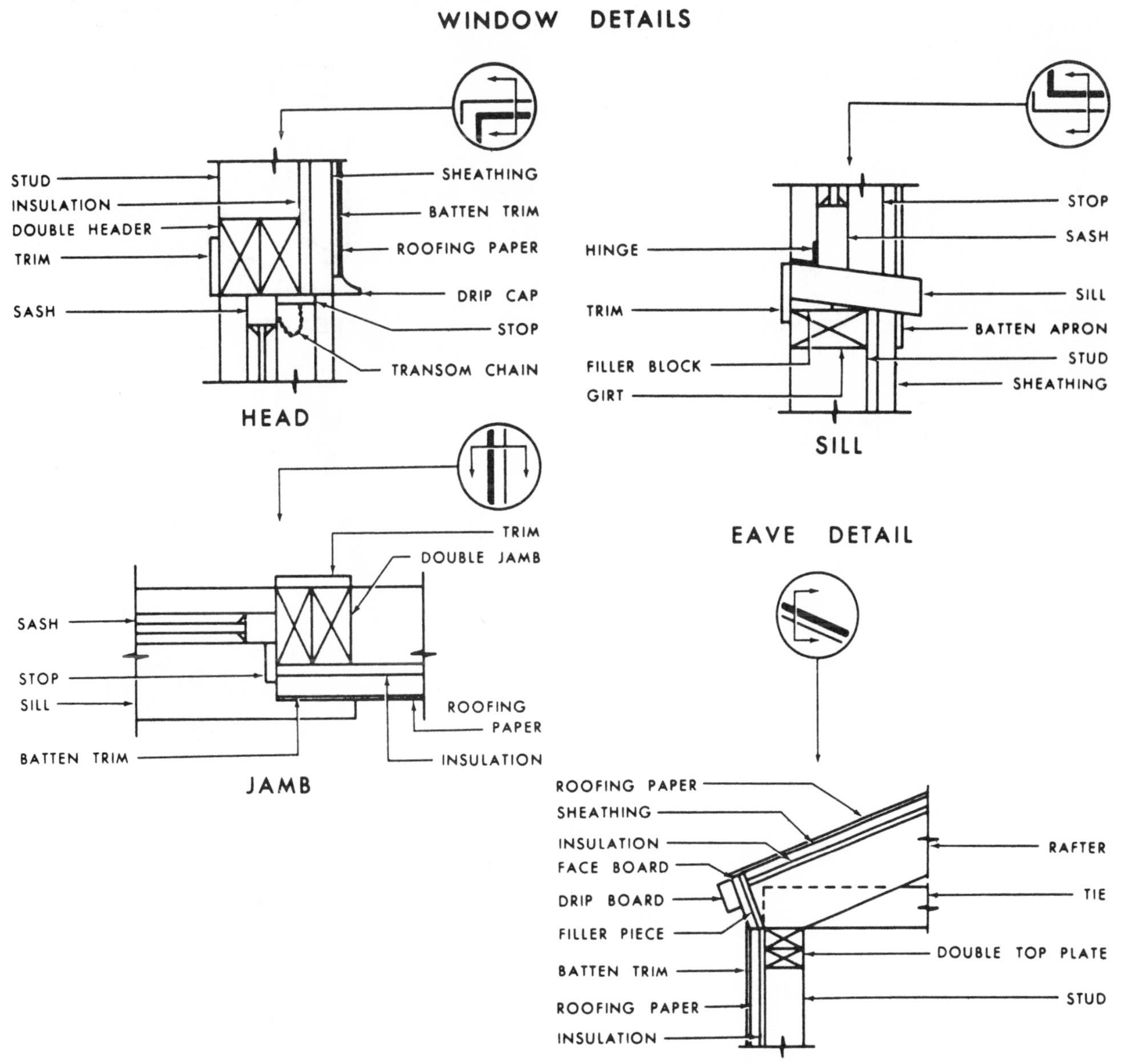

WINDOW DETAILS

HEAD

STUD
INSULATION
DOUBLE HEADER
TRIM
SASH

SHEATHING
BATTEN TRIM
ROOFING PAPER
DRIP CAP
STOP
TRANSOM CHAIN

SILL

HINGE
TRIM
FILLER BLOCK
GIRT

STOP
SASH
SILL
BATTEN APRON
STUD
SHEATHING

JAMB

SASH
STOP
SILL
BATTEN TRIM

TRIM
DOUBLE JAMB
ROOFING PAPER
INSULATION

EAVE DETAIL

ROOFING PAPER
SHEATHING
INSULATION
FACE BOARD
DRIP BOARD
FILLER PIECE
BATTEN TRIM
ROOFING PAPER
INSULATION

RAFTER
TIE
DOUBLE TOP PLATE
STUD

Figure 2–10. Typical window and eave details.

section with the parts identified by name and/or size is illustrated in figure 2–8.

2–7. Details
Details are large scale drawings which show features that do not appear (or appear on too small a scale) on the plans, elevations, and sections. Details do not have a cutting-plane indication, but are simply noted by a code. The construction of doors, windows, and eaves is usually shown in detail drawings. Figure 2–9 shows some typical door framing details and figure 2–10 shows that of window wood framing and an eave detail for a simple type of cornice. Other details which are customarily shown are sills, girder and joist connections, and stairways.

Section II. LIGHT AND HEAVY WOOD FRAMING

2–8. Light Wood Framing
Framing is the rough timberwork of a building. It includes exterior walls, flooring, roofing, beams, trusses, partitions, and ceilings. Working prints for theater of operations type buildings usually show details of all framing. Light framing is used in barracks, bathhouses, administration buildings, light shop buildings, hospital build-

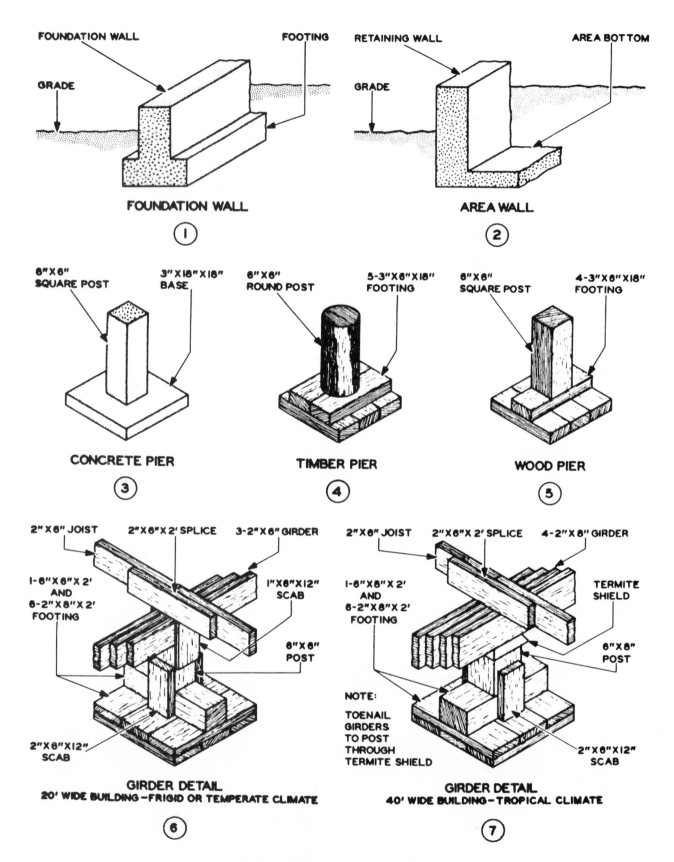

Figure 2–11. Typical foundation walls, piers,
footings, and girder details.

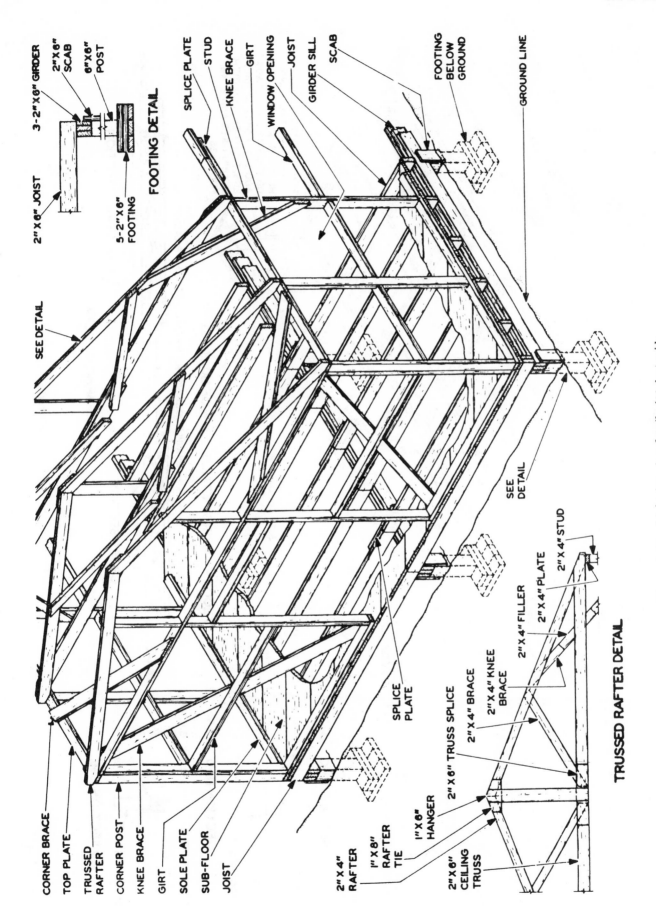

FOOTING DETAIL

2"X6" JOIST

3-2"X6" GIRDER
2"X6" SCAB
6"X6" POST

5-2"X6" FOOTING

SPLICE PLATE
STUD
KNEE BRACE
GIRT
WINDOW OPENING
JOIST
GIRDER SILL
SCAB

FOOTING BELOW GROUND

GROUND LINE

SEE DETAIL

SEE DETAIL

CORNER BRACE
TOP PLATE
TRUSSED RAFTER
CORNER POST
KNEE BRACE
GIRT
SOLE PLATE
SUB-FLOOR
JOIST

SPLICE PLATE

2"X6" TRUSS SPLICE
I"X8" RAFTER TIE
I"X6" HANGER
2"X8" CEILING TRUSS

2"X4" RAFTER

2"X4" BRACE
2"X4" KNEE BRACE
2"X4" FILLER
2"X4" PLATE
2"X4" STUD

TRUSSED RAFTER DETAIL

Figure 2–12. Light framing details (20-foot-wide building).

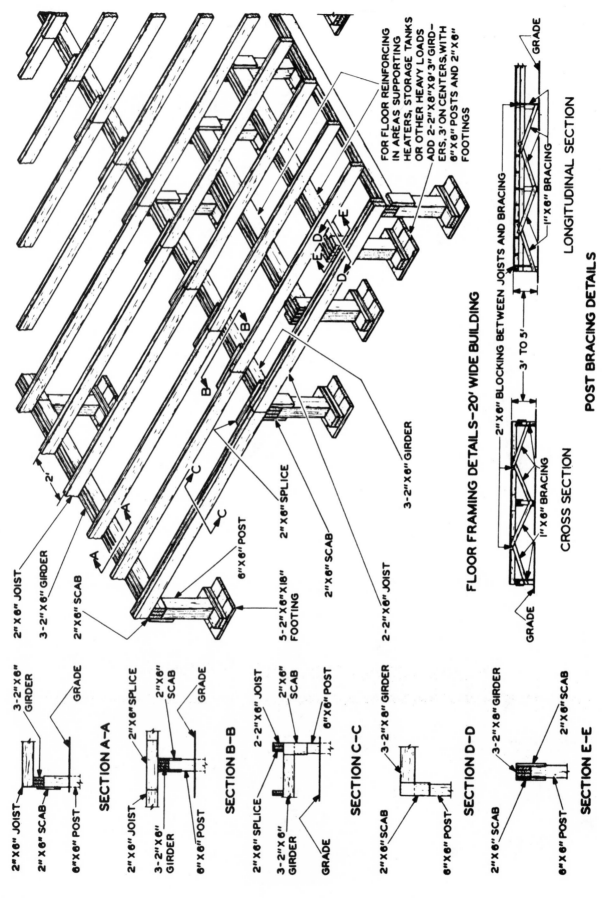

2"x6" JOIST

3-2"x6" GIRDER

2"x6" SCAB

2'

FOR FLOOR REINFORCING IN AREAS SUPPORTING HEATERS, STORAGE TANKS OR OTHER HEAVY LOADS ADD 2-2"x8"x9'3" GIRDERS, 3' ON CENTERS, WITH 6"x6" POSTS AND 2"x6" FOOTINGS

3-2"x6" GIRDER

2"x6" JOIST

2-2"x6" JOIST

2"x6" SPLICE

6"x6" POST

2"x6" SCAB

5-2"x6"x18" FOOTING

2"x6" SCAB

FLOOR FRAMING DETAILS–20' WIDE BUILDING

2"x6" BLOCKING BETWEEN JOISTS AND BRACING

GRADE

GRADE

I"X6" BRACING

LONGITUDINAL SECTION

3' TO 5'

I"X6" BRACING

GRADE

GRADE

CROSS SECTION

POST BRACING DETAILS

Figure 2–13. Floor framing details.

2"x6" JOIST

3-2"x6" GIRDER

GRADE

2"x6" SCAB

6"x6" POST

SECTION A–A

2"x6" JOIST

2"x6" SPLICE

2"x6" SCAB

GRADE

3-2"x6" GIRDER

6"x6" POST

SECTION B–B

2"x6" SPLICE

2-2"x6" JOIST

2"x6" SCAB

6"x6" POST

3-2"x6" GIRDER

GRADE

SECTION C–C

3-2"x6" GIRDER

2"x6" SCAB

6"x6" POST

SECTION D–D

3-2"x6" GIRDER

2"x6" SCAB

6"x6" POST

SECTION E–E

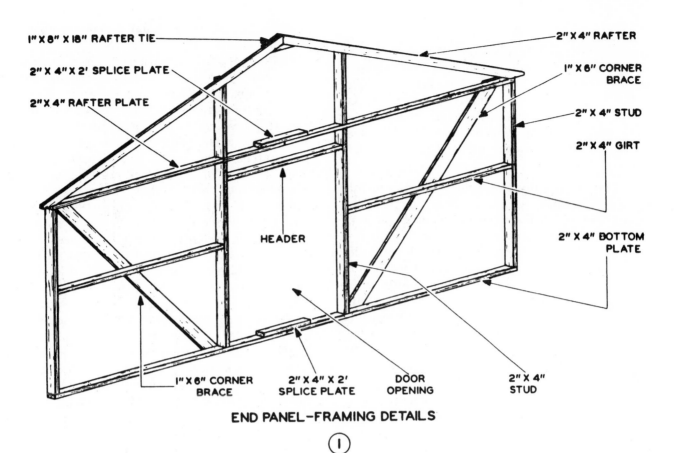

1" X 8" X 18" RAFTER TIE

2" X 4" X 2' SPLICE PLATE

2" X 4" RAFTER PLATE

2" X 4" RAFTER

1" X 6" CORNER BRACE

2" X 4" STUD

2" X 4" GIRT

HEADER

2" X 4" BOTTOM PLATE

1" X 6" CORNER BRACE

2" X 4" X 2' SPLICE PLATE

DOOR OPENING

2" X 4" STUD

END PANEL—FRAMING DETAILS

(1)

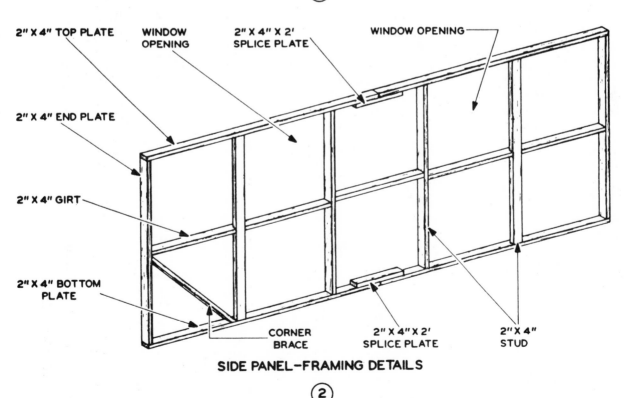

2" X 4" TOP PLATE

WINDOW OPENING

2" X 4" X 2' SPLICE PLATE

WINDOW OPENING

2" X 4" END PLATE

2" X 4" GIRT

2" X 4" BOTTOM PLATE

CORNER BRACE

2" X 4" X 2' SPLICE PLATE

2" X 4" STUD

SIDE PANEL—FRAMING DETAILS

(2)

Figure 2-14. Typical wall panels—framing details.

ings, and similar structures.

a. The types of foundation walls, footings, and girder details normally used in standard theater of operations type construction are shown in figure 2–11. The various details for overall framing of a 20-foot-wide building showing ground level and including window openings, braces, splices, and nomenclature of framing are shown in figure 2–12.

b. Figure 2–13 illustrates floor framing details showing footings, posts, girders, joists, reinforced section of floor for heavy loads, section views covering makeup of certain sections, scabs for joining girders to posts, and post bracing details as placed for cross sections and longitudinal sections. On a construction print the type of footings and size of the various members are shown. In some cases the lengths are given while in others the bill of materials which accompanies the print specifies the required lengths of the various members.

c. Wall framing details for end panels are shown in ①, figure 2–14. The height of panels is usually shown and from this height the length of wall studs is determined by deducting the thickness of the top or rafter plate and the bottom plate. The space between studs is given in the drawing as well as height of girt from bottom plate, type of door opening, if any, and window opening. Details for side panels, ②, figure 2–14, cover the same type of information as listed for end panels. For window openings, the details specify whether the window is hinged to swing in or out or whether it is to be a sliding panel. Studs placed next to window openings may be

placed either on edge or flat depending upon the type of window used.

d. The makeup of various trussed rafters is shown in figure 2–14. A 40-foot trussed rafter showing a partition bearing in the center is shown in ①, figure 2–15. This figure shows the splices required, bracing details, stud and top plate at one end of rafter, and size of members. The typical 20-foot truss rafter is shown in ②, figure 2–15. The use of filler blocks to keep the brace members in a vertical plane is needed since the rafter and bottom chord are nailed together rather than spliced. The rafter tie is placed on the opposite side from the vertical brace. Usually the splice plate for the bottom chord, if one is needed, is placed on the side on which it is planned to nail the rafters so that it can also serve as a filler block. A modified truss rafter is shown in ③, figure 2–15. This type of truss is used only when specified in plans for certain construction. It will not be used in areas subject to high wind velocities or moderate to heavy snowfall. In this type of trussed rafter, the bottom chord is placed on the rafters at a height above the top plate.

2–9. Heavy Wood Framing

Heavy wood framing consists of framing members at least 6 inches in dimension (timber construction). Examples of this type of framing can be found in heavy roof trusses, timber trestle bridges, and wharfs. The major differences between light and heavy framing are the size of timber used and the types of fasteners used. Fasteners for both light and heavy framing will be covered in a later chapter. Figure 2–16 shows the framing details for a heavy roof truss.

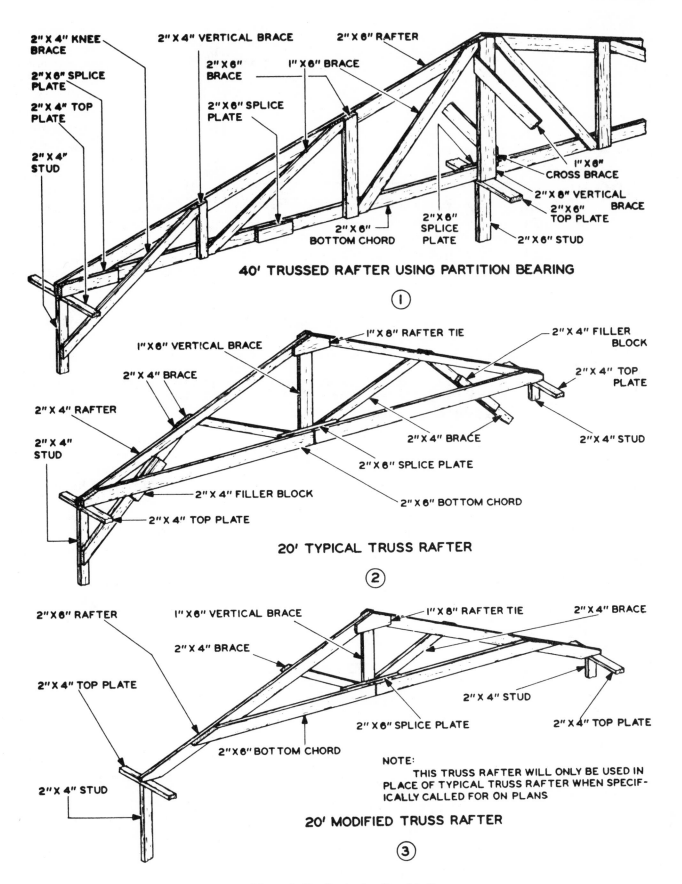

2" X 4" KNEE BRACE

2" X 4" VERTICAL BRACE

2" X 6" RAFTER

2" X 6" SPLICE PLATE

2" X 6" BRACE

1" X 6" BRACE

2" X 4" TOP PLATE

2" X 6" SPLICE PLATE

2" X 4" STUD

1" X 6" CROSS BRACE

2" X 8" VERTICAL BRACE

2" X 6" TOP PLATE

2" X 6" BOTTOM CHORD

2" X 6" SPLICE PLATE

2" X 6" STUD

40' TRUSSED RAFTER USING PARTITION BEARING

①

1" X 6" VERTICAL BRACE

1" X 8" RAFTER TIE

2" X 4" FILLER BLOCK

2" X 4" BRACE

2" X 4" TOP PLATE

2" X 4" RAFTER

2" X 4" BRACE

2" X 4" STUD

2" X 4" STUD

2" X 6" SPLICE PLATE

2" X 4" FILLER BLOCK

2" X 6" BOTTOM CHORD

2" X 4" TOP PLATE

20' TYPICAL TRUSS RAFTER

②

2" X 6" RAFTER

1" X 6" VERTICAL BRACE

1" X 8" RAFTER TIE

2" X 4" BRACE

2" X 4" BRACE

2" X 4" TOP PLATE

2" X 4" STUD

2" X 6" SPLICE PLATE

2" X 4" TOP PLATE

2" X 6" BOTTOM CHORD

NOTE:
THIS TRUSS RAFTER WILL ONLY BE USED IN PLACE OF TYPICAL TRUSS RAFTER WHEN SPECIFICALLY CALLED FOR ON PLANS

2" X 4" STUD

20' MODIFIED TRUSS RAFTER

③

Figure 2–15. Trussed rafter details.

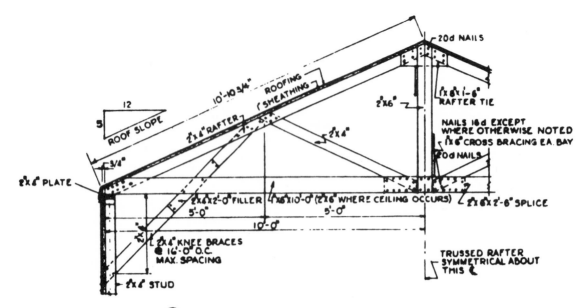

① TYPICAL LIGHT ROOF TRUSS

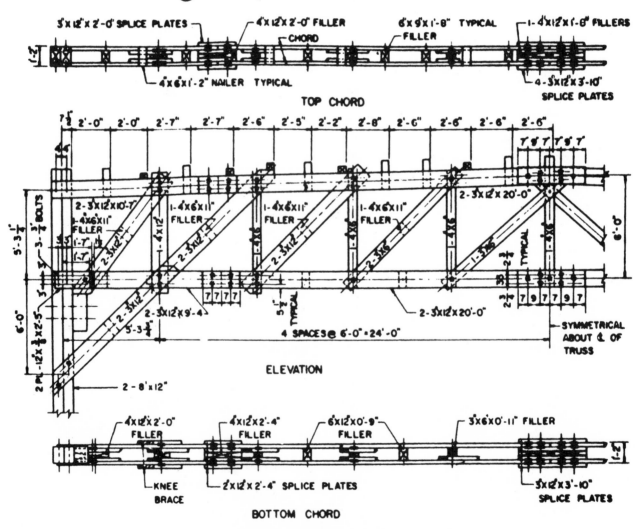

② TYPICAL HEAVY ROOF TRUSS

Figure 2–16. Typical heavy roof trusses.

CHAPTER 3

CONSTRUCTION TECHNIQUES

Section I. METHODS OF FRAME CONSTRUCTION

3–1. Methods

The method of erecting buildings directly affects the time, labor, and material needed. The methods may be divided into two types.

a. Built in Place. In this method each piece is separtely erected in its proper place.

b. Panel Method. In this method a complete section is built up as a unit and then set in the building in the proper place. It is used extensively because it makes for greater speed, better control over working parties and better use of manpower. It also allows the use of a standard list of sizes for each similar section; standard plans shown in TM 5–302 further simplify construction.

3–2. Factors Considered in Selection of Method to be Used

Construction planning permits an orderly series of operations and prevents duplication of effort and waste of material. Factors considered in planning are construction plant layout, distribution of material, number of skilled and semiskilled men available, and number and type of units to be constructed. From a list of the various separate operations required, an estimate of the total number of man-hours needed is made. This estimate forms the basis for determining the number and type of men needed and for organizing the erection crew or crews. Arrangements for assembling the necessary materials at the job site and for doing the preliminary cutting and assembly are made in advance.

3–3. Procedures, Built-In-Place Method

When using the built-in-place method, the officer in charge of construction divides the men into working parties, whose duties may be as follows:

a. Laying Out the Foundation.
b. Grading and Excavating.
c. Laying Out and Cutting Various Sizes of Material.

d. Carrying Material to the Cutting and Erecting Parties.

If a party completes its task before the building is completed, it is assigned a new task. For example, if the party laying out the foundation completes its work before erection of the building is begun, it is assigned a new duty such as cutting rafters. Parts are built in the following order: footings, piers, sills, joists, floor, soles, studs, plates, girts, rafters, bracing, siding, sheathing, roofing, doors, windows, steps, and inside finish (if used).

3–4. Procedures, Panel Method

The panel method (preassembly method) requires careful planning before the actual construction. Most Army buildings are now built by this method, as follows:

a. Before measuring and cutting lumber, the number and size of sections that are alike should be determined from the blueprint. This insures the correct numbers of each piece. The carpenter assigns a crew to cut and assemble one section. In most cases, a template is built as a guide for assembling the section. It should be built square, correct in size, and level.

b. The number and size of each piece in a section is given to the man in charge of the cutting party. The cutting party cuts the timber to the correct length with a handsaw or power saw. The length is measured by the use of square and tape. After one piece has been cut, it may be used

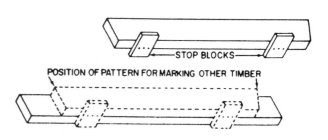

Figure 3–1. Marking a pattern.

as a pattern for marking the remaining pieces. The pattern is set up by nailing two blocks to the piece of correct size, one near each end, as shown in figure 3–1. These blocks act as stops to hold the pattern in place on the timber to be marked. Several cutting and assembling parties may be used at one time on different types of sections.

c. The plate and sole are placed in the template with the studs and girts between; then the door and window posts, if any, are placed (fig. 3–2).

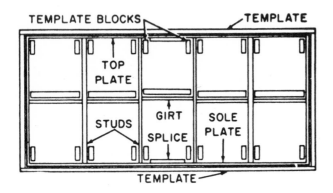

TEMPLATE BLOCKS

TEMPLATE

TOP PLATE

STUDS

GIRT SPLICE

SOLE PLATE

TEMPLATE

Figure 3–2. Template for framing walls.

The girts, sole, and plate are nailed to the studs with 16- or 20-penny nails. If insulation board is used, it and the wall sheathing are put on the section before it is taken out of the template. By applying the wall finish before raising the section, no scaffold or ladders need be used.

d. The erecting party sets the sections into place, braces them temporarily, and nails them together. The end section should be first, and it may be erected on graded earth. The sidewall sections are next and should be erected so as to keep the two walls even. The rafter party can then place the rafters on the walls. Parties should be set up as follows: layout party, cutting party, assembling party, carrying party, erecting party for sidewalls, erecting party for rafters, sheathing party, roofing party, and door-and-window party.

e. The preassembly method of erection may be used for all types of small buildings and large warehouses. When this method is used for large buildings, cranes are used to place sections too heavy to be handled by hand. Where machinery is used, caution in fastening the cable or rope avoids damaging the section.

Section II. LUMBER

3–5. Description

Lumber varies greatly in structural characteristics. A carpenter must learn about wood so that he can choose the most suitable material for a particular job. This section describes the various types of lumber for construction carpentry, its use, the standard sizes, and the methods of measuring lumber quantities in terms of board feet— the units in which it is procured and ordered.

a. *Size.* Lumber is usually sawed into standard size, length, width, and thickness. This permits uniformity in planning structures and in ordering materials. Table 3–1 lists the common widths and thicknesses of wood in rough and in dressed dimensions in the United States. Standards have been established for dimension differences between the quoted size of lumber and its standard sizes when dressed. Quoted sizes refer to dimensions prior to surfacing. These dimension differences must be taken into consideration. A good example of the dimension difference is the common 2 x 4. As may be seen in table 3–1, the familiar quoted size 2 x 4 is the rough or nominal dimension but the actual dressed size is 1 5/8 by 3 5/8 inches.

Table 3–1. Nominal Sizes and Standard Sizes of Lumber

Nominal size (in.)	American standard (in.)
1 x 3	25/32 x 2 5/8
1 x 4	25/32 x 3 5/8
1 x 6	25/32 x 5 5/8
1 x 8	25/32 x 7 1/2
1 x 10	25/32 x 9 1/2
1 x 12	25/32 x 11 1/2
2 x 4	1 5/8 x 3 5/8
2 x 6	1 5/8 x 5 5/8
2 x 8	1 5/8 x 7 1/2
2 x 10	1 5/8 x 9 1/2
2 x 12	1 5/8 x 11 1/2
3 x 8	2 5/8 x 7 1/2
3 x 10	2 5/8 x 9 1/2
3 x 12	2 5/8 x 11 1/2
4 x 12	3 5/8 x 11 1/2
4 x 16	3 5/8 x 15 1/2
6 x 12	5 1/2 x 11 1/2
6 x 16	5 1/2 x 15 1/2
6 x 18	5 1/2 x 17 1/2
8 x 16	7 1/2 x 15 1/2
8 x 20	7 1/2 x 19 1/2
8 x 24	7 1/2 x 23 1/2

b. *Grade.* Lumber as it comes from the sawmill is divided into three main classes: yard lumber, structural material, and factory and shop lumber. Only yard lumber will be considered here. It is classified on a quality basis into sizes, shapes, and qualities needed for ordinary construction and general building purposes. It is subdivided into classifications of select lumber and common lumber.

(1) *Select lumber.* Select lumber is of good appearance and finishing, and is identified by the following grade names:

(a) *Grade A.* Grade A is suitable for natural finishes and practically clear.

(b) *Grade B.* Grade B is suitable for natural finishes, of high quality, and generally clear.

(c) *Grade C.* Grade C is adapted to high quality paint finishes.

(d) *Grade D.* Grade D is suitable for paint finishes between higher finishing grades and common grades, and has somewhat the nature of both.

(2) *Common lumber.* Common lumber is suitable for general construction and utility purposes and has the following grade names:

(a) *No. 1 common.* No. 1 common is suitable for use without waste; it is sound and tight-knotted; and it may be considered watertight lumber.

(b) *No. 2 common.* No. 2 common is less restricted in quality than No. 1 but of the same general quality. It is used for framing, sheathing, and other structural forms where the stress or strain is not too great.

(c) *No. 3 common.* No. 3 common permits some waste with prevailing grade characteristics less than in No. 2. It is used for such rough work as footings, guardrails, and rough flooring.

(d) *No. 4 common.* No. 4 common permits waste, is of low quality, and may have coarse features, such as decay and holes. It is used for sheathing, subfloors, and roof boards in the cheaper types of construction, but its most important industrial outlet is for boxes and crates.

(e) *No. 5 common.* No. 5 common is not produced in some species of lumber. The only requirement is that it must be usable. It is used for boxes, crates, and dunnage.

3–6. Types and Standard Sizes of Lumber

a. *Frame.* The building frame is the wood form constructed to support the finished members of the structure. It includes posts, girders (beams), joists, subfloor, sole plates, girts, knee braces, and rafters. Softwoods are usually used for lightwood framing and all other construction carpentry described in this manual. Yard tim-

ber is cut into those standard sizes required for light framing, including 2 x 4, 2 x 6, 2 x 8, 2 x 10, 2 x 12 pieces and all other sizes required for framework, with the exception of those sizes classed as structural lumber: that is, 5 inches and thicker in least dimensions. Although 1 to No. 3 common are used for framing, No. 2 common is most often used and is therefore most often stocked and available in lumber yards in the common sizes used for various framing members. However, the size of lumber needed may vary with the design of the building (light frame, heavy frame) and the design of the particular member (beams or girders, for example). Such sizes are made from single pieces of structural timber, or built up as required. When lumber requirements are specified in a materials list, the symbols listed under the column "Type" (or "dressed") show the number of surfaces or edges of the lumber which have been planed. S1S shows that the piece has been surfaced on one side; S2S, surfaced on two sides; S1E, surfaced on one edge; S2E, surfaced on two edges; S1S1E, S1S2E, S2S1E, or S4S show combinations of surfaced edges and sides.

b. *Walls.* The exterior wall of a frame structure usually has three layers: sheathing, building paper, and siding. Sheathing lumber is 1 x 6 or 1 x 8 of No. 1, No. 2, or No. 3 common softwood, but No. 2 is most often used. It may be plain, tongued and grooved, or shiplapped. Siding lumber may be B and better, C, D, No. 1 or No. 2 grade, and varies in size from ½ x 4 to

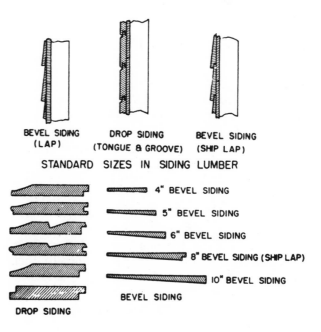

BEVEL SIDING (LAP) DROP SIDING (TONGUE & GROOVE) BEVEL SIDING (SHIP LAP)

STANDARD SIZES IN SIDING LUMBER

4" BEVEL SIDING
5" BEVEL SIDING
6" BEVEL SIDING
8" BEVEL SIDING (SHIP LAP)
10" BEVEL SIDING

BEVEL SIDING

DROP SIDING

Figure 3–3. Types of siding.

1 x 12. C grade is most often used. The two principal types of siding lumber are bevel and drop. Plain or clapboard siding is often used but has a tendency to warp and separate. For standard sizes in siding lumber, see figure 3–3. Siding is usually procured in bundles consisting of a given number of square feet per bundle.

3–7. Computation of Board Feet

a. Dimensions. Sizes of softwood or building construction lumber are standardized for convenience in ordering and handling. Building materials sizes run 8, 10, 12, 14, 16, 18, and 20 feet in length, 2, 4, 6, 8, 10, and 12 inches in width, and 1, 2, and 4 inches in thickness. The actual width and thickness of dressed lumber are considerably less than the standard, or quoted, width and thickness. For the relative difference between standard or nominal, and actual sizes of construction lumber, see table 3–1. Hardwoods, which have no standard lengths or widths, run 1/4, 1/2, 1, 1 1/4, 1 1/2, 2, 2 1/2, 3, and 4 inches in thickness. Plywoods are usually 4 x 8 and vary in thickness from 1/8 to 1 inch. Stock panels are usually available in widths of 48 inches and lengths varying in multiples of 16 inches up to 8 feet. Panel lengths run in 16-inch multiples because the accepted spacing for studs and joists is 16 inches. The amount of lumber required is measured in board feet. A board foot is a unit measure representing an area of 1 square foot and a thickness of 1 inch actual or nominal size. The number of board feet in a piece of lumber can be computed by the arithmetic method or by the tabular method.

b. Arithmetic Method. To determine the number of board feet in one or more pieces of lumber, the following formula is used:

$$\frac{\text{Pieces X Thickness in inches x Width in inches X Length in feet}}{12}$$

Example 1: Find the number of board feet in a piece of lumber 2 inches thick, 10 inches wide, and 6 feet long (fig. 3–4).

$$\frac{1 \times 2 \times 10 \times 6}{12} = 10 \text{ bd ft}$$

Example 2: Find the number of board feet in 10 pieces of lumber 2 inches thick, 10 inches wide, and 6 feet long.

$$\frac{10 \times 2 \times 10 \times 6}{12} = 100 \text{ bd ft}$$

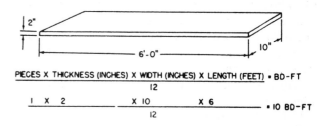

Figure 3–4. Board feet computation.

If all three dimensions are in inches, divide by 144 instead of 12.

Example: Find the number of board feet in a piece of lumber 2 inches thick, 10 inches wide, and 18 inches long.

$$\frac{1 \times 2 \times 10 \times 18}{144} = 2\frac{1}{2} \text{ bd ft}$$

c. Tabular Method. The standard essex board measure table (fig. 3–5), on the back of the blade of the framing square, is a quick aid in computing board feet. In using the board measure table, all computations are made on the basis of 1-inch thickness. The inch markings along the outer edge of the blade represent the width of a board 1 inch thick. The third dimension, length, is provided in the vertical column of figures under the 12-inch mark. The compute the number of board feet in a piece of lumber 4 inches thick, 8 inches wide, and 14 feet long, find the number 14 in the vertical column under the 12-inch mark. Then follow the guideline under the figure 14 laterally across the blade until it reaches the

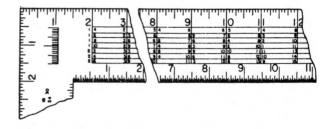

Figure 3–5. Essex board measure table.

figure on that line directly under the inch mark corresponding to the width of the piece. Under the 8-inch mark on the guideline indicated by the 14, the figures 9 and 4 appear. The figure to the left of the vertical line represents feet and that on the right represents inches. In this case, these figures mean that there are 9 and 4/12 or

9 1/3 board feet in a piece of lumber 14 feet long, 8 inches wide, and 1 inch thick. To convert this figure to the proper number of board feet in a piece of the same width and length but 4 inches thick, as is the piece under discussion, simply multiply the proper answer for a board 1 inch thick by 4. The proper total number in this case is 37 1/3 board feet.

d. Rapid Estimation of Board Feet by Use of Tables. Rapid estimation of board feet can be estimated rapidly by the use of table 3-2 or table 3-3.

Table 3-2. Rapid Calculation of Board Measure.

Width	Thickness	Board feet
3″	1″ or less	1/4 of the length
4″	1″ or less	1/3 of the length
6″	1″ or less	1/2 of the length
9″	1″ or less	3/4 of the length
12″	1″ or less	Same as the length
15″	1″ or less	1 1/4 of the length

Table 3-3. Board Feet

Nominal size (in.)	Actual length in feet								
	8	10	12	14	16	18	20	22	24
1 x 2		1 2/3	2	2 1/3	2 2/3	3	3 1/2	3 2/3	4
1 x 3		2 1/2	3	3 1/2	4	4 1/2	5	5 1/2	6
1 x 4	2 3/4	3 1/3	4	4 2/3	5 1/3	6	6 2/3	7 1/3	8
1 x 5		4 1/6	5	5 5/6	6 2/3	7 1/2	8 1/3	9 1/6	10
1 x 6	4	5	6	7	8	9	10	11	12
1 x 7		5 5/8	7	8 1/6	9 1/3	10 1/2	11 2/3	12 5/6	14
1 x 8	5 1/3	6 2/3	8	9 1/3	10 2/3	12	13 1/3	14 2/3	16
1 x 10	6 2/3	8 1/3	10	11 2/3	13 1/3	15	16 2/3	18 1/3	20
1 x 12	8	10	12	14	16	18	20	22	24
1 1/4 x 4		4 1/6	5	5 5/6	6 2/3	7 1/2	8 1/3	9 1/6	10
1 1/4 x 6		6 1/4	7 1/2	8 3/4	10	11 1/4	12 1/2	13 3/4	15
1 1/4 x 8		8 1/3	10	11 2/3	13 1/3	15	16 2/3	18 1/3	20
1 1/4 x 10		10 5/12	12 1/2	14 7/12	16 2/3	18 3/4	20 5/6	22 11/12	25
1 1/4 x 12		12 1/2	15	17 1/2	20	22 1/2	25	27 1/2	30
1 1/2 x 4	4	5	6	7	8	9	10	11	12
1 1/2 x 6	6	7 1/2	9	10 1/2	12	13 1/2	15	16 1/2	18
1 1/2 x 8	8	10	12	14	16	18	20	22	24
1 1/2 x 10	10	12 1/2	15	17 1/2	20	22 1/2	25	27 1/2	30
1 1/2 x 12	12	15	18	21	24	27	30	33	36
2 x 4	5 1/3	6 2/3	8	9 1/3	10 1/3	12	13 1/3	14 2/3	16
2 x 6	8	10	12	14	16	18	20	22	24
2 x 8	10 2/3	13 1/3	16	18 2/3	21 1/3	24	26 2/3	29 1/3	32
2 x 10	13 1/3	16 2/3	20	23 1/3	26 2/3	30	33 1/3	36 2/3	40
2 x 12	16	20	24	28	32	36	40	44	48
3 x 6	12	15	18	21	24	27	30	33	36
3 x 8	16	20	24	28	32	36	40	44	48
3 x 10	20	25	30	35	40	45	50	55	60
3 x 12	24	30	36	42	48	54	60	66	72
4 x 4	10 2/3	13 1/3	16	18 2/3	21 1/3	24	26 2/3	29 1/3	32
4 x 6	16	20	24	28	32	36	40	44	48
4 x 8	21 1/3	26 2/3	32	37 1/3	42 2/3	48	53 1/3	58 2/3	64
4 x 10	26 2/3	33 1/3	40	46 2/3	53 1/3	60	66 2/3	73 1/3	80
4 x 12	32	40	48	56	64	72	80	88	96

Section III. CONSTRUCTION HARDWARE

3-8. General

The fasteners used for frame construction is the theater of operations are made of metal. They are classified as nails, screws, bolts, driftpins, corrugated fasteners, and timber connectors.

3-9. Nails

a. Use. The standard nail used by the Army carpenter is made from steel wire. There are many types of nails, classified according to use and form. The wire nail is round, straight, pointed, and varies in size, weight, shape of head, type of point, and finish. The following rules are followed in using nails:

(1) The nail should be at least three times as long as the thickness of wood it is intended to hold. Two-thirds of the length of the nail is driven into the second piece for proper anchorage;

one-third anchors the piece being fastened.

(2) Nails should be driven at an angle slightly toward each other and placed to provide the greatest holding power. Nails driven with the grain do not hold as well as nails driven across the grain.

(3) A few nails of proper type and size, properly placed and properly driven, will hold better than a great many driven close together.

(4) Nails are the cheapest and easiest fasteners to be used. Screws of comparable size provide more holding power; bolts provide still more.

b. *Types.*

(1) *Common wire nails* (1, fig. 3–6). Common wire nails and box nails are the same except that the wire sizes are one or two numbers smaller for a given length of the box nail than they are for the common nail. The common wire nail is used for housing-construction framing.

(2) *Finishing nails* (2, fig. 3–6). The finishing nail is made from finer wire and has a smaller head than the common nail. It may be set below the surface of the wood and leaves only a small hole easily filled with putty. It is generally used for interior or exterior finishing work and for finished carpentry and cabinetmaking.

(3) *Scaffold or form nails* (3, fig. 3–6). The scaffold, form, or staging nail (as it is sometimes called) appears to have two heads. The lower head (shoulder) permits the nail to be driven securely home while the upper head projects above the wood to make it easy to pull. The scaffold nail is not meant to be permanent.

(4) *Roofing nails* (4, fig. 3–6). Roofing nails are round-shafted, diamond-pointed, galvanized nails of relatively short length and large heads.

They fasten flexible roofing and resist continuous exposure to weather. If shingles or roll roofing is put on over old roofing, the roofing nails must be long enough to go through the old material and secure the new. Asphalt roofing must be fastened with corrosion resistant nails, never with plain nails. Nailing is begun in the center of the shingle, just above the cutouts or slots, to avoid buckling.

(5) *Cut nails* (5, fig. 3–6). Cut nails are wedge shaped with a head on the large end. They are often used to nail flooring because they are of very hard steel and have good holding power.

c. *Sizes.* Nail sizes are designated by the term "penny". This term applies to the length of the nail (1 penny, 2 penny, etc.), which is the same for all types. The approximate number of nails per pound varies according to the type and size. The wire gage number varies according to type. Figure 3–7 explains the term "penny" for each of the nails referred to in this section. The "d" next to the numbers in the "Size" column is the abbreviation of "penny" and should be read "2 penny", "3 penny", etc. Table 3–4 gives the general size and type of nail preferred for specific uses.

3–10. Screws

Screws instead of nails are more expensive in time and money but sometimes necessary for superior results. Screws provide more holding power than nails, can be easily tightened to draw material securely together, are neater in appearance, and may be withdrawn without damaging the material. The common wood screw is usually made of unhardened steel, stainless steel, aluminum, or brass. The steel may be bright finished or blued, or zinc, cadmium, or chrome plated. Wood screws are threaded from a gimlet point for approximately 2/3 of the length of the screw and are provided with a slotted head for use of a screwdriver.

a. *Types and Uses.*

(1) *Wood screws* (1, fig. 3–8). Wood screws are designated according to head style. The most common types are flathead, ovalhead, and roundhead with either slotted or phillips heads. To prepare wood for receiving the screws, a pilot hole the diameter of the screw is bored in the piece of wood that is to be fastened (fig. 3–9). Then a smaller, starter hole is bored in the piece of wood that is to act as anchor or hold the threads of the screw. The starter hole is drilled

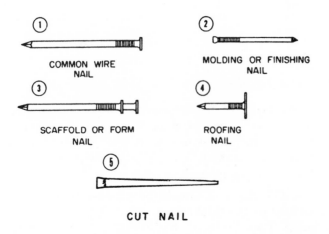

Figure 3–6. Types of nails.

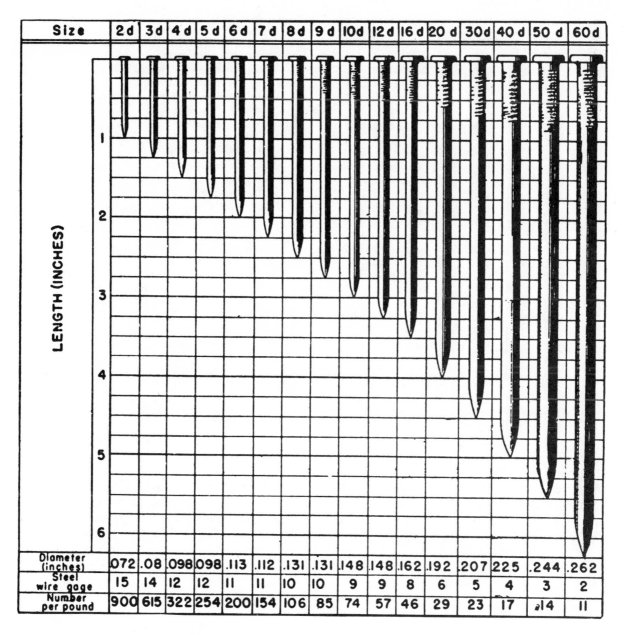

Size	2d	3d	4d	5d	6d	7d	8d	9d	10d	12d	16d	20d	30d	40d	50d	60d
Diameter (inches)	.072	.08	.098	.098	.113	.112	.131	.131	.148	.148	.162	.192	.207	.225	.244	.262
Steel wire gage	15	14	12	12	11	11	10	10	9	9	8	6	5	4	3	2
Number per pound	900	615	322	254	200	154	106	85	74	57	46	29	23	17	14	11

Figure 3–7. Sizes of nails.

with a diameter less than that of the screw threads and to a depth 1/2 or 2/3 the length of the threads to be anchored. This assures accuracy in placing the screws, reduces the possibility of splitting the wood, and reduces the time required. Properly set slotted and phillips flathead and ovalhead screws are countersunk enough to permit a covering material to be used. Slotted roundhead and phillips roundhead screws are not countersunk, but driven firmly flush with the surface. The slot of the roundhead screw is left parallel with the grain of the wood.

(2) *Lag screws* (2, fig. 3–8). The Army name for lag screws is lag bolt, wood screw type. They are longer and heavier than the common wood screw and have coarser threads which extend from a cone or gimlet point slightly more than half the length of the screw. Squarehead and hexagonhead lag screws are usually placed with a wrench. They are used when ordinary wood screws would be too short or too light and spikes would not be strong enough. For sizes of lag screws, see table 3–7. Combined with expansion anchors, they are used to frame timbers to existing masonry.

(3) *Expansion shields.* Expansion shields (expansion anchors) are inserted in a predrilled hole, usually in masonry, to provide a gripping base or anchor for a screw, bolt, or nail. The shield may be obtained separately or may include

Table 3-4. Size, Type, and Use of Nails

Size	Lgth (in.)	Diam (in.)	Remarks	Where used
2d	1	.072	Small head	Finish work, shop work.
2d	1	.072	Large flathead	Small timber, wood shingles, lathes.
3d	1¼	.08	Small head	Finish work, shop work.
3d	1¼	.08	Large flathead	Small timber, wood shingles, lathes.
4d	1½	.098	Small head	Finish work, shop work.
4d	1½	.098	Large flathead	Small timber, lathes, shop work.
5d	1¾	.098	Small head	Finish work, shop work.
5d	1¾	.098	Large flathead	Small timber, lathes, shop work.
6d	2	.113	Small head	Finish work, casing, stops, etc., shop work.
6d	2	.113	Large flathead	Small timber, siding, sheathing, etc., shop work.
7d	2¼	.113	Small head	Casing, base, ceiling, stops, etc.
7d	2¼	.113	Large flathead	Sheathing, siding, subflooring, light framing.
8d	2½	.131	Small head	Casing, base, ceiling, wainscot, etc., shop work.
8d	2½	.131	Large flathead	Sheathing, siding, subflooring, light framing, shop work.
8d	1¼	.131	Extra-large flathead	Roll roofing, composition shingles.
9d	2¾	.131	Small head	Casing, base, ceiling, etc.
9d	2¾	.131	Large flathead	Sheathing, siding, subflooring, framing, shop work.
10d	3	.148	Small head	Casing, base, ceiling, etc., shop work.
10d	3	.148	Large flathead	Sheathing, siding, subflooring, framing, shop work.
12d	3¼	.148	Large flathead	Sheathing, subflooring, framing.
16d	3½	.162	Large flathead	Framing, bridges, etc.
20d	4	.192	Large flathead	Framing, bridges, etc.
30d	4½	.207	Large flathead	Heavy framing, bridges, etc.
40d	5	.225	Large flathead	Heavy framing, bridges, etc.
50d	5½	.244	Large flathead	Extra-heavy framing, bridges, etc.
60d	6	.262	Large flathead	Extra-heavy framing, bridges, etc.

¹ This chart applies to wire nails, although it may be used to determine the length of cut nails.

the screw, bolt, or nail. After the expansion shield is inserted in the predrilled hole, the fastener is driven into the hole in the shield, wedging it firmly against the surface of the hole.

(4) *Sheet metal screws.* For the assembly of metal parts, sheet metal screws are used. These screws are made regularly in steel and brass with four types of heads: flat, round, oval, and fillister, as shown in that order in 3, figure 3-8.

b. *Wood Screw Sizes.* Wood screw sizes vary from 1/4 to 6 inches. Screws up to 1 inch in length increase by eighths, screws from 1 to 3 inches increase by quarters, and screws from 3 to 6 inches increase by half-inches. Screws vary in length and size of shaft. Each length is made in a number of shaft sizes identified by a number that shows relative differences in the diameter of the screws. Proper nomenclature of a screw includes the type, material, finish, length, and screw size number which indicates the wire gage of the body, drill or bit size for the body hole, and drill or bit size for the starter hole. Tables 3-5 and 3-6 provide size, length, gage, and applicable drill and auger bit sizes for screws; table 3-7 gives lengths and diameters of lag screws.

3-11. Bolts

Bolts are used when great strength is required or when the work must be frequently disassembled. Nuts are usually used for fastening, and sometimes washers are used to protect the surface of the material they fasten. Bolts are selected for a specific use in terms of length, diameter, threads, style of head, and type. Washers between the nut and a wood surface or between both the nut and the head and their opposing surfaces will avoid marring the surfaces and permit additional torque in tightening.

a. *Carriage Bolts.* Carriage bolts come in three types: bolt, square neck (1, fig. 3-10); bolt, finned neck (2, fig. 3-10); and bolt, ribbed neck (3, fig. 3-10). They have roundheads that are not made to be driven. They are threaded only part of the way up the shaft; usually the threads are two to four times as long as the diameter of the bolt. In each type of carriage bolt, the upper part of the shank, immediately below the head grips the materials in which the bolt is inserted and keeps it from turning when a nut is tightened down on it or removed. The finned type has two or more fins extending from the head to the shank. The ribbed type has longitudinal

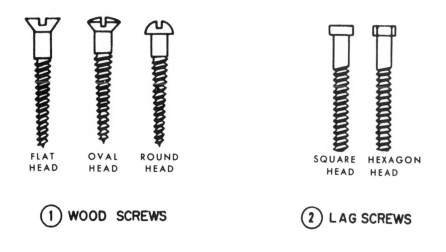

① WOOD SCREWS

② LAG SCREWS

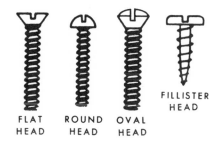

③ METAL SCREWS

Figure 3-8. Types of screws.

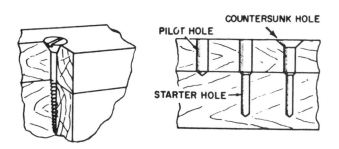

Figure 3-9. Sinking a screw properly.

Table 3-5. Screw Sizes and Dimensions

Length (in.)	Size numbers																								
	0	1	2	3	4	5	6	7	8	9	10	11	12	13	14	15	16	17	18	20	22	24	26	28	30
¼		x	x	x																					
⅜	x	x	x	x	x	x	x	x	x	x															
½		x	x	x	x	x	x	x	x	x	x	x	x												
⅝		x	x	x	x	x	x	x	x	x	x	x	x	x	x										
¾			x	x	x	x	x	x	x	x	x	x	x	x	x	x	x								
⅞			x	x	x	x	x	x	x	x	x	x	x	x	x	x	x								
1				x	x	x	x	x	x	x	x	x	x	x	x	x	x	x	x	x					
1¼					x	x	x	x	x	x	x	x	x	x	x	x	x	x	x	x	x	x			
1½					x	x	x	x	x	x	x	x	x	x	x	x	x	x	x	x	x	x			
1¾						x	x	x	x	x	x	x	x	x	x	x	x	x	x	x	x	x			
2						x	x	x	x	x	x	x	x	x	x	x	x	x	x	x	x	x			
2¼						x	x	x	x	x	x	x	x	x	x	x	x	x	x	x	x	x			
2½						x	x	x	x	x	x	x	x	x	x	x	x	x	x	x	x	x			
2¾							x	x	x	x	x	x	x	x	x	x	x	x	x	x	x	x			
3							x	x	x	x	x	x	x	x	x	x	x	x	x	x	x	x	x		
3½									x	x	x	x	x	x	x	x	x	x	x	x	x	x	x		
4									x	x	x	x	x		x		x	x	x	x	x	x	x	x	
4½													x		x		x		x	x	x	x	x	x	x
5													x		x		x		x	x	x	x	x	x	x
6															x		x		x	x	x	x	x	x	x

Gage and diameter													
Steel wire gage	17	15	14	13	12	11	10	9	8	7	6½	6	5
Diameter (inches)	.054	.072	.080	.091	.105	.120	.135	.148	.162	.177	.184	.192	.207
Steel wire gage	4½	4	3	2½	2	1	½	0	00	00½	000	0000	
Diameter (inches)	.216	.225	.243	.253	.262	.283	——	.306	.331	——	.362	.393	

Table 3-6. Drill and Auger Bit Sizes for Wood Screws

Screw size No.		1	2	3	4	5	6	7	8	9	10	12	14	16	18
Nominal screw		.073	.086	.099	.112	.125	.138	.151	.164	.177	.190	.216	.242	.268	.294
Body diameter		5/64	3/32	3/32	7/64	1/8	9/64	5/32	11/64	11/64	3/16	7/32	15/64	17/64	19/64
Pilot hole	Drill size	5/64	3/32	7/64	7/64	1/8	9/64	5/32	11/64	3/16	3/16	7/32	1/4	17/64	19/64
	Bit size	-----	-----	-----	-----	-----	-----	-----	-----	-----	-----	4	4	5	5
Starter hole	Drill size	-----	1/16	1/16	5/64	5/64	3/32	7/64	7/64	1/8	1/8	9/64	5/32	3/16	13/64
	Bit size	-----	-----	-----	-----	-----	-----	-----	-----	-----	-----	-----	-----	-----	4

Table 3-7. Lag Screw Sizes

Lengths (inches)	Diameters (inches)			
	1/4	3/8, 7/16, 1/2	5/8, 3/4	7/8, 1
1	x	x	-----	-----
1½	x	x	x	-----
2, 2½, 3, 3½, etc., 7½, 8 to 10.	x	x	x	x
11 to 12	-----	x	x	x
13 to 16	-----	------	x	x

ribs, splines, or serrations on all or part of a shoulder located immediately beneath the head. Holes bored to receive carriage bolts are bored to be a tight fit for the body of the bolt and counterbored to permit the head of the bolt to fit flush with or below the surface of the material being fastened. The bolt is then driven through the hole with a hammer. Carriage bolts are chiefly for wood-to-wood use but may also be used for wood-to-metal. If used for wood-to-metal application, the head should be fitted to the wood item. Metal surfaces are sometimes predrilled and countersunk to permit the use of carriage bolts metal-to-metal. Carriage bolts can be obtained from 1/4 inch to 1 inch in diameter, and from 3/4 to 20 inches long (table 3-8). A common flat washer should be used with carriage bolts between the nut and the wood surface.

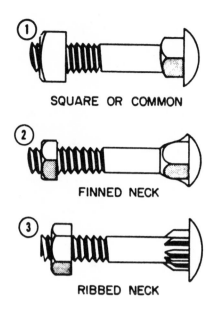

SQUARE OR COMMON

FINNED NECK

RIBBED NECK

Figure 3–10. Carriage bolts.

b. Screw, Cap (Machine Bolts). Machine bolts (fig. 3–11) are made with cut National Fine or National Coarse threads extending in length from twice the diameter of the bolt plus 1/4 inch (for bolts less than 6 inches in length), to twice the diameter of the bolt plus 1/2 inch (for bolts over 6 inches in length). They are precision made and generally applied metal-to-metal where close tolerance is desirable. The head may be square, hexagon, double hexagon, rounded, or flat countersunk. The nut usually corresponds in shape to the head of the bolt with which it is used. Machine bolts are externally driven only. The proper machine bolt is selected on the basis of head style, length, diameter, number of threads per inch, and coarseness of thread. The hole through which the bolt is to pass is bored to the same diameter as the bolt. Machine bolts are made in diameters from 1/4 inch to 3 inches and may be obtained in any length desired (table 3–9).

Table 3–8. Carriage Bolt Sizes

Lengths (inches)	Diameters (inches)			
	3/16, 1/4, 5/16, 3/8	7/16, 1/2	9/16, 5/8 3/4	
¾ - - - - - - - - - - -	x			
1 - - - - - - - - - - -	x	x		
1¼ - - - - - - - - - - -	x	x	x	
1½, 2, 2½, etc., 9½, 10 to 20.	x	x	x	x

c. Stove Bolts. Stove bolts (fig. 3–12) are less precisely made than machine bolts. They are made with either flat or round slotted heads and may have threads extending over the full

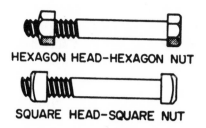

HEXAGON HEAD–HEXAGON NUT

SQUARE HEAD–SQUARE NUT

Figure 3–11. Machine bolts.

length of the body, over part of the body, or over most of the body. They are generally used with square nuts and applied metal-to-metal, wood-to-wood, or wood-to-metal. If flatheaded, they are countersunk; if roundheaded, they are drawn flush to the surface.

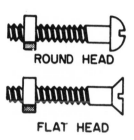

ROUND HEAD

FLAT HEAD

Figure 3–12. Stove bolts.

Table 3–9. Machine Bolt Size

Lengths (inches)	Diameters (inches)			
	¼, ⅜	7/16	½, 9/16, ⅝	¾, ⅞, 1	1⅛, 1¼
¾ - - - - - - - - - - -	x				
1, 1¼ - - - - - - - - -	x	x	x		
1½, 2, 2½ - - - - - - -	x	x	x	x	
3, 3½, 4, 4½, etc., 9½, 10 to 20.	x	x	x	x	x
21 to 25 - - - - - - -			x	x	x
26 to 39 - - - - - - -				x	x

d. Expansion Bolts. An expansion bolt (fig. 3–13) is a bolt used together with an expansion shield to provide anchorage in substances in which a threaded fastener is useless. The shield,

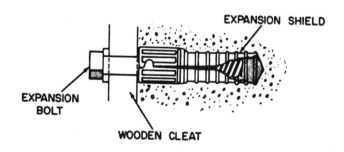

EXPANSION SHIELD

EXPANSION BOLT

WOODEN CLEAT

Figure 3–13. Expansion bolts.

or expansion anchor (para 3–10*b*(3)), inserted in a predrilled hole expands when the bolt is driven into it and becomes wedged firmly in the hole, providing a secure base for the grip of the fastener.

3–12. Driftpins

Driftpins (called driftbolt for supply purposes) are long, heavy, threadless bolts used to hold heavy pieces of timber together (fig. 3–14).

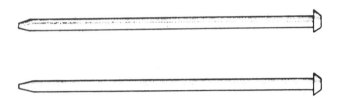

Figure 3–14. Driftpins (driftbolts).

a. Types. Driftpins have heads and vary in diameter from 1/2 to 1 inch, and in length from 18 to 26 inches.

b. Uses. To use the driftpin, a hole slightly smaller than the diameter of the pin is made in the timber. The pin is driven into the hole and is held in place by the compression action of the wood.

3–13. Corrugated Fasteners

Corrugated fasteners are one way to fasten joints and splices in small timber and boards. They are used particularly in the miter joint (joints and splices are discussed in the next section). They are made of sheet metal of 18 to 22 gage with alternate ridges and grooves; the ridges vary from 3/16 to 5/16 inch, center to center. One end is cut square; the other end is sharpened with beveled edges.

a. Types. There are two types of corrugated fasteners: one with ridges running parallel (1, fig. 3–15), the other with ridges running at a slight angle to one another (2, fig. 3–15). The latter type tends to compress the material since the ridges and grooves are closer at the top than at the bottom.

b. Size. These fasteners are made in several different lengths and widths. The width varies from 5/8 to 1 1/8 inches, while the length varies from 1/4 to 3/4 inch. The fasteners also are made with different numbers of ridges, ranging from three to six ridges per fastener.

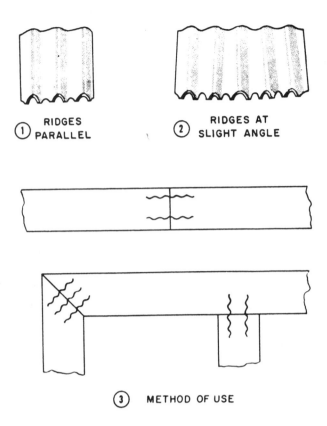

Figure 3–15. Corrugated fasteners and their uses.

c. Use. Corrugated fasteners are used in a number of ways; to fasten parallel boards together, as in fastening tabletops; to make any type of joint; and as a substitute for nails where nails may split the timber. The fasteners have a greater holding power than nails in small timber. The proper method of using the fasteners is shown in 3, figure 3–15.

3–14. Timber Connectors

Timber connectors are metal devices for increasing the joint strength in timber structures. Efficient connections for either timber-to-timber joints or timber-to-steel joints are provided by the several types of timber connectors. The right type is determined mostly by the kind of joint to be made and the load to be carried. The connectors eliminate much complicated framing of joints. They simplify the design of heavy construction; they give greater efficiency of material; they reduce the amount of timber and hardware used; and they save much time and labor.

a. Types. Split rings are made of low-carbon steel and have 2 1/2- and 4-inch diameters. They are used between two timber faces for heavy construction. The fit into grooves which are cut

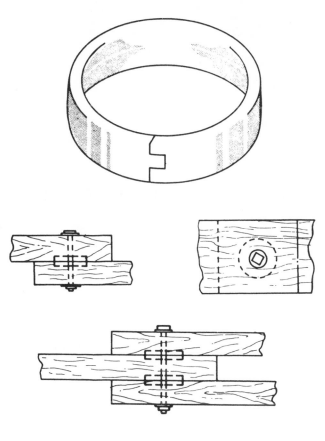

Figure 3–16. Split ring and its installation.

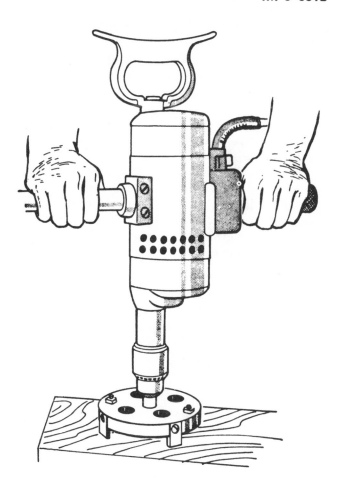

Figure 3–17. Method of cutting grooves.

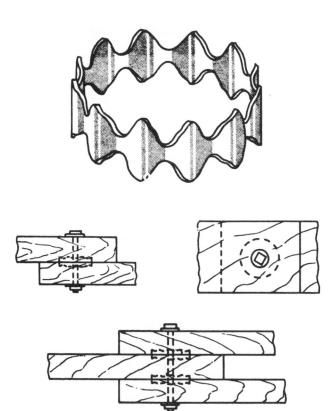

Figure 3–18. Toothed ring.

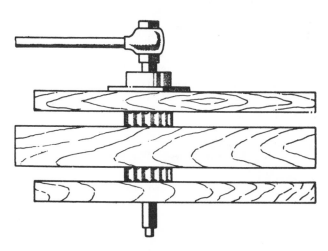

Figure 3–19. Installation of toothed ring.

half the depth of the ring into each of the timber faces (fig. 3–16). The grooves are made with a special bit used in an electric, air, or hand drill (fig. 3–17). The tongue-and-groove split in the ring permits ring bearing simultaneously against the cone wall and outer wall of the groove into which the ring is placed. The inside bevel and mill edge make installation into and removal from the groove easier.

b. Uses. Toothed rings are corrugated and toothed, and are made from 16-gage plate low-carbon steel (fig. 3-18). They are used between two timber frames for comparatively light construction and are embedded into the contact faces of the joint members by means of pressure (fig. 3-19).

Section IV. JOINTS AND SPLICES

3-15. General

a. The weak points in a structure usually occur where there are connections between materials. The existence of such weak points is usually a sign of faulty workmanship, since connections can be made so that the strength of the structure at these points is not weakened at all.

b. All connections between pieces of timber are classified as either joints or splices. Joints are connections between two pieces of timber which come together at an angle. Splices are connections between two pieces of timber which extend in the same line.

3-16. Types of Joints

The types of joints most commonly used in carpentry are the butt and lap joints (fig. 3-20). The butt joint is constructed by placing the end of one board on another board in such a way that the boards are at an angle (usually a right angle), forming a corner. The lap joint is constructed by overlapping two pieces of wood and securing them to form a joint, or by cutting away corresponding portions (usually half) in equal lengths from the thickness of two boards and then joining them in such a way that they overlap and form a corner. The various types of joints are discussed in the following paragraphs.

3-17. Butt Joints

a. Straight Butt Joint. The straight butt joint is formed by bringing the square-cut end of one board against the square face of another (1 and 2, fig. 3-20). The butt end of one board should be square and the face of the other smooth so that the pieces fit perpendicular to each other. Nails or screws are used to hold the two pieces together. Properly selected screws will hold such a joint securely. However, for framing, butt joints are secured by 8- or 10-penny nails which are toenailed to strengthen the joint. Toenailing is done by driving the nail diagonally through both pieces. End grain is the weakest part of a piece of wood when used in joint connections. Since a butt joint connection is made at either

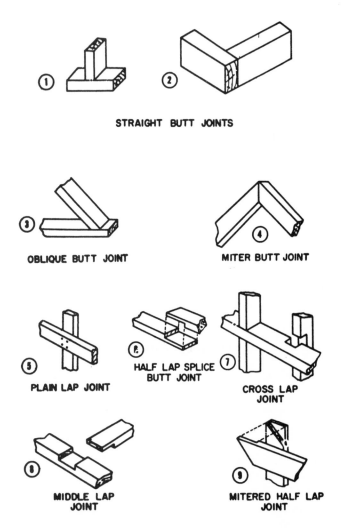

Figure 3-20. Butt and lap joints.

one or two end-grain parts, the connection will be no stronger than the characteristics of the end-grain parts. A butt joint is therefore the weakest type of joint. This is especially true if the joint is of two pieces of wood only.

b. Oblique Butt Joint. The oblique butt joint is formed by bringing the end of one board, cut to form the desired angle against the face of another board with which it is to be joined (3, fig. 3-20). Bracing is a typical application for this joint. This joint should not be used where great strength is required. The strength of the joint depends upon the nailing; the size of the nails used depends entirely upon the size of the timber. Nails should be toenailed as in the case of the straight butt joint and not too many nails should be used.

c. Miter Butt Joint. The miter butt joint is formed by bringing the mitered ends of two boards together to form the desired angle (4, fig. 3–20). The miter butt joint is usually used at corners where the straight butt joint is not satisfactory. To make a miter joint, the angle of cut is the same for both pieces. To form a right-angle miter joint (the most commonly used miter joint), each piece is cut at a 45-degree angle so that when the pieces are joined they will form a 90-degree angle. The miter joint is used mostly in framing but is a very weak joint and is not to be used where strength is important.

3–18. Lap Joints

a. Plain Lap Joint. The plain lap joint is formed by laying one board over another and securing the two by means of screws or nails (5, fig. 3–20). This is the simplest and most often used method of joining in framing and construction. This joint is as strong as the fasteners and material used.

b. Half-Lap Splice Joint. The half-lap splice joint is constructed by cutting away portions (usually half) in equal lengths from the thickness of two boards and joining them in such a way that the cutaway portions overlap to form the joint (6, fig. 3–20). The half-lap is a relatively strong, easily made joint. Overlapping surfaces must fit snugly and smoothly. Saw on the waste side of the gage line when cutting out the laps to avoid cutting laps oversize by the thickness of the kerf. Several useful variations of the half-lap are cross lap (7, fig. 3–20), middle lap (8, fig. 3–20), and mitered half-lap (9, fig. 3–20).

3–19. Other Useful Joints
(fig. 3–21)

a. Dado and Rabbet. The dado is a rectangular, square-bottomed groove cut in wood, and a rabbet is a corner cut out of an edge of a piece of wood. Both the dado and the rabbet are used to form the following joints: dado joint (1, fig. 3–21), rabbet joint (2, fig. 3–21), dado-rabbet joint (3, fig. 3–21), and stopped dado (4, fig. 3–21).

b. Dovetail, Mortise, and Tenon. Locked joints give added strength at the cost of added work and workmanship and are not used unless parti-

cular strength is required of the joint. The most common locked joints are lap dovetail (5, fig. 3–21), through single dovetail (6, fig. 3–21), open mortise and tenon (7, fig. 3–21), and through mortise and tenon (8, fig. 3–21).

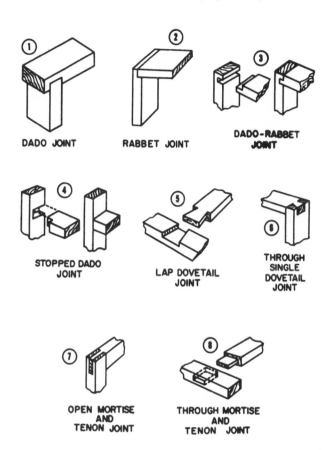

Figure 3–21. Dado, rabbet, dovetail, and mortise and tenon joints.

3–20. Splices

Splices connect two or more pieces of timber so they will be as strong as a single timber of the same length and the joint will be as strong as the unjoined portions. The type of splice used is determined by the way in which the spliced timber is to be subjected to the stress and strain it must support. Timbers subjected to direct longitudinal stress (1, fig. 3–22) as vertical supports or in exerting pressure require splices designed to resist compression. Timbers subjected to transverse and angular stresses when used as trusses, braces, or joists require splices designed to resist tension (2, fig. 3–22). Timbers used as horizontal supports require splices designed to resist bending (3, fig. 3–22). Splices for resisting compression are usually worthless for tension or bending; therefore, splices should be made to meet the conditions for which they are to be used. The carpenter should know each type of splice and should be able to make and apply each properly.

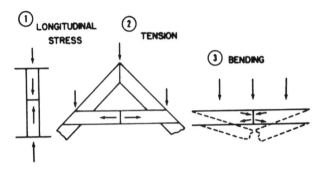

Figure 3–22. Splice stresses.

3–21. Compression Resistant Splices

General. Compression resistant splices support weight or exert pressure and will resist compression stress only. The butt splice and the halved splice are the most common types of compression resistant splices.

a. *Butt Splice.* The butt splice is constructed by butting the squared ends of two pieces of timber together and securing them in this position by means of two wood or metal pieces fastened on opposite sides of the timber (1 and 2, fig. 3–23). The two short supporting pieces keep the splice straight and prevent buckling. Metal plates used as supports in constructing a butt splice are called fishplates (1, fig. 3–23). Wood plates are called scabs (2, fig. 3–23). Fishplates are fastened in place with bolts or screws. Bolts, nails, or corrugated fasteners may be used to secure scabs. If nails are used with scabs, they are staggered and driven at an angle away from the splice. Too many nails, or nails that are too large, will weaken a splice.

b. *Halved Splice.* The halved splice is made by cutting away half the thickness of equal lengths from the ends of two pieces of timber and fitting the complementary tongues or laps together. The laps should be long enough to have enough bearing surfaces. Nails or bolts may be used to fasten the halved splice (3, fig. 3–23). In order to give this type of splice resistance to some tension as well as compression, fishplates or scabs may be used as with the butt splice.

3–22. Tension Resistant Splices

In tension members such as trusses, braces, and joists, the joint undergoes stress that is exerted in more than one direction and creates a tension

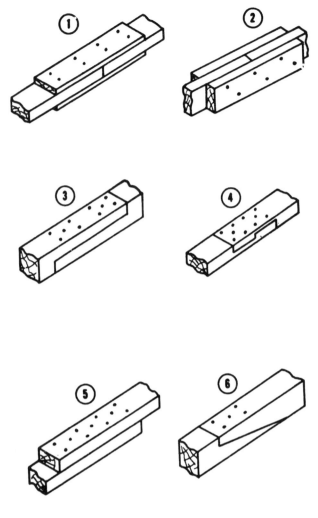

Figure 3–23. Compression, tension, and bending splices.

tending to buckle the member in a predictable direction. Tension splices are designed to provide the greatest practicable number of bearing surfaces and shoulders within the splice to resist the buckling tension.

a. *Square Splice.* The square splice is a modification of the compression halved splice. Notches are cut in the tongues or laps to provide an additional locking shoulder (4, fig. 3–23). The square splice may be fastened with nails or bolts or may be greatly strengthened by the use of fishplates or scabs.

b. *Plain Splice.* A hasty substitute for the square splice is the long plain splice (5, fig. 3–23). A long overlap of the two pieces is desirable to provide adequate bearing surface and enough room for fasteners to make up for the lack of shoulder lock.

3–23. Bend Resistant Splices

a. *General.* Horizontal timbers supporting

weight undergo stress at a splice which results in a compression of the upper part that has a tendency to crush the fibers and in a tension of the lower part that tends to pull the fibers apart. Bend resistant splices resist both compression and tension; they combine the features of the compression and tension splices.

b. Construction. The bend resistant splice is constructed by cutting oblique complementary laps in the ends of two pieces of timber. The upper tongue (bearing surface) is squared to butt against the square of the complementary lap (6, fig. 3-23) to offer maximum resistance to crushing, and the lower tongue is beveled. A scab or fishplate may be fastened along the bottom of the splice to resist the tendency of the pieces to separate. In any case where it is not desirable to lap or halve the timber ends for a splice subject to tension, a butt joint secured by fishplates may be used.

CHAPTER 4

BILLS OF MATERIALS

4–1. Definition

a. A bill of materials is a list of all materials needed to complete a structure. It includes item number (parts and materials), name, description, unit of measure, quantity and, where called for, the stock size and number, and sometimes the weight.

b. Bills of materials are based on takeoffs and estimates of the materials needed. They are usually made up by the draftsman when he prepares the original drawings; the carpenter simply uses them when ordering materials. However,

where no bills of materials accompany field prints, they must be drawn up by the constructing forces; thus, a carpenter should be able to work with or develop bills of materials. Reasonable accuracy can best be obtained by having separate bills of materials prepared by at least two estimators. They can then be compared and one copy corrected or both used to make up a final bill of materials.

4–2. Materials Takeoff List

a. The first step in preparing a bill of mater-

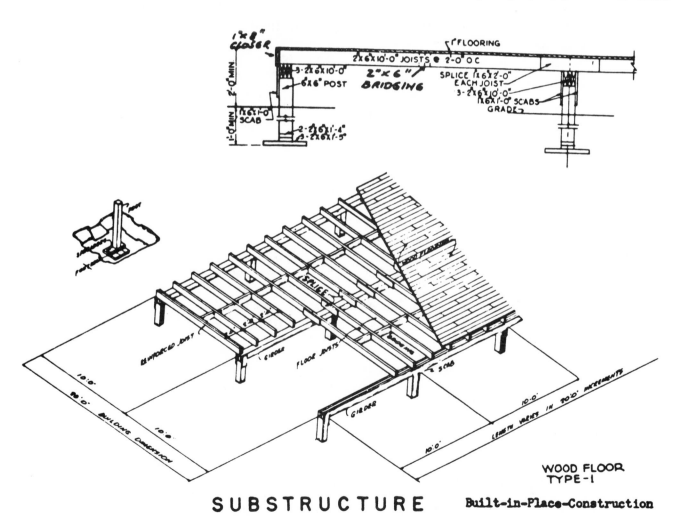

SUBSTRUCTURE   Built-in-Place-Construction

Figure 4–1. 20-foot wide TO building substructure.

Table 4–1. Materials Takeoff List for 20' x 40' TO Building

Item Name or use of piece	No of pieces	Unit	Length in place	Size	Length	No. per length	Quantity
1. Footers	45	Pc	1'–5"	2x6	10'	7	7
2. Spreaders	30	Pc	1'–4"	2x6	8'	6	5
3. Foundation post	15	Pc	3'–0"	6x6	12'	4	4
4. Scabs	20	Pc	1'–0"	1x6	8'	8	3
5. Girders	36	Pc	10'–0"	2x6	10'	1	36
6. Joists	46	Pc	10'–0"	2x6	10'	1	46
7. Joist splices	21	Pc	2'–0"	1x6	8'	4	6
8. Block bridging	40	Pc	1'–10⅜"	2x6	8'	4	10
9. Closers	12	Pc	10'–0"	1x8	10'	1	12
10. Flooring	800	BF	RL	1x6	RL	--	--

ials is to prepare a materials takeoff list. This is an individual listing of all parts of the building, "taken off" the plans, usually by an actual tally and checkoff of the items shown, noted, or specified on the drawings and specifications. Both architectural and engineering plans provide the names and sizes of the various items which are to be listed.

b. Figure 4–1 shows the plan for the substructure of a 20 foot wide building. Table 4–1 is a materials takeoff list prepared for the plans in figure 4–1. This list contains all parts of the building, starting with its bottom and working upward until all its parts are listed.

c. Look at the first item on the materials takeoff list as an example. The item number is followed by the name of the item. Next is the total number of pieces needed to make up the item. In the example there are 15 posts in a 20' x 40' building. With three pieces needed for each footer, a total of 45 pieces are needed. The length in place is the actual length of the member after it has been cut and is ready to be nailed in place. The length in place of the footer is 1'–5". The size refers to the quoted size of the lumber, such as 2 x 4 or 2 x 6. Since 2 x 6 stock is being used in the example, that dimension is put into the size column. The commercial length refers to the standard lengths available from the lumber yard or depot, such as 8', 10', and 12' long pieces of stock.

d. It must be decided which length is the most economical to use in making the footers, which are built from 45 pieces of 2 x 6 x 1'–5". If the standard lengths of 8'–0", 10'–0", and 12'–0" are changed to 96", 120", and 144", the length in place can be divided into the commercial lengths in inches. This will give the number of pieces that can be obtained from each commercial length, plus the amount of waste per commercial length. For example, the length in place of the footers is 1'–5", or 17". Dividing 17" into 96", the 8' commercial length, an answer of five pieces 1'5" long with 11" waste is obtained. In a 10' piece, dividing 17" into 120" gives seven pieces 1'–5" long with 1" waste. When there is only 1" waste or no waste at all, that commercial length can be used without going further. Since seven pieces 1'–5" long are obtained from each 10'–0" stock and since 45 pieces 1'–5" long are needed, seven 2" x 6" x 10'–0" pieces are ordered to give the required 45 pieces 1'–5" long. Four extra 1'–5" lengths of 2' x 6" will be left, but they may be used elsewhere on the job.

4–3. Materials Estimate List

a. The materials estimate list puts into a shorter form the information on the materials takeoff list, adds an allowance for waste and breakage, and makes an estimate of quantities of materials known to be necessary but which may not have been placed on the drawings, such as nails, cement, concrete-form lumber and tie wire, temporary bracing or scaffold lumber, and so on.

b. The first step in preparing the materials estimate list (table 4–2) is to consoliate the information on the takeoff list. This means to group all pieces of the same size and length in a logical order. For example, start with the largest size lumber that can be found on the material takeoff list. Add together all the pieces of that same size and length that appear anywhere on

Table 4-2. Materials Estimate List

Item	Size & length	Unit	Takeoff quantity	Waste allowance	Additional requirements	Total quantity	b.m.
1	6 x 6 x 12	Pc	4	1	None	5	180
2	2 x 6 x 10	Pc	89	9	None	98	980
3	2 x 6 x 8	Pc	15	2	3 for temporary bracing	20	160
4	1 x 8 x 10	Pc	12	2	None	14	91
5	1 x 6 x 8	Pc	9	2	2 for batter boards	13	52
6	1 x 6 x RL	BF	800	160	None	960	960
7	16d	lb	- - -	- - -	36 nails, framing	36	- - -
8	8d	lb	- - -	- - -	23 nails, flooring	23	- - -

the list. This gives the total number of pieces of that particular size and length that will be needed for the project. Continue in this way with the next smaller size of lumber, and work down to the smallest size and length of material.

c. To each total number of pieces of one length and size, the waste factor must be added. For flooring, sheathing, and other 1 inch material, add a waste allowance of 20 percent to the total number of pieces. For all other materials 2 inches and larger, add 10 percent to the total number. In the next column, estimate the amount of additional requirements for materials not shown on the plans. Add up the total quantity for each size and length of material, and then convert it to board feet, using one of the methods given in paragraph 3–7.

d. The sizes and pounds of nails needed should be added to the list. Two nail formulas are used for estimating the number of pounds of nails needed:

(1) For flooring and sheathing, and other 1-inch material, the following formula is used:

$$\text{No. of lb (2d to 12d, sheathing)} = \frac{d}{4} \times \frac{b.m.}{100}$$

(2) For framing materials which are 2 inches or more, the following formula is used:

$$\text{No. of lb (12d to 60d, framing)} = \frac{d}{4} \times \frac{b.m.}{100}$$

4–4. Bill of Materials

The actual bill of materials is the final step. Although the materials estimate list contains all of the information on all the material needed for the project, it contains much information of little interest to the depot personnel, so it is simplified into the bill of materials format shown in table 4–3. This is the document submitted to supply personnel to requisition the material. The rest of the building would be analyzed in the same way.

Table 4-3. Bills of Materials

Item	Quantity	Unit	Size & length	b.m.	Description or where used
1.	5	Pc	6″ x 6″ x 12′	180	Posts
2.	98	Pc	2″ x 6″ x 10′	980	Footing, girder, joist
3.	20	Pc	2″ x 6″ x 8′	160	Spreader, bridging
4.	14	Pc	1″ x 8″ x 10′	94	Closers
5.	13	Pc	1″ x 6″ x 8′	52	Scabs, splices
6.	960	BF	1 x 6 x RL	960	Flooring
7.	36	lb	16d	- - -	Nails, framing
8.	23	lb	8d	- - -	Nails, area coverage
9.					
10.					

CHAPTER 5

BUILDING LAYOUT AND FOUNDATION

5-1. Introduction

Layout means the actions performed in preparing the materials and work area before beginning construction. As soon as the construction site has been selected, layout may begin.

5-2. Tools and Materials

Tools and materials used in layout must be carefully selected. The most commonly used are as follows: figure 5-1.

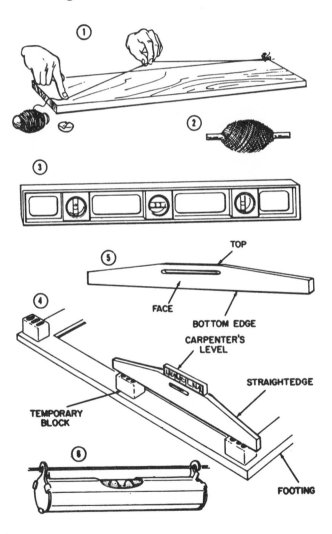

Figure 5-1. Layout tools.

a. *Sledge Hammer or Maul.* The sledge hammer or maul is used to sink corner stakes or batter board posts.

b. *Post-Hole Auger.* The post hole auger is used to dig the holes required to set posts properly in some soils.

c. *Hand Saw.* The hand saw is used to cut batter boards and posts.

d. *Chalkline.* A chalkline is a white, twisted mason's line consisting of a reel, line, and chalk. It is coated with chalk and stretched taut between points to be connected by a straight line, just off the surface. When snapped, the line makes a straight guideline.

e. *Tracing Tape.* Tracing tape is a cotton tape approximately 1 inch wide. It is generally in a 200-foot length for laying out excavation or foundation lines.

f. *Ax or Hatchet.* The ax or hatchet is used to sharpen batter boards and stakes.

g. *Hammer.* The hammer is used for building batter boards.

h. *Posts and Stakes.* Batter board posts are made from 2 x 4 or 4 x 4 material; corner stakes, from 4 x 4's. Batter boards are made from 1 x 4 or 1 x 6 pieces.

i. *Carpenter's Level.* The carpenter's level (4, fig. 5-1) determines levelness of surface and sights level lines. It may be used directly on the surface or used with a straightedge (fig. 5-1). Levelness is determined by the bubbles suspended within glass tubes parallel to one or more surfaces of the level.

j. *Straightedge.* The straightedge usually has a handhole, a bottom edge at least 30 inches long used as a leveling surface, and a top edge 8 to 10 inches long used as a working surface. It may be used with the level to increase the area checked (5, fig. 5-1). It is most often used to lay out straight lines between points close enough together to use the edge as a ruler.

k. *Line Level.* The line level has a spirit bubble

to show levelness; it can be hung from a line (6, fig. 5–1). Placement halfway between the points to be leveled gives the greatest accuracy.

l. Engineer's Transit or Leveling Instrument. The engineer's transit establishes reference points or grade lines which permit building up or down with accuracy as to vertical level. It locates corners and lays out lines for buildings or excavation.

(1) *Engineer's transit.* The engineer's transit has an adjustable tripod and head. It measures horizontal or vertical angles (fig. 5–2).

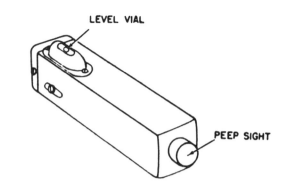

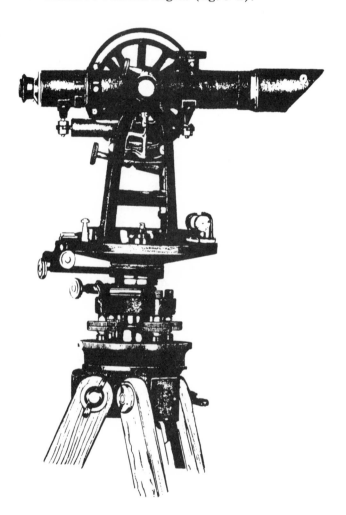

Figure 5–2. Engineer's transit.

(2) *Locator's hand level.* The locator's hand level measures approximately differences in elevation and can establish grades over limited distances (fig. 5–3). The landscape, level bubble, and index line are seen in the tube.

5–3. Use of the Engineer's Transit

The carpenter ordinarily does not use the engineer's transit but many of them learn how to

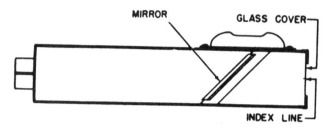

LEVELING INSTRUMENT

Figure 5–3. Leveling instrument.

do so on the job. TM 5–232 and TM 5–233 provide information needed in the use of this instrument. The following guidance will help those who wish to review the procedure.

a. Set up the transit directly over station mark (A) (fig. 5–4), the point from which layout is sighted. A bench mark (B) may be provided by surveying engineers as a point of reference. The bench mark may be on the foundation of an adjacent building or a buried stone marker. If bench marks have been established in the area and the architect's drawings have been created specifically for that particular area, the bench mark will appear on the drawings and the plans

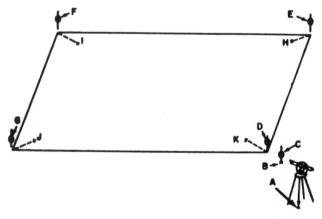

Figure 5–4. Layout of a plot with a transit.

will be oriented to that point. If no bench mark exists, a post may be driven into the ground to provide this reference point. This post can establish floor levels, foundation levels, or any definite point of elevation. When setting up the engineer's transit or leveling instrument, a plumb bob may be used to center the instrument directly over the selected station mark.

b. Adjust the tripod so that it rests firmly on the ground with the sighting tube at eye level. Level up the head of the instrument by turning the leveling screws, so that the sight tube and head are level when turned in any direction. Once set up, all contact with the legs of the tripod should be avoided.

c. Place a leveling rod (C) upright on any point to be checked, and sight through the sight tube of the instrument at the leveling rod. In accurate work, a spirit level may be attached to the leveling rod. An assistant should hold the leveling rod, and should move the target on the rod up or down until the crossline on the target comes in line with the crosshair sights in the sighting tube.

d. To obtain the difference in elevation between two points, such as the surveyor's bench mark (B) and the target point (D), hold the rod on the point (B) and take a rod reading. This will be the length of the bottom of the rod below the line of sight. Take a rod reading at point (D). The difference between the two rod readings is the difference.

e. To establish a level for the depth of an excavation or for the level of foundation walls, measure equal distances at all corners from these target points to the desired elevations (H, I, J, and K).

f. To lay out a right angle with an engineer's transit, set up the transit directly over the line (use plumb bob) at the point where the right angle is to occur (A, fig. 5-5). Sight a reference point on that line (B) to be sure the transverse axis of the engineer's transit is parallel to the line. Turn the eyepiece end of the sight tube to the left until the scale indicates that an arc of 90° has been completed. Establish a leveling rod in position along this line of sight at the desired distance. A line extended from the leveling rod (D) to the point from which the sight was taken will be perpendicular to the base line and will form a right angle at the point at which they bisect (DAB).

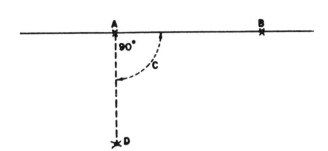

Figure 5-5. Laying out a right angle with an engineer's transit.

5-4. Staking Out

When the location and alinement of a building have been determined, a rectangle comprising the exterior dimensions of the structure is staked out. If the building is other than rectangular, a rectangle large enough to comprise the major outline of the irregular structure is staked out and the irregularities plotted and proved by smaller rectangles within or without the basic form.

5-5. Laying Out a Rectangle Without a Transit

If the construction is parallel to an identifiable line that may be used as a guide, staking out may be accomplished without a builder's transit. If a clearly defined line which construction is to parallel is present (AB) (fig. 5-6) and the maximum outer perimeter of the building area (AC, CD, DB) is known, proceed in the following manner:

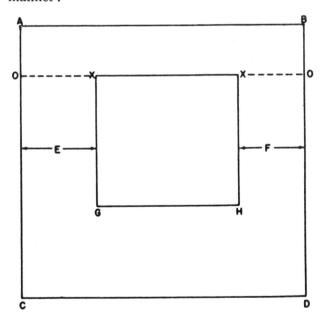

Figure 5-6. Laying out a rectangle without use of transit.

a. Measure away from the front line (AB) along the side lines (AC and BD) the distances (AO and BO) desired to the dimension of the project that is to run parallel to the front line.

b. Stretch a line tightly from point O to O. This line will mark out what will be frontage of the project.

c. Measure in from lines AC and BD along line OO, one-half the difference between the length of OO and the desired length of the project. The points (X and X) will constitute the front corners of the project.

d. The two distances, OX and XO, establish the distance E and F. Extending lines from the two front corners, X and X, parallel to AC and BD at the distances established as E and F for the required depth of the project provides the side lines of the project XG and XH.

e. Joining the extreme ends of side lines XG and XH will provide the rear line of the project.

f. After the four corners (X, X, G, and H) have been located, drive stakes at each corner. Batter boards may be erected at these points either after all the stakes have been set or while they are being set. Dimensions are determined accurately during each step.

g. If the building is not rectangular, several lines such as OO may be run and appropriate adjacent rectangles constructed from these lines in the same fashion as indicated above.

5-6. Laying out a Simple Rectangle With an Engineer's Transit or Leveling Instrument

a. Working from an established line AB (fig. 5-7) such as a road or street line, property line, or an established reference line, select a point to represent the lateral limit for a front corner of the project.

b. Set up the engineer's transit at point C and establish point D, a front corner of the project.

c. Set up the engineer's transit at a point E a greater distance along line AB from point C than the intended length of the project. Set a stake at F, the same distance from AB as D. CD and EF are equal.

d. Establish the front line of the project by marking off the length of the project DG along the established line DF. The two front corners of the project will be located at D and G.

e. With engineer's transit at point C, shoot E and then swing the transit 90 degrees and sight along this position to establish H, the rear corner of the project.

f. With the engineer's transit set up at G, sight D and swing the transit sight tube 90 degrees and shoot I, the other rear corner of the project.

g. To prove the work, set up the transit at I and take a sighting on H. If IH is equal to DG, the work is correct. If it is not, the work must be repeated until correct.

5-7. Laying Out an Irregularly Shaped Project

Where the outline of the building is not a rectangle, the procedure in establishing each point is the same as described above, but more points have to be located and the final proving of the work is more likely to reveal a small error. It is usually advisable with an irregularly shaped building to lay out first a large rectangle which will comprise the entire building or a greater part of it. This is shown in 2, figure 5-7, as the rectangle HOPQ. Having once established this accurately, the remaining portion of the layout will consist of small rectangles, each of which can be laid out and proved separately. The other rectangles as LMNP, ABCQ, DEFG, and LJKO are illustrated in 2, figure 5-7.

5-8. Batter Boards

a. Staking Procedure. At the points at which the various corners of the project are located, a corner stake is driven to mark the exact spot (fig. 5-8). If the area must be excavated for a foundation, the excavating will disturb the pegs. Batter boards are therefore set up to preserve definite and accurate building lines to work toward or from. This is done by stretching heavy cord or fine wire from one batter board to the

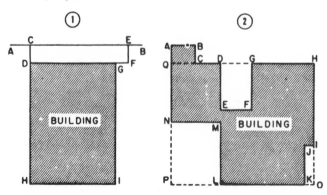

Figure 5-7. Laying out regular and irregular projects.

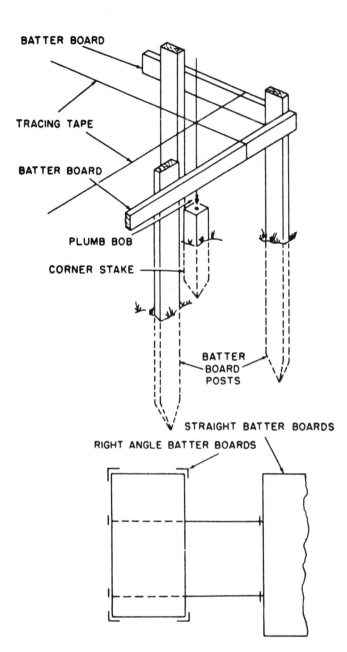

BATTER BOARD

TRACING TAPE

BATTER BOARD

PLUMB BOB

CORNER STAKE

BATTER BOARD POSTS

STRAIGHT BATTER BOARDS

RIGHT ANGLE BATTER BOARDS

Figure 5–8. Batter boards.

other to define the lines of excavations.

b. Locating Batter Boards. Right-angle batter boards are erected 3 or 4 feet outside each corner stake (fig. 5–8). Straight batter boards are erected 3 or 4 feet outside of the line stakes set at points provided for the extension of foundation lines (fig. 5–8) which intercept side lines.

c. Construction of Batter Boards. Batter board stakes may be 2 x 4's, 2 x 6's, or 4 x 4's. Right-angle batter boards usually are two 1 x 6 boards and three stakes. They can be nailed or bolted to the stakes either before or after they are sunk. Batter boards are firmly anchored. Since the

boards should be at the exact height of the top of the foundation, it may be desirable to adjust the height by nailing the boards to the stakes after the stakes have been sunk. Right-angle batter boards may be nailed at close to perpendicular by the use of a framing square and should be leveled by means of a carpenter's level before they are secured. When the final adjustments have been made for accuracy and squareness, saw cuts may be made or nails driven into the tops of the boards to hold the lines and keep them in place. Separate cuts or nails may be used for the building line, the foundation line, footing line, and excavation lines. These grooves permit the removal and replacement of the lines in the correct position.

5–9. Extending Lines

The following procedure applies to a simple layout (fig. 5–9) and must be amended to apply to different or more complex layout problems:

a. After locating and sinking stakes A and B, erect batter boards 1, 2, 3, and 4. Extend the chalkline X from batter board 1 over stakes A and B to batter board 3.

b. After locating and sinking stake C, erect batter boards 5 and 6. Extend the chalkline Y from batter board 2 over stakes A and C to batter board 6.

c. After locating and sinking stake D, erect batter boards 7 and 8. Extend chalkline Z from batter board 5 over stakes C and D to batter board 7.

d. Extend line O from batter board 8 over stakes D and B to batter board 4.

e. Where foundation walls are wide at the bottom and extend beyond the outside dimensions of the building, the excavation must be larger than the size laid out. To lay out dimensions for this excavation, measure out as far as required from the building line on each batter board, and stretch lines between these points and outside the first layout.

f. The lines may be brought to an approximate right angle where they cross by holding a plumb bob over the corner layout stakes and adjusting the lines until they touch the plumb bob line perfectly.

g. The lines should be checked by means of a line level, or carpenter's level.

5–10. Squaring Foundation Lines

There are two methods for squaring extended

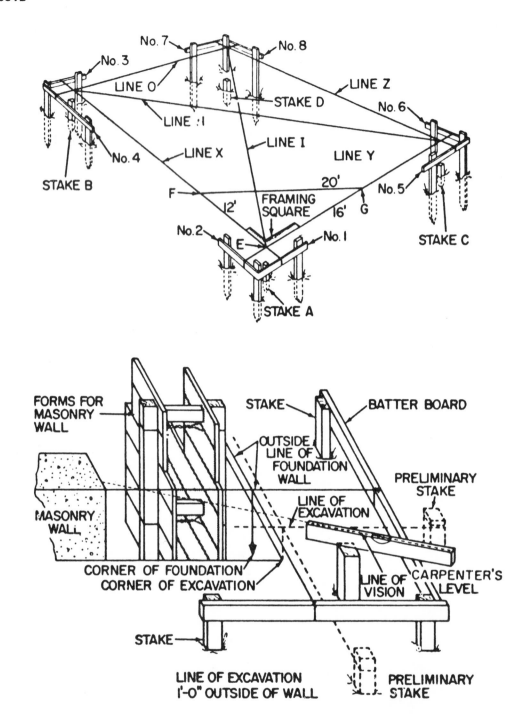

Figure 5-9. Laying out building lines from batter boards.

lines commonly used by the carpenter: the 6-8-10 method and the diagonal method.

a. 6-8-10 Method (fig. 5-9). After lines have been extended and are in place, measure the distance EF (6 feet or a multiple thereof, such as 12 feet). Measure off EF (to a distance of 8 feet if the previous figure used was 6 feet, or to a distance 16 feet if the previous figure

was 12 feet). Adjust the lines until FG equals 10 feet if the other two measurements used are 6 feet and 8 feet, or 20 feet if the other two are 12 feet and 16 feet.

b. The Diagonal Method (fig. 5-9). If the layout is rectangular, line H and I cutting the rectangle from opposing corners will form two triangles. If the rectangle is perfect, these lines will be equal in length and the corners perfectly square. If lines H and I are not equal in length, adjust the corners by moving the lines right or left until H and I are equal.

5-11. Foundations

Foundations vary according to their use, the bearing capacity of the soil, and the type of material available. The material may be cut stone, rock, brick, concrete, tile, or wood, depending upon the weight which the foundation is to support. Foundations may be classified as wall or column (pier) foundations.

a. Wall Foundations. Wall foundations are built solid for their total length when heavy loads are to be carried or where the earth has low supporting strength. These walls may be made of concrete, rock, brick, or cut stone, with a footing at the bottom (fig. 5-10). Because of the time, labor, and material required to built it, this type of wall will be used in the theater of operations only when other types cannot be used. Steel rod reinforcements should be used in all concrete walls.

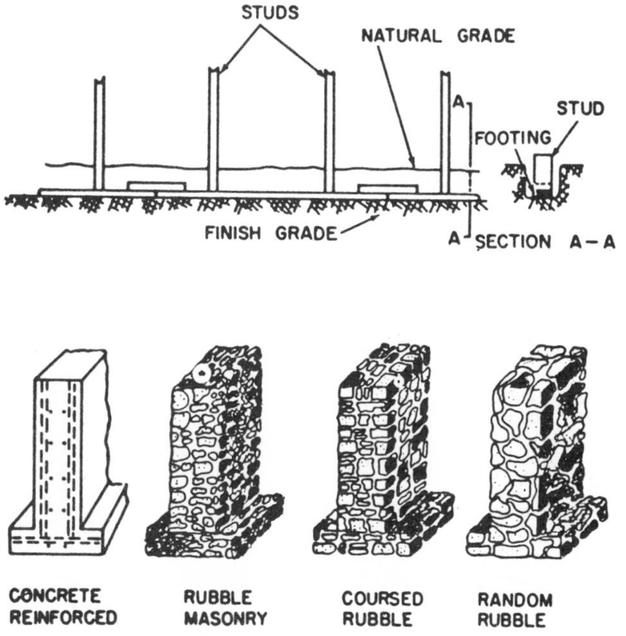

Figure 5-10. Foundation walls.

(1) *Rubble masonry.* Rubble stone masonry is used for walls both above and below ground and for bridge abutments. In military construction, it is used when form lumber or masonry units are not available. Rubble masonry may be laid up with or without mortar; if strength and stability are desired, mortar must be used.

(2) *Coursed rubble.* Coursed rubble is assembled of roughly squared stones in such a manner as to produce approximately continuous horizontal bed joints.

(3) *Random rubble.* This is the crudest of all types of stonework. Little attention is paid to laying the stone in courses. Each layer must contain bonding stones that extend through the wall. This produces a wall that is well tied together.

b. Column or Pier Foundations. Column or pier foundations save time and labor. They may be constructed from masonry or wood. The piers or columns are spaced according to the weight to be carried. In most cases, the spacing is from 6 to 10 feet. Figure 5-11 shows the different types of piers with different types of footing. Wood piers are generally used since they are installed with the least time and labor. Where wood piers are 3 feet or more above the ground, braces are necessary (fig. 5-12).

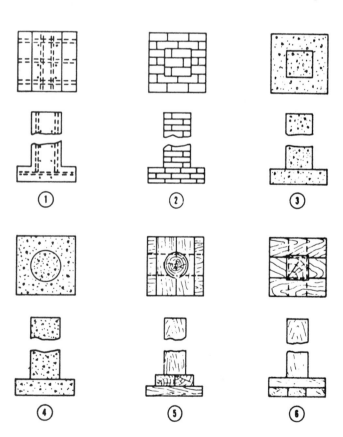

Figure 5-11. Column and piers.

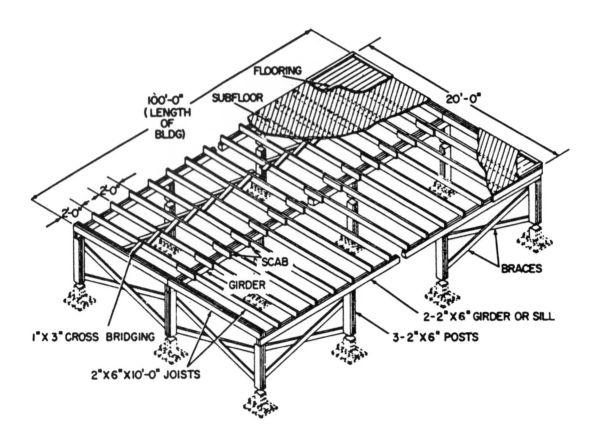

Figure 5–12. Braced piers, sills, girders, and joist construction.

CHAPTER 6

FORMS FOR CONCRETE

6–1. Use

Forms are a major part of concrete construction work. They must support the plastic concrete until it hardens. Forms protect the concrete, assist in curing it, and support any reinforcing rods or conduit embedded in it.

6–2. Design

Forms for concrete must be tight, rigid, and strong. If not tight, loss of mortar may cause a honeycomb effect or loss of water may cause sand streaking. The forms must be braced enough to stay in alinement. Special care is needed in bracing and tying down forms, such as for retainer walls, where the mass of concrete is large at the bottom and tapers toward the top. In this type of construction and in the first pour for walls and columns, the concrete tends to lift the form above its proper elevation. TM 5–742, Concrete and Masonry, gives formulas and tables for designing forms of proper strength.

6–3. Construction Materials

Forms are generally constructed from one of four different materials: earth, metal, wood, and fiber. The carpenter usually constructs wood and fiber forms.

a. Wood. Wood forms are the most common in building construction; they are economical, easy to handle, easy to produce, and adaptable to many shapes. Form lumber can be reused for roofing, bracing, or similar purposes.

(1) Lumber should be straight, strong, and only partially seasoned. Kiln-dried timber tends to swell when soaked with water. Swelling may cause bulging and distortion. If green lumber is used, allowance should be made for shrinkage or it should be kept wet until the concrete is in place. Softwoods (pine, fir, and spruce) are the most economical, light, easy to work, and generally available.

(2) Wood coming in contact with concrete should be surfaced (smooth) on the side towards the concrete and on both edges. The edges may be square, shiplap, or tongue and groove.

Tongue-and-groove lumber makes a more water-tight joint, which reduces warping.

(3) Plywood can be used economically for wall and floor forms if made with waterproof glue and marked for use in concrete forms. Plywood is warp resistant and can be used more often than other lumber. It is made in thicknesses of 1/4, 3/8, 9/16, 5/8, and 3/4 of an inch and in widths up to 48 inches. The 8-foot lengths are most commonly used. The 5/8- and 3/4-inch thicknesses are most economical; thinner plywood requires solid backing to prevent deflection. The 1/4-inch thickness is useful for curved surfaces.

b. Waterproof cardboard and other fiber materials are used for round concrete columns and other preformed shapes. Forms are made by gluing layers of fiber together and molding them to the right shape. The advantage is that fabrication at the job site is not necessary.

6–4. Oiling

a. Oiling. Before concrete is placed, forms are treated with oil or other coating material to prevent the concrete from sticking. The oil should penetrate the wood and prevent water absorption. A light-bodied petroleum oil will do. On plywood, shellac is more effective than oil. If forms are to be reused, painting helps preserve the wood. Occasionally, lumber contains enough tannin to cause softening of the concrete surface; if so, the form surface should be treated with whitewash or limewater before the oil is used.

b. Wetting. If form oil is not available, wetting with water may be substituted to prevent sticking but only in an emergency.

6–5. Form Removal

Forms should be built so as to permit easy removal without danger to the concrete. When necessary to wedge against the concrete, only wood wedges should be used rather than a pinchbar or other metal tool. Forms should not be jerked off after wedging has been started at one end to avoid breaking the edges of the concrete.

Forms to be reused should be cleaned and oiled immediately. Nails should be removed as forms are stripped.

6-6. Components of Wall Forms

Figure 6-1 shows the various parts of a wall form. These parts are described as follows:

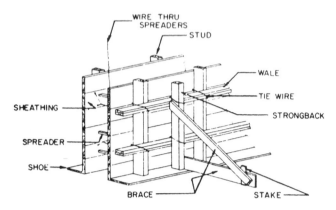

Figure 6-1. Form for a concrete wall.

a. Sheathing. Sheathing forms the surface of the concrete. It should be smooth, especially if the finished surface is to be exposed. Since concrete is plastic when placed in the form, sheathing should be watertight. Tongue-and-groove lumber or plywood gives a watertight surface.

b. Studs. The weight of the concrete causes the sheathing to bulge if it is not reinforced. Vertical studs make the wall form rigid. They are generally made from 2x4 or 3x6 lumber.

c. Wales (walers). Studs also require reinforcing when they extend more than 4 or 5 feet. Double wales give this reinforcing; they also tie prefabricated panels together and keep them in a straight line. They run horizontally and are lapped at the corners.

d. Braces. Many types of braces give the forms stability. The most common brace is a horizontal member and a diagonal member nailed to a stake and to a stud or wale. The diagonal member should make a 30-degree angle with the horizontal member. Additional bracing may be strongbacks (vertical members) behind the wales or in the corner formed by intersecting wales. Braces are not part of the form design and are not considered as providing additional strength.

e. Shoe Plates. The shoe plate is nailed into the foundation or footing and must be carefully placed to maintain the wall dimensions and alinement. Studs are tied into the shoe.

f. Spreaders. Spreaders are cut to the same length as the thickness of the wall and placed between the forms. They are not nailed but held in place by friction because they must be removed before the concrete hardens. A wire is attached to the spreaders to pull them out of the form after the concrete has put enough pressure on the walls to permit easy removal.

g. Tie Wires. Tie wires hold the forms secure against the lateral pressure of unhardened concrete. Double strands are always used.

6-7. Construction of Wall Forms

a. Wall panels should be about 10 feet long so they can be easily handled. Panels are made by nailing the sheathing to the studs. Sheathing is normally 1-inch (13/16 inches dressed) tongue and groove lumber or 3/4-inch plywood. Figure 6-2 shows how panels are connected: figure 6-3 shows details for the corner of a wall.

b. Figure 6-4 shows how to use a wood strip as a wedge when curtain walls and columns are placed at the same time. In removing the forms, the wedge is removed first.

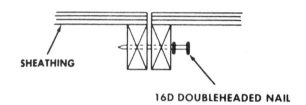

Figure 6-2. Method of connecting wall form panels together.

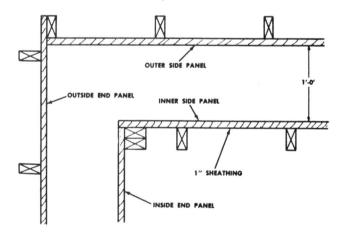

Figure 6-3. Details of corner of wall form.

c. Ties keep wall forms together as the concrete is poured; figures 6-5 and 6-6 show two ways of doing this. Figure 6-5 shows how to use wire ties, which are for low walls only or when tie rods are not available. The wire should be No.

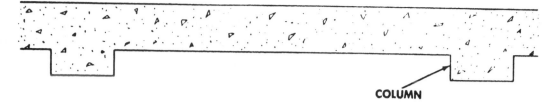

PLAN VIEW OF THE WALL

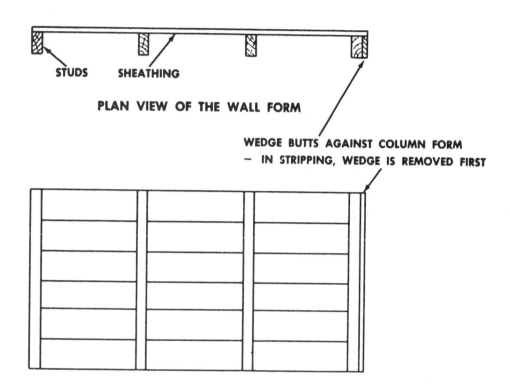

STUDS   SHEATHING

PLAN VIEW OF THE WALL FORM

WEDGE BUTTS AGAINST COLUMN FORM
— IN STRIPPING, WEDGE IS REMOVED FIRST

ELEVATION OF WALL FORM

Figure 6–4. Wall form for curtain walls.

8 or No. 9 gage, soft, black, annealed iron wire, but barbed wire can be used in an emergency. Tie spacing should be the same as the stud spacing, but never more than 3 feet. Each tie is formed by looping the wire around a wale, bringing it through the form, crossing it inside the form walls, and looping it around the wale on the opposite side. The tie wire is made taut by twisting it with a wedge.

d. Spreaders keep the wall forms together as the concrete is placed. Spreaders must be placed near each tie wire; they are removed as the forms are filled so they will not become embedded in the concrete. Figure 6–7 shows how to remove spreaders. A wire fastened to the bottom spreader passes through a hole drilled in each spreader above it. Pulling on the wire will remove the

spreaders one after another as the concrete level rises in the forms.

e. Figure 6–6 shows a tie rod and spreader combination. After the form is removed, each rod is broken off at the notch. If appearance is important, the holes should be filled with a mortar mix.

6–8. Foundation and Footing Forms

a. *Footing Forms.* When possible, earth is excavated to form a mold for concrete wall footings. If wood forms are needed, the four sides are built in panels. Panels for two opposite sides are made at exact footing width (*a*, figure 6–8); the other pair (*b*, figure 6–8) have two end cleats on the inside spaced the length of the footing *plus* twice the sheathing thickness. The 1-inch

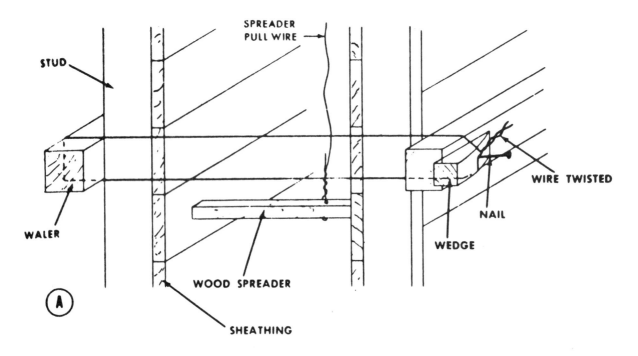

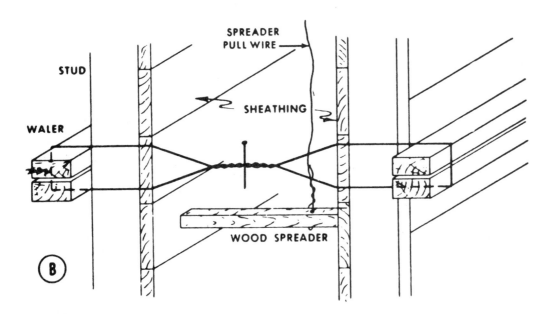

Figure 6-5. Wire ties for form walls.

thick sheathing is nailed to vertical cleats spaced on 2-foot centers. Two-inch dressed lumber should be used for the cleats.

(1) Panels are held in place with form nails until the tie wire is installed; nails should be driven from the outside part way so they can be easily removed.

(2) Tie wires are wrapped around the center cleats. Wire holes on each side of the cleat should be less than 1-inch diameter to prevent

leakage of mortar. All reinforcing bars must be placed before the wire is installed.

(3) For forms 4 feet square or larger, stakes are driven as shown in figure 6-8. These stakes and 1 x 6 boards nailed across the top prevent spreading. Panels may be higher than the required depth of footing since they can be marked on the inside to show the top of the footing. If the footings are less than 1 foot deep and 2 feet square, forms can be constructed of 1-inch sheathing without cleats as shown in figure 6-9.

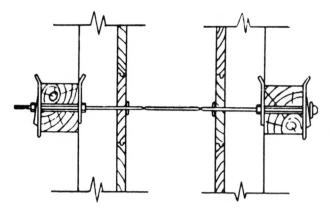

Figure 6-6. Tie rod and spreader for wall form.

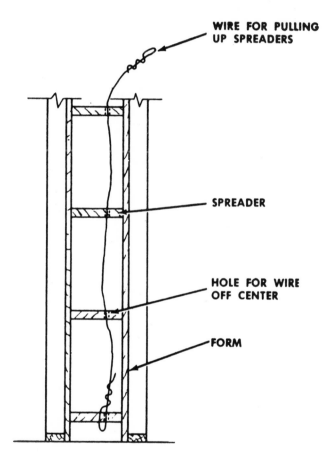

Figure 6-7. Removing wood spreaders.

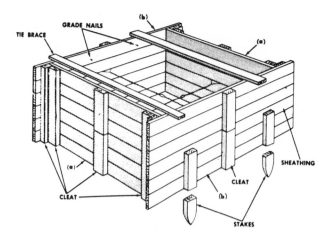

Figure 6-8. Typical large footing form.

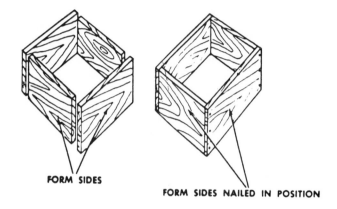

Figure 6-9. Small footing forms.

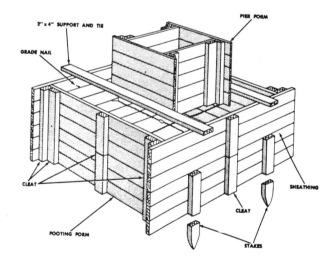

Figure 6-10. Footing and pier form.

b. *Footing and Pier Forms.* When placing a footing and a small pier at the same time, the form is built as shown in figure 6-10. Support for the upper form must not interfere with the placement of concrete in the lower form. This is done by nailing 2 x 4 or 4 x 4 pieces to the lower form as shown. The top form is then nailed to these pieces.

c. *Wall Footings.* Figures 6-11 and 6-12 show how to construct and brace forms for wall foot-ings. The sides are 2-inch lumber held in place by stakes and apart by spreaders. The short brace shown at each stake holds the form in line.

6-9. Column Forms

Figure 6-13 shows elements of column forms.

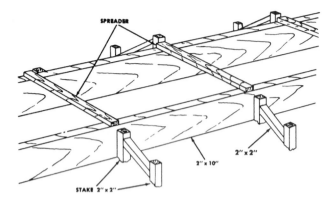

Figure 6–11. Wall footing form.

a. *Components.* Sheathing runs vertically to save the number of sawcuts; corner joints are firmly nailed to insure water-tightness. Batten are narrow strips of boards (cleats) placed directly over the joints to fasten the several pieces of vertical sheathing together.

b. *Construction.* Figure 6–13 shows a column and footing form. The column form is erected after the steel reinforcing is assembled and tied to dowels in the footing. The form should have a cleanout hole in the bottom to help remove debris. The lumber removed to make the cleanout

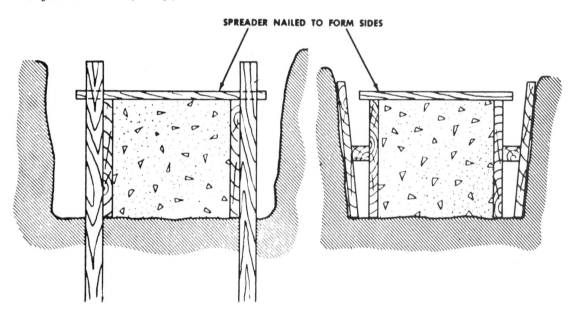

Figure 6–12. Bracing the wall footing form.

holes should be nailed to the form so it can be put back in the hole before concrete is placed.

6–10. Beam and Girder Forms

Figure 6–14 shows a beam form. The type of construction depends on whether the form is to be removed in one piece or whether the bottom is to be left until the concrete is strong enough to remove the shoring. Beam forms receive little bursting pressure but must be shored at close intervals to prevent sagging.

a. *Construction.* The bottom has the same width as the beam and is in one piece the full width. Form sides are 1-inch tongue and groove material and lap over the bottom as shown in figure 6–14. The sheath is nailed to 2 x 4 struts placed on 3-foot centers. A 1 x 4 piece is nailed along the struts to support the joists for the floor panel. The sides of the form are not nailed

to the bottom but held in position by continuous strips. Crosspieces nailed on top serve as spreaders. After erection, the slab panel joints hold the beam in place.

b. *Assembly.* Beam and girder assembly is shown in figure 6–15. The beam bottom butts up tightly against the side of the girder and rests on a 2 x 4 nailed to the girder side. Details in the figure show the clearances for stripping and allow for movement caused by the weight of the concrete. The 4 x 4 posts are spaced to support the concrete and are wedged at bottom or top for easy removal.

6–11. Floor Forms

Floor panels are built as shown in figure 6–16. The 1-inch tongue and groove sheathing or 3/4-inch plywood is nailed to 1 x 4 cleats on 3-foot centers. These panels are supported by 2 x 6

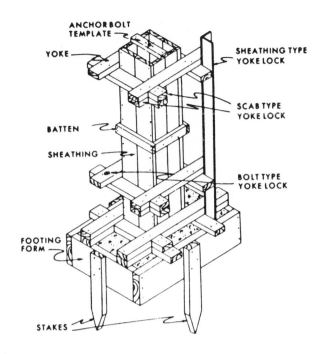

ANCHOR BOLT
TEMPLATE
YOKE
SHEATHING TYPE
YOKE LOCK
SCAB TYPE
YOKE LOCK
BATTEN
SHEATHING
BOLT TYPE
YOKE LOCK
FOOTING
FORM
STAKES

Figure 6-13. Form for a concrete column.

joists. Spacing of joists depends on the thickness of the concrete slab and the span of the beams. If the slab spans the distance between two walls, the panels are used in the same manner as when beams support the floor slab.

6-12. Stair Forms

Figure 6-17 shows a method for building stair forms up to 3 feet in width. The sloping wood platform forming the underside of the steps should be 1-inch tongue and groove sheathing. This platform should extend 12 inches beyond each side of the stairs to support stringer bracing

blocks. The back of the panel is shored with 4 x 4 pieces as shown. The 2 x 6 cleats nailed to the shoring should rest on wedges to make adjustment easy and to make removal of the posts easy. The side stringers are 2 x 12 pieces cut as required for the tread and risers. The riser should be 2-inch material beveled as shown.

6-13. Safety Precautions

The following safety rules apply to form construction and removal.

a. Construction.

(1) Consider protruding nails as the principal source of accidents on form work.

(2) Inspect tools frequently.

(3) Place mud sills under shoring that rests on the ground.

(4) On elevated forms, take care to protect men on scaffolds and on the ground.

(5) Do not raise large form panels in heavy gusts of wind.

(6) Brace all shoring securely to prevent collapse of form work.

b. Stripping.

(1) Permit only workmen doing the stripping in the immediate area.

(2) Do not remove forms until the concrete has set.

(3) Pile stripped forms immediately to avoid congestion, exposed nails, and other hazards.

(4) Cut wires under tension with caution to avoid backlash.

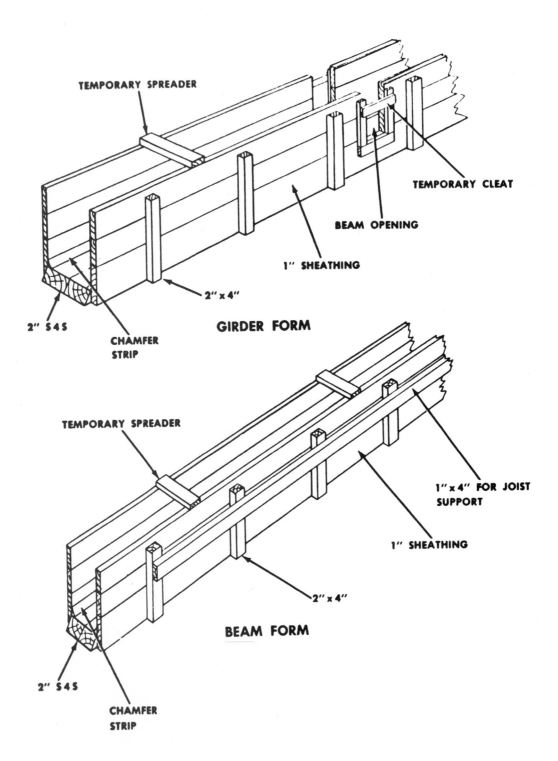

TEMPORARY SPREADER

TEMPORARY CLEAT

BEAM OPENING

1" SHEATHING

2" x 4"

2" S4S

CHAMFER
STRIP

GIRDER FORM

TEMPORARY SPREADER

1" x 4" FOR JOIST
SUPPORT

1" SHEATHING

2" x 4"

BEAM FORM

2" S4S

CHAMFER
STRIP

Figure 6–14. Beam and girder forms.

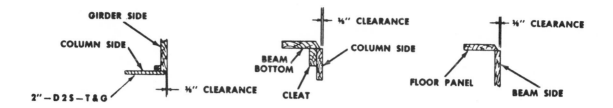

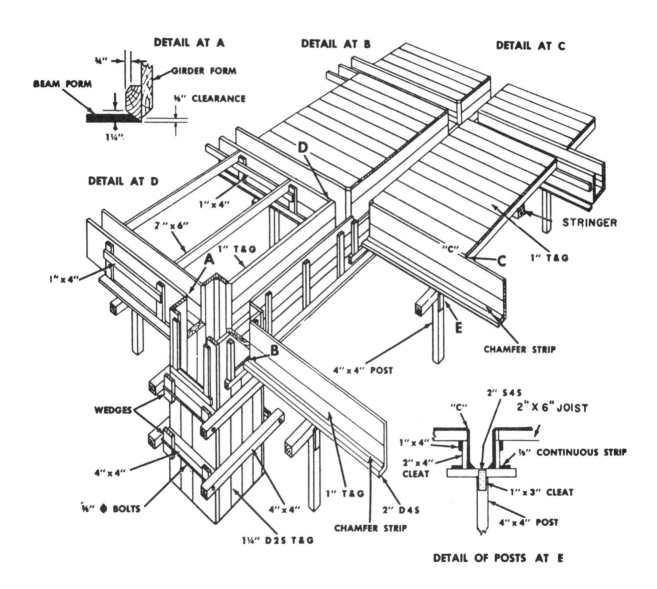

Figure 6–15. Assembly details, beam and floor forms.

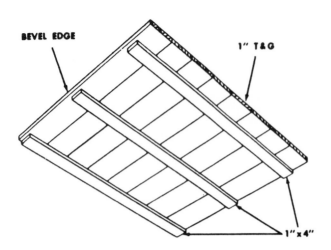

Figure 6–16. Form for floor slab.

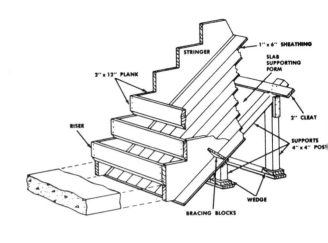

Figure 6–17. Stairway form.

CHAPTER 7

FRAME CONSTRUCTION

Section I. FLOOR FRAMES AND FLOOR COVERINGS

7–1. Framing

After the foundation is built and the batter-boards placed, the carpenter builds the framework. The framework includes the beams, trusses, foundation walls, outside walls, flooring, partitions, roofing, and ceiling.

a. Light Framing. Light framing is used in barracks, bathhouses, administration buildings, light shop buildings, hospitals, and similar buildings. Figure 7–1 shows some details for a 20-foot-wide building; the ground level; window openings, braces, and splices; and names the framing parts.

b. Light Frame Construction. Much of the

framing can be done while staking out and squaring is being completed. When the skeleton is far enough along, boards can be nailed on without need for cutting if they are standard 8-, 10-, 12-, 16-, or 18-foot lengths. The better skilled men should construct the frame. With good organization, a large force of men can be kept busy during framing.

c. Expedient Framing. Expedient framing depends on the conditions. The ideas below may suggest other expedients.

(1) *Light siding.* Chicken wire and water resistant bituminous paper can be sandwiched to provide adequate temporary framing in temperate climates.

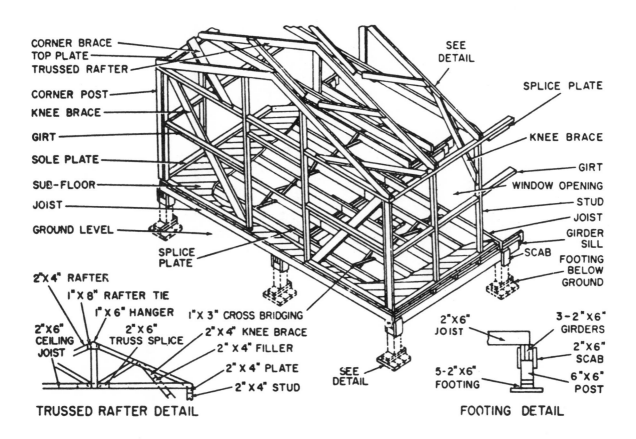

Figure 7–1. View of a light frame building substructure.

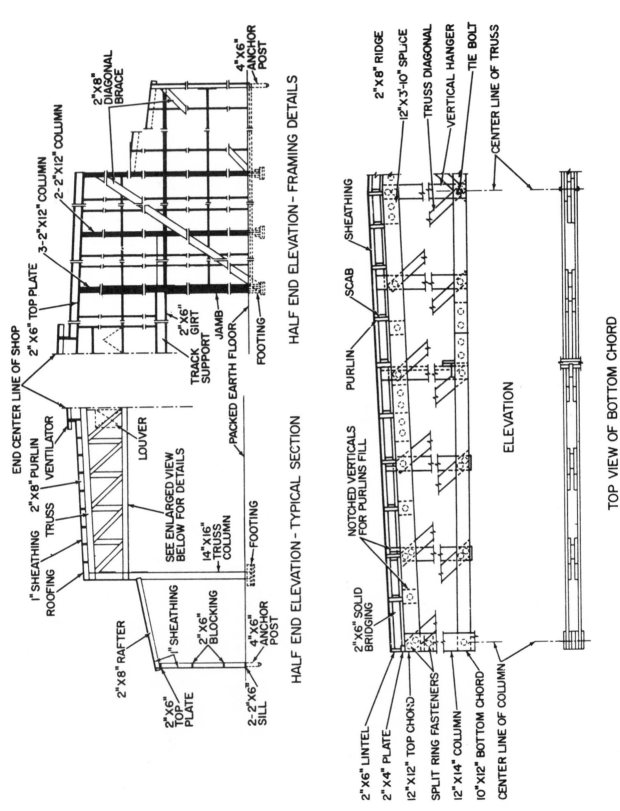

2"x8" DIAGONAL BRACE

2-2"X12" COLUMN

3-2"X12" COLUMN

2"x6" TOP PLATE

END CENTER LINE OF SHOP

2"X6" GIRT

JAMB

TRACK SUPPORT

FOOTING

PACKED EARTH FLOOR

4"X6" ANCHOR POST

HALF END ELEVATION – FRAMING DETAILS

I" SHEATHING

ROOFING

TRUSS

2"X8" PURLIN

VENTILATOR

LOUVER

SEE ENLARGED VIEW BELOW FOR DETAILS

14"X16" TRUSS COLUMN

FOOTING

2"X8" RAFTER

2"X6" TOP PLATE

2"X6" BLOCKING

I" SHEATHING

4"X6" ANCHOR POST

2-2"X6" SILL

HALF END ELEVATION – TYPICAL SECTION

2"X8" RIDGE

12"X3'-10" SPLICE

TRUSS DIAGONAL

VERTICAL HANGER

TIE BOLT

CENTER LINE OF TRUSS

SHEATHING

SCAB

PURLIN

NOTCHED VERTICALS FOR PURLINS FILL

2"X6" SOLID BRIDGING

ELEVATION

2"X6" LINTEL

2"X4" PLATE

12"X12" TOP CHORD

SPLIT RING FASTENERS

12"X14" COLUMN

10"X12" BOTTOM CHORD

CENTER LINE OF COLUMN

TOP VIEW OF BOTTOM CHORD

Figure 7–2. Sectional view of a heavy frame building.

(2) *Salvaged framing.* Salvaged sheet metal such as corrugated material or gasoline cans can be used as siding in the construction of emergency housing.

(3) *Local timber.* Poles trimmed from saplings or bamboo can be constructed into reasonably sound framing. Such materials may be secured with native vines as a further expedient.

(4) *Wood substitute framing.* Adobe soil, straw, and water puddled to proper consistency can be used for form walls, floors, and foundations. A similar mixture may be used to form sun-dried bricks for construction use.

(5) *Excavations.* Proper excavation and simple log cribbing may be covered with sod and carefully drained to provide adequate shelter.

d. Heavy Framing. Heavy frame buildings are more permanent, generally warehouses, depots, and shops. Figure 7–2 shows the details of heavy frame construction.

7–2. Sills

a. Types. The sill (fig. 7–1) is the foundation that supports all the building above it. It is the first part of the building to be set in place. It rests directly on the foundation piers or on the ground; it is joined at the corners and spliced when necessary. Figure 7–3 shows the most common sills. The type used depends on the type of construction used in the frame.

(1) *Box sills.* Box sills are used often with the very common style of platform framing, either with or without the sill plate. In this type of sill (1 and 2, fig. 7–3), the part that lies on the foundation wall or ground is called the sill plate. The sill is laid edgewise on the outside edge of the sill plate.

(2) *T-sills.* There are two types of T-sill construction; one commonly used in dry, warm climates (3, fig. 7–3), and one commonly used in less warm climates (4, fig. 7–3). Their construction is similar except that in the latter case the joists are nailed directly to the studs, as well as to the sills, and headers are used between the floor joists.

(3) *Braced framing sill.* The sill shown in 5, figure 7–3, is generally used in braced-framing construction. The floor joists are notched out and nailed directly to the sill and studs.

(4) *Built-up sills.* Where built-up sills are used, the joints are staggered (1, fig. 7–4). The corner joints are made as shown in 2, figure 7–4.

b. Sill Requirement for Piers. If piers are used in the foundation, heavier sills are used. They

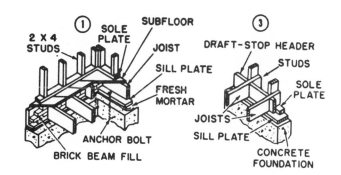

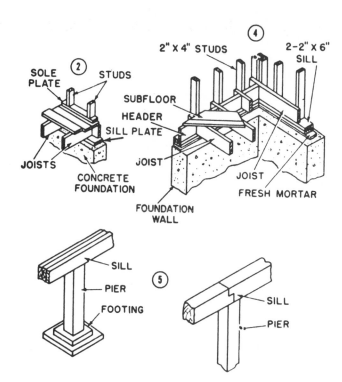

Figure 7–3. Types of sills.

are single heavy timbers or built up of two or more pieces of timber. Where heavy timber or built-up sills are used, the joints should occur over piers. The size of the sill depends upon the load to be carried and upon the spacing of the piers. The sill plates are laid directly on graded earth or on piers. Where earth floors are used, the studs are nailed directly to the sill plate.

7–3. Girders

The distance between two outside walls is often too great to be spanned by a single joist. When two or more joists are needed to cover the span, intermediate support for inboard joist-ends is provided by one or more girders. A girder is a large beam that supports other smaller beams or joists.

a. Construction. A girder may be made up of

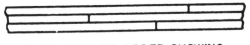

PLAN VIEW OF GIRDER SHOWING
METHOD OF STAGGERING JOINTS

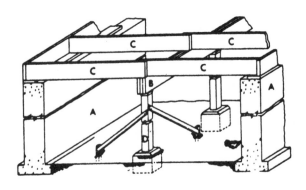

Figure 7-5. Built-up girder.

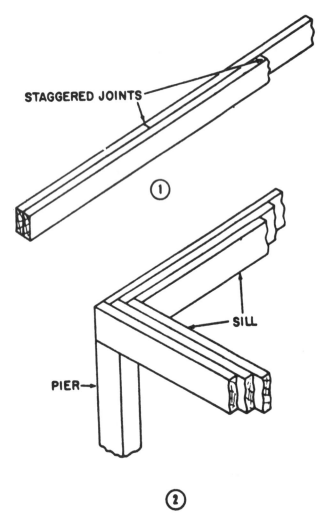

Figure 7-4. Sill fabrication.

several beams nailed together with 16d common nails; or it may be solid wood, steel, reinforced concrete, or a combination of these materials.

b. Design Requirements. Girders carry a very large proportion of the weight of a building. They must be well designed, rigid, and properly supported at the foundation walls and on the columns. Precautions must be taken to avoid or counteract any future settling or shrinking that might cause distortion of the building. The girders must also be installed so that they will properly support joists.

c. Illustration. Figure 7-5 shows a built-up girder. A shows the two outside masonry walls, B the built-up girder, C the joists, and D the support columns which support the girder B. Notice that the joists rest on top of the girder. This type of girder is commonly used in house construction. It is generally made of three planks spiked together (fig. 7-5) with 16d common nails.

d. Use of Ledger Board. A girder with a ledge board upon which the joists rest is used where vertical space is limited. This arrangement is useful in providing more headroom in basements.

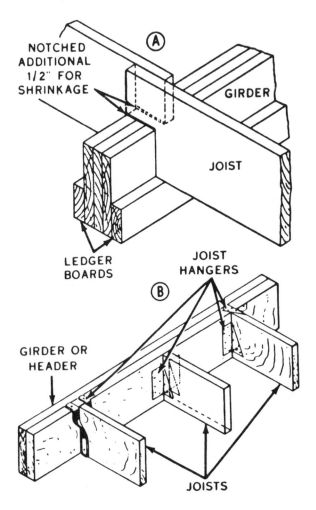

Figure 7-6. Joist-to-girder attachment.

e. Joist Hangers. A girder over which joist hangers have been placed to carry the joists is also used where there is little headroom or where the joists carry an extremely heavy load and nailing cannot be relied on. These girders are illustrated in figure 7–6.

f. Size Requirements. The principles which govern the size of a girder are—

(1) The distance between girder posts.

(2) The girder load area.

(3) The total floor load per square foot on the girder.

(4) The load per linear foot on the girder.

(5) The total load on the girder.

(6) The material to be used.

g. Size Determination. A girder should be large enough to support any ordinary load placed upon it; any size larger than that is wasted material. The carpenter should understand the effect of length, width, and depth on the strength of a wood girder before attempting to determine its size.

h. Depth. When the depth of a girder is doubled, the safe load is increased four times. In other words, a girder that is 3 inches wide and 12 inches deep will carry four times as much wight as a girder 3 inches wide and 6 inches deep. In order to obtain greater carrying capacity through the efficient use of material, it is better to increase the depth within limits than it is to increase the width of the girder. The sizes of built-up wood girders for various loads and spans may be determined by using table 7–1. (LOCATED IN BACK OF CHAPTER)

i. Load Area. The load area of a building is carried by both foundation walls and the girder. Because the ends of each joist rest on the girder, there is more weight on the girder than there is on either of the walls. Before considering the load on the girder, it may be well to consider a single joist. Suppose that a 10-foot plank weighing 5 pounds per foot is lifted by two men. If the men were at opposite ends of the plank, they would each be supporting 25 pounds.

(1) Now assume that one of these men lifts the end of another 10-foot plank with the same weight as the first one, and a third man lifts the opposite end. The two men on the outside are each supporting one-half of the weight of one plank, or 25 pounds apiece, but the man in the center is supporting one-half of each of the two planks, or a total of 50 pounds.

(2) The two men on the outside represent the foundation walls, and the center man represents the girder; therefore, the girder carries one-half of the weight, while the other half is equally divided between the outside walls. However, the girder may not always be located halfway between the outer walls. To explain this, the same three men will lift two planks which weigh 5 pounds per foot. One of the planks is 8 feet long and the other is 12 feet long. Since the total length of these two planks is the same as before and the weight per foot is the same, the total weight in both cases is 100 pounds.

(3) One of the outside men is supporting one-half of the 8-foot plank, or 20 pounds. The man on the opposite outside end is supporting one-half of the 12-foot plank, or 30 pounds. The man in the center is supporting one-half of each plank, or a total of 50 pounds. This is the same total weight he was lifting before. A general rule that can be applied when determining the girder load area is that a girder will carry the weight of the floor on each side to the midpoint of joists which rest upon it.

j. Floor Load. After the girder load area is known, the total floor load per square foot must be determined in order to select a safe girder size. Both dead and live loads must be considered in finding the total floor load.

(1) The first type of load consists of all weight of the building structure. This is called the dead load. The dead load per square foot of floor area, which is carried to the girder either directly or indirectly by way of bearing partitions, will vary according to the method of construction and building height. The structural parts included in the dead load are—

Floor joists for all floor levels.

Flooring materials, including attic if it is floored.

Bearing partitions.

Attic partitions.

Attic joists for top floor.

Ceiling lath and plaster, including basement ceiling if it is plastered.

(2) For a building of light-frame construction similar to an ordinary frame house, the dead load allowance per square foot of all the structural parts must be added together to determine the total dead load. The allowance for average subfloor, finish floor, and joists without basement plaster should be 10 pounds per square foot. If the basement ceiling is plastered, an additional 10 pounds should be allowed. When girders (or bearing partitions) support the first floor partition, a load allowance of 20 pounds must be

allowed for ceiling plaster and joists when the attic is unfloored. If the attic is floored and used for storage, an additional 10 pounds (per sq ft) should be allowed.

(3) The second type of load to be considered is the weight of furniture, persons, and other movable loads which are not actually a part of the building but are still carried by the girder. This is called the live load. Snow on the roof is considered a part of the live load. The live load per square foot will vary according to the use of the building and local weather conditions. The allowance for the live load on floors used for living purposes is usually 30 pounds per square foot. If the attic is floored and used for light storage, an additional 20 pounds per square foot should be allowed. The allowance per square foot for live loads is usually governed by specifications and regulations.

(4) When the total load per square foot of floor area is known, the load per linear foot on the girder is easily figured. Assume that the girder load area of the building shown in figure 7–7 is sliced into 1-foot lengths across the girder. Each slice represents the weight supported by 1 foot of the girder. If the slice is divided into 1-foot units, each unit will represent 1 square foot of the total floor area. The load per linear foot of girder is determined by multiplying the number of units by the total load per square foot. Note in figure 7–7 that the girder is off center. Therefore, the joist length on one side of the girder is 7 feet (one-half of 14 feet) and the other side is 5 feet (one-half of 10 feet), for a total distance of 12 feet across the load area. Since each slice is 1 foot wide, it has a total floor area of 12 square feet. Now, if we assume that the total floor load for each square foot is 70 pounds, multiply the length times the width (7′ x 12′) to get the total square feet supported by the girder (7′ x 12′ = 84 sq ft).

  84 sq ft
x 70 lb per sq ft (live and dead load)
‾‾‾‾‾‾‾‾‾‾‾
5,880 lb total load on girder

k. Material. Wooden girders are more common than steel in small frame-type buildings. Solid timber may be used or they may be built up by using two or more 2-inch planks. Built-up girders have the advantage of not warping as easily as solid wooden girders and are less likely to have decayed wood in the center.

(1) When built-up girders are used, the pieces should be securely spiked together to prevent them from buckling individually. A two-

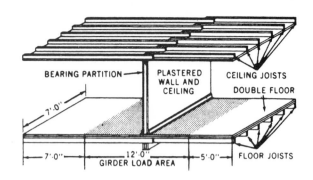

Figure 7–7. Girder load area.

piece girder of 2-inch planks should be spiked on both sides with 16d common nails. The nails should be located near the bottom, spaced approximately 2 feet apart near the ends and 1 foot apart in the center. A three-piece girder should be nailed in the same way as a two-piece girder.

(2) Regardless of whether the girder is built-up or solid, it should be of well-seasoned material. For a specific total girder load and span, the size of the girder will vary according to the kinds of wood used. The reason for this variation is that some kinds are stronger than others.

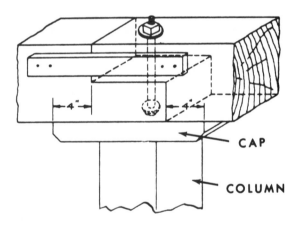

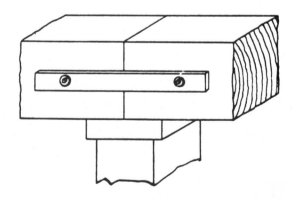

Figure 7–8. Half-lap and butt joints.

l. Splicing. To make a built-up girder, select straight lumber free from knots and other defects. The stock should be long enough so that no more than one joint will occur over the span between footings. The joints in the beam should be staggered, with care taken to insure that the planks are squared at each joint and butted tightly together. Sometimes a half-lap joint is used to join solid beams. In order to do this correctly, the beam should be placed on one edge so that the annual rings run from top to bottom. The lines for the half-lap joint are then laid out as illustrated in figure 7–8, and the cuts are made along these lines. The cuts are then checked with a steel square to assure a matching joint. To make the matching joint on the other beam, proceed in the same way and repeat the process.

(1) The next step is to tack a temporary strap across the joint to hold it tightly together. Now drill a hole through the joist with a bit about 1/16 inch larger than the bolt to be used. Fasten together with a bolt, washer, and nut.

(2) Another type of joint is called the strapped butt joint. The ends of the beam should be cut square, and the straps, which generally are 18 inches long, are bolted to each side of the beams.

m. Supports. When building small houses where the services of an architect are not available, it is important that the carpenter have some knowledge of the principles that determine the proper size of girder supports.

(1) A column or post is a vertical member designed to carry the live and dead loads imposed upon it. It may be made of wood, metal, or masonry. The wooden columns may be solid timbers or may be made up of several wooden members spiked together with 16d or 20d common nails. Metal columns are made of heavy pipe, large steel angles, or I-beams.

(2) Regardless of the material used in a column, it must have some form of bearing plate at the top and bottom. These plates distribute the load evenly over the cross sectional area of the column. Basement posts that support girders should be set on masonry footings. Columns should be securely fastened to the load-bearing member at the top and to the footing on which they rest at the bottom. Figure 7–9 shows a solid wooden column with a metal bearing cap drilled to provide a means of fastening it to the column and to the girder. The bottom of this type of column may be fastened to the masonry footing by a metal dowel inserted in a hole drilled in the bottom of the column and in the

masonry footing. The base at this point is coated with asphalt to prevent rust or rot.

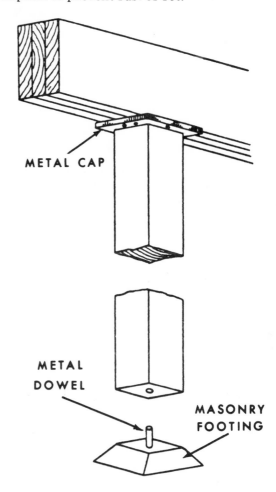

Figure 7–9. Solid wood column with metal bearing cap.

(3) When locating columns, it is well to avoid spans of more than 10 feet between columns that are to support the girders. The farther apart the columns are spaced, the heavier the girder must be to carry the joists over the span between the columns.

(4) A good arrangement of the girder and supporting columns for a 24- x 40-foot building is shown in figure 7–10. Column B will support one-half of the girder load existing in the half of the building lying between the wall A and column C. Column C will support one-half of the girder load between columns B and D. Likewise, column D will share equally the girder loads with column C and the wall E.

n. Girder Forms. Girder forms for making concrete girders and beams are constructed from 2-inch-thick material (fig. 7–11) dressed on all sides. The bottom piece of material should be constructed in one piece to avoid the necessity of cleats. The bottom piece of the form should never

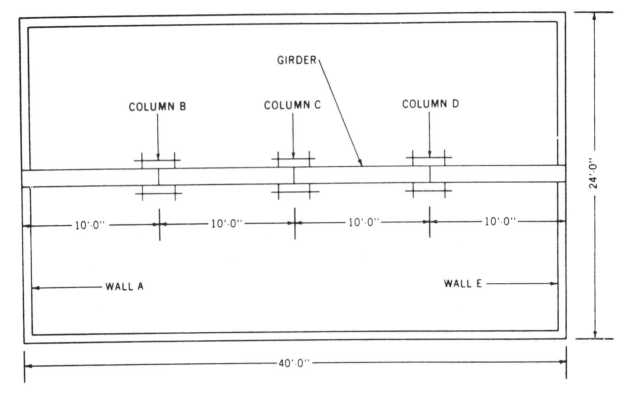

Figure 7–10. Column spacing.

overlap the side pieces. The side pieces must always overlap the bottom. The temporary cleats shown in figure 7–11 are tacked on to prevent the form from collapsing when handled.

7–4. Floor Joists

Joists are the wooden members that make up the body of the floor frame. The flooring or subflooring is nailed to them. They are usually 2 or 3 inches thick. Joists as small as 2 by 6 inches are sometimes used in light buildings. These are too small for floors with spans over 10 feet but are frequently used for ceiling joists. Joists usually carry a uniform load of materials and personnel. The latter loads carry a uniform

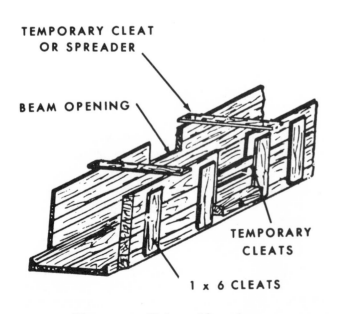

Figure 7–11. Girder and beam form.

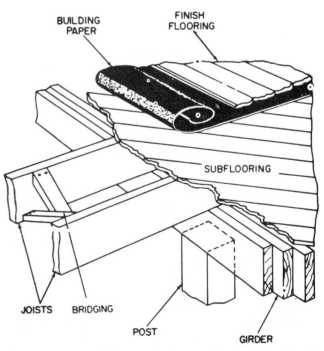

Figure 7–12. Floor joists.

load of materials and personnel. The latter loads are "live loads"; the weight of joists and floors is a "dead load". The joists carry the flooring directly on their upper surface and they are supported at their ends by sills, girders, bearing partitions, or bearing walls (fig. 7–12). They are spaced 16 or 24 inches apart, center to center; sometimes the spacing is 12 inches, but where such spacing is necessary, heavier joists should

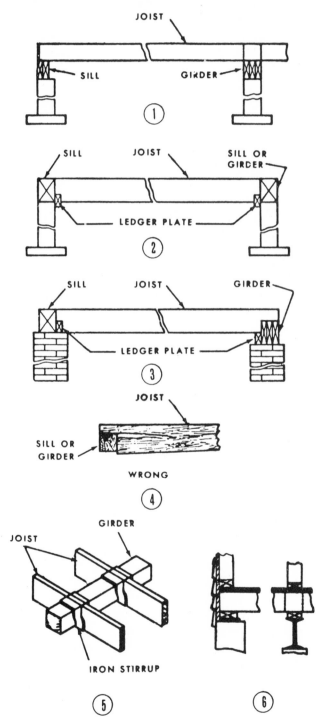

Figure 7–13. Sill and joist connections.

be used. Two-inch material should not be used for joists more than 12 inches apart.

7–5. Connecting Joists to Sills, Girders, and I-Beams

a. Joining to Sills. In joining joists to sills, be sure that the connection is able to hold the load that the joists will carry. A joist resting upon the sill is shown in 1, figure 7–13. This method (of several methods) is most commonly used because it provides the strongest possible joint. The methods shown in 2 and 3, figure 7–13, are used where it is not desirable to use joists on top of the sill. The ledger plate (*e* below) should be securely nailed and the joist should not be notched over one-third of its depth to prevent splitting (4, fig. 7–13).

b. Joining to Girders. In the framing of the joists to the girders, the joists must be level. Therefore, if the girder is not the same height as the sill, the joist must be notched as shown in 3, figure 7–13. If the girder and sill are of the same height, the joist must be connected to the sill and girder to keep the joist level. In placing joists, always have the crown up since this counteracts the weight on the joist; in most cases there will be no sag below a straight line. Overhead joists are joined to plates as shown in 1 and 2, figure 7–14. The inner end of the joist rests on the plates of the partition walls. When a joist is to rest on plates or girders, either the joist is cut long enough to extend the full width of the plate or girder, or it is cut so as to meet in the center of the plate or girder and is connected with a scab. Where two joist ends lie side by side on a plate, they should be nailed together. Joists may also be joined to girders by using ledger strips (3 and 4, fig. 7–14).

c. Iron Stirrups. One of the strongest supports for the joists is straps or hangers (iron stirrups) as shown in 5 of figure 7–13.

d. I-Beams. The simplest and probably the best way to carry joists on steel girders is to rest them on top, as shown in 6, figure 7–13, provided headroom is not too much restricted. If there is a lack of headroom, use the method shown in 5, figure 7–13.

e. Use of Ledger Plates (fig. 7–14). In connecting joists to girders and sills where piers are used, a 2 by 4 is nailed to the face of the sill or girder, flush with the bottom edge; this is called a "ledger plate" (1, fig. 7–14). These pieces should be nailed securely with 20-penny nails about 12 inches apart. Where 2 by 4 or 2

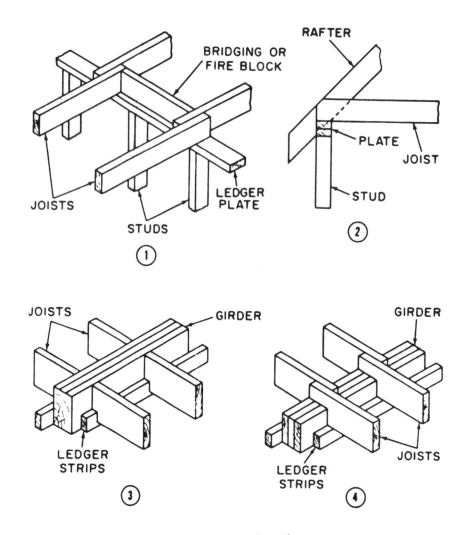

Figure 7-14. Ledger plates.

by 8 joists are used, it is better to use 2 by 2's to prevent the joists from splitting at the notch. When joists are 10 inches deep and deeper, 2 by 4's may be used without reducing the strength of the joists. If a notch is used, joist ties may be used to overcome this loss of strength. These ties are short 1 by 4 boards nailed across the joist; the ends of the boards are flush with the top and bottom edge of the joists.

7-6. Bridging

a. General. When joists are used over a long span, they have a tendency to sway from side to side. Floor frames are bridged in order to stiffen the floor frame, to prevent unequal deflection of the joists, and to enable an overload joist to receive some help from the joists on either side of it. A pattern for the bridging stock is obtained by placing a piece of material between the joists as shown in figure 7-15, then marking and sawing it. When sawed, the cut will form the correct

angle. Always nail the top of the bridging with 8- or 10-penny nails. Do not nail the bottom of the bridging until the rough floor has been laid, in order to keep the bridging from pushing up any joist which might cause an unevenness in the floor.

b. Construction. Bridging is of two kinds: solid (or horizontal) bridging (1, fig. 7-15) and cross bridging (2, fig. 7-15). Cross bridging is the one most generally used; it is very effective and requires less material than horizontal bridging. Cross bridging looks like a cross and consists of pieces of lumber, usually 1 by 3 or 2 by 3 inches in size, cut in diagonally between the floor joists. Each piece is nailed to the top of each joist and forms a cross (x) between the joists. These pieces between joists should be placed as near to each other as possible. Bridging should be nailed and the bottoms left until the subfloor is laid. This permits the joists to adjust themselves to their final positions. The bottom ends of bridging

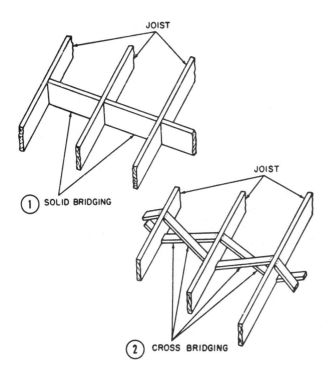

Figure 7-15. Types of bridging.

may then be nailed, forming a continuous truss across the whole length of the floor and preventing any overloaded joist from sagging below the others. Cutting and fitting the bridging by hand is a slow process; a power saw should be used if it is available. After joists have once been placed, a pattern may be made and used to speed up the process of cutting. On joists over 8 feet long, one line of bridging should be placed and on joists over 16 feet long, two lines.

7-7. Floor Openings

a. General. Floor openings for stairwells, ventilators, and chimneys are framed by a combination of headers and trimmers (fig. 7-16). Headers run at right angles to the direction of the joists and are doubled. Trimmers run parallel to the joists and are actually doubled joists. The joists are framed to the headers where the headers form the opening frame at right angles to the joists. These shorter joists, framed to the headers, are called tail beams, tail joists, or header joists. The number of headers and trimmers needed at any opening depends upon the shape of the opening, whether it is a simple rectangle or contains additional angles; upon the direction in which the opening runs in relation to the direction in which the joists run; and upon the position of the opening in relation to partitions or walls. Figure 7-16 gives examples of openings, one of which runs parallel to the

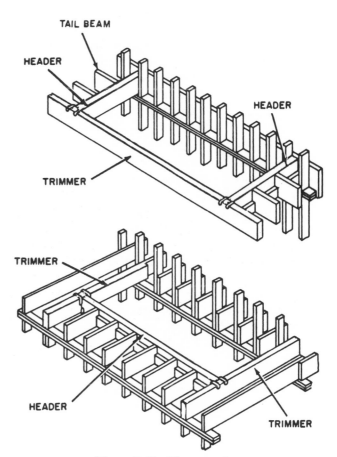

Figure 7-16. Floor openings.

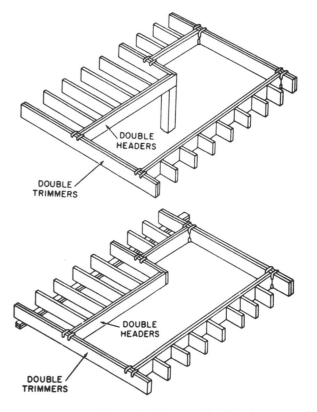

Figure 7-17. Double headers and double trimmers.

joist and requires two headers and one trimmer, while the other runs at right angles to the run of the joists and, therefore, requires one header and two trimmers. The openings shown in figure 7-17 are constructed with corner angles supported in different ways. The cantilever method requires that the angle be fairly close to a supporting partition with joists from an adjacent span that run to the header.

b. Construction. To frame openings of the type shown in figure 7-18, first install joists A and C, then cut four pieces of timber that are the same size as the joists with their length corresponding to the distance between the joists A and C at the outside wall. Nail two of these pieces between the joists at the desired distances from the ends of the joists; these pieces are shown as headers Nos. 1 and 2, figure 7-18. Install short joists X and Y, as shown. The nails should be 16- or 20-penny nails. By omitting headers Nos. 3 and 4 and joists B and D, the short joists X and Y can be nailed in place through the header and the headers can be nailed through the joists A and B into its end. After the header and short joists have been securely nailed, headers Nos. 3 and 4 are nailed beside Nos. 1 and 2. Then joist B is placed beside joists A and joist D beside C, and all are nailed securely.

7-8. Subfloors and Finish Floors

a. Subfloors. After the foundation and basic framework of a building are completed, the floor is constructed. The subfloor, if included in the plans, is laid diagonally on the joists and nailed with 8- to 10-penny nails. The floor joists form a framework for the subfloor. Subflooring boards 8 inches wide or over should have three or more nails per joist. Where the subfloor is over 1 inch thick, larger nails should be used. Figure 5-12

shows the method of laying a subfloor. Preferably it is laid before the walls are framed so that it can be used as a floor to work on while framing the walls.

b. Finish Floors.

(1) *General.* A finish floor in the theater of operations, in most cases, is of 3/4-inch material, square edged (fig. 7-19) or tongued and grooved (fig. 7-20), and varying from 3 1/4 to 7 1/4 inches wide. It is laid directly on floor joists or on a subfloor and nailed with 8-penny common nails in every joist. When laid on a subfloor, it is best to use building paper between the two floors to keep out dampness and insects. In warehouses, where heavy loads are to be carried on the floor, 2-inch material should be used. The flooring, in this case, also is face-nailed with 16- or 20-penny nails. It is not tongued and grooved and ranges in width from 4 to 12 inches. The joints are made on the center of the joist.

(2) *Wood floors.* Wood floors must be strong enough to carry the load. The type of building and the use for which it is intended determines the general arrangement of the floor system,

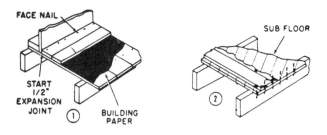

Figure 7-19. Methods for nailing square-edged flooring.

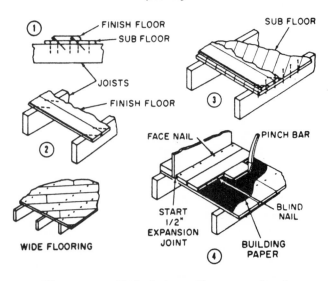

Figure 7-20. Methods for nailing tongued-and-grooved flooring.

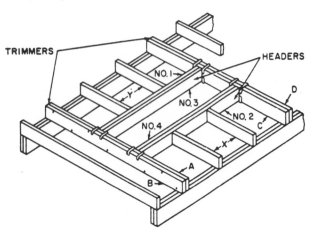

Figure 7-18. Floor opening construction.

thickness of the sheathing, and approximate spacing of the joists.

(3) *Concrete floors.* Concrete floors may be constructed for shops where earthen or wood floors are not suitable such as in repair and assembly shops for airplanes and heavy equipment and in certain kinds of warehouses. These floors are made by pouring concrete on the ground after the earth has been graded and tamped. This type of floor is likely to be damp unless protected. Drainage is provided, both for the floor area and for the area near the floor, to prevent flooding after heavy rains. The floor should be reinforced with steel or wire mesh. Where concrete floors are to be poured, a foundation wall may be poured first and the floor poured after the building is completed. This gives protection to the concrete floor while it sets.

(4) *Miscellaneous types of floors.* Miscellaneous floors may include earth, adobe brick, duckboard, or rushes. Use of miscellaneous flooring is usually determined by a shortage of conventional materials, the need to save time or labor, the extremely temporary nature of the facilities, or the special nature of the structure. The selection of material is usually determined by availability. Duckboard is widely used for shower flooring; earthen floors are common and conserve both materials and labor if the ground site is even without extensive grading. Rush or thatch floors are primarily an insulating measure and must be replaced frequently.

(5) *Supports.* In certain parts of the floor frame, in order to support some very heavily concentrated load or a partition wall, it may be necessary to double the joist or to place two joists together (fig. 7–21).

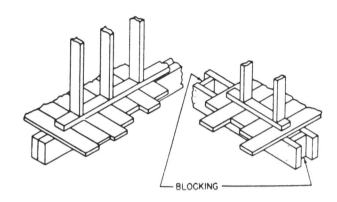

BLOCKING

Figure 7–21. Reinforced joists.

Section II. WALLS AND WALL COVERINGS

7–9. General
Wall framing (fig. 7–22) is composed of regular studs, diagonal bracing, cripples, trimmers, headers, and fire blocks and is supported by the floor sole plate. The vertical members of the wall framing are the studs, which support the top plates and all of the weight of the upper part of the building or everything above the top plate line. They provide the framework to which the wall sheathing is aniled on the outside and which supports the lath, plaster, and insulation on the inside.

7–10. Wall Components
Walls and partitions which are classed as framed constructions (fig. 7–23) are composed of structural elements which are usually closely spaced, slender, vertical members called studs. These are arranged in a row with their ends bearing on a long horizontal member called a bottom plate or sole plate, and their tops capped with another plate, called a top plate. Double top plates are used in bearing walls and partitions. The bearing strength of stud walls is determined by the strength of the studs.

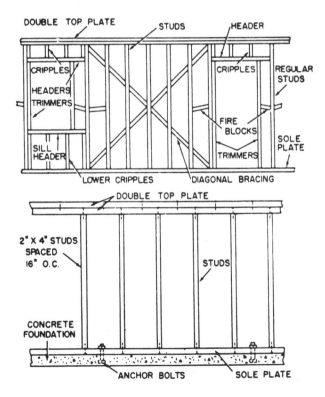

Figure 7–22. Typical wall frame details.

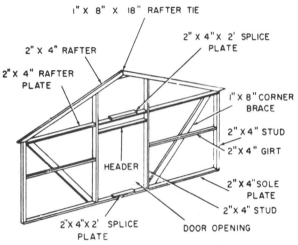

① END PANEL - FRAMING DETAILS

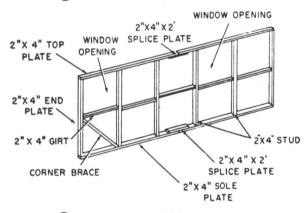

② SIDE PANEL - FRAMING DETAILS

Figure 7–23. Typical wall construction showing openings.

a. *Corner Posts.* The studs used at the corners of frame construction are usually built up from three or more ordinary studs to provide greater strength. These built-up assemblies are corner-partition posts. The corner posts are set up, plumbed, and temporarily braced. The corner posts (fig. 7–24) may be made in the following ways:

(1) A corner post may consist of a 4 by 6 with a 2 by 4 nailed on the board side, flush with one edge, as shown in figure 7–24. This type of corner is for a 4-inch wall. Where walls are thicker, heavier timber is used.

(2) A 4 by 4 may be used with a 2 by 4 nailed to two of the adjoining sides, shown in 2, figure 7–24.

(3) Two 2 by 4's may be nailed together with blocks between and a 2 by 4 flush with one edge, shown in 3, figure 7–24.

(4) A 2 by 4 may be nailed to the edge of another 2 by 4, the edge of one flush with the

side of the other (4, fig. 7–24). This type is used extensively in the theater of operations where no inside finish is needed.

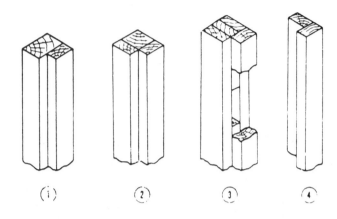

Figure 7–24. Corner post construction.

b. *T-Posts.* Whenever a partition meets an outside wall, a stud wide enough to extend beyond the partition on both sides is used; this provides a solid nailing base for the inside wall finish. This type of stud is called a T-post (fig. 7–25) and is made in the following different ways:

(1) A 2 by 4 may be nailed and centered on the face side of a 4 by 6 (1, fig. 7–25).

(2) A 2 by 4 may be nailed and centered on two 4 by 4's nailed together (2, fig. 7–25).

(3) Two 2 by 4's may be nailed together with a block between them and a 2 by 4 centered on the wide side (3, fig. 7–25).

(4) A 2 by 4 may be nailed and centered on the face side of a 2 by 6, with a horizontal bridging nailed behind them to give support and stiffness (4, fig. 7–25).

c. *Partition and Double T-Posts.* Where a partition is finished on one side only, the partition post used consists of a simple stud, set in the outside wall, in line with the side of the partition

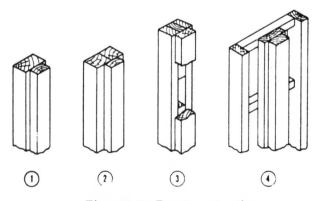

Figure 7–25. T-post construction.

wall, and finished as stud A in 1, figure 7–26. These posts are nailed in place along with the corner post. The exact position of the partition walls must be determined before the posts are placed. Where the walls are more than 4 inches thick, wider timber is used. In special cases, for example where partition walls cross, a double T-post is used. This is made by using methods in *b*(1), (2), or (3) above, and nailing another 2 by 4 to the opposite wide side, as shown in 2, 3, and 4, figure 7–26.

d. Studs.

(1) After the sills, plates, and braces are in place, and the window and door openings are laid out, the studs are placed and nailed with two 16- or 20-penny nails through the top plate. Then the remaining or intermediate studs are laid out on the sills or soles by measuring from

one corner the distances the studs are to be set apart. Studs are normally spaced 12, 16, and 24 inches on centers, depending upon the type of outside and inside finish. Where vertical siding is used, studs are set wider apart since the horizontal girts between them provide nailing surface.

(2) When it is desirable to double the post of the door opening, first place the outside studs into position and nail them securely. Then cut short studs, or *filler studs,* the size of the opening, and nail these to the inside face of the outside studs as shown in figure 7–27. In making a window opening, a bottom header must be framed; this header is either single or double. When it is doubled, the bottom piece is nailed to the opening studs at the proper height and the top piece of the bottom header is nailed into place flush with the bottom section. The door header is framed as shown in figure 7–27. The filler stud rests on the sole at the bottom.

e. Girts. Girts are always the same width as the studs and are flush with the face of the stud, both outside and inside. Girts are used in hasty construction where the outside walls are covered with vertical siding. Studs are placed from 2 to 10 feet apart, with girts, spaced about 4 feet apart, running horizontally between them (fig. 7–27). The vertical siding acts in the same way as to studs and helps to carry the weight of the roof. This type of construction is used extensively in the theater of operations.

f. Top Plate and Sole Plate.

(1) *Top plate.* The top plate ties the studding together at the top and forms a finish for the walls; it furnishes a support for the lower ends of the rafters (fig. 7–22). The top plate serves as a connecting link between the wall and the roof, just as the sills and girders are connecting links between the floors and the walls.

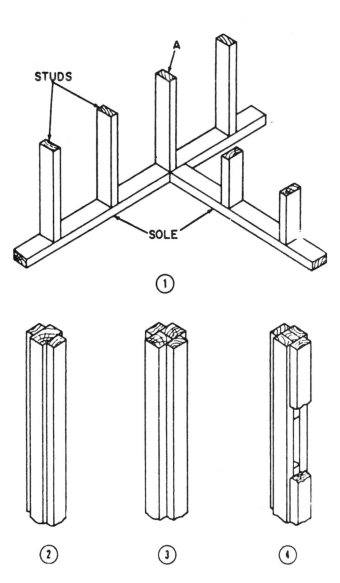

Figure 7–26. Partition posts.

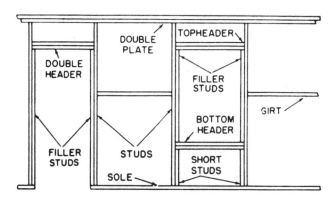

Figure 7–27. Door and window framing.

The plate is made up of one or two pieces of timber of the same size as the studs. In cases where the studs at the end of the building extend to the rafters, no plate is used at the end of the building. When it is used on top of partition walls, it is sometimes called the cap. Where the plate is doubled, the first plate or bottom section is nailed with 16- or 20-penny nails to the top of the corner posts and to the studs. The connection at the corner is made as shown in 1, figure 7–28. After the single plate is nailed securely and the corner braces are nailed into place, the top part of the plate is then nailed to the bottom section with 16- or 20-penny nails either over each stud, or spaced with two nails every 2 feet. The edges of the top section should be flush with the bottom section and the corner joints lapped as shown in 1 and 2, figure 7–28.

(2) *Sole plate.* All partition walls and outside walls are finished either with a 2 by 4 or with a piece of timber corresponding to the thickness of the wall; this timber is laid horizontally on the floor or joists. It carries the bottom end of the studs (fig. 7–22). This timber is called the "sole" or "sole plate". The sole should be nailed with two 16- or 20-penny nails at each joist that it crosses. If it is laid lengthwise on top of a girder or joist, it should be nailed with two nails every 2 feet.

g. Bridging. Frame walls are bridged, in most cases, to make them more sturdy. There are two methods of bridging:

(1) *Diagonal bridging.* Diagonal bridging is nailed between the studs at an angle (1, fig. 7–29). It is more effective than the horizontal type since it forms a continuous truss and tends to keep the walls from sagging. Whenever possible, both interior partitions and exterior walls should be bridged alike.

(2) *Horizontal bridging.* Horizontal bridging is nailed between the studs horizontally and halfway between the sole and the plate (2, fig. 7–29). This bridging is cut to lengths which correspond to the distance between the studs at the bottom. Such bridging not only stiffens the wall but also will help straighten studs.

7–11. Partitions

Partition walls divide the inside space of a building. These walls in most cases are framed as part of the building. Where floors are to be installed after the outside of the building is completed, the partition walls are left unframed. There are two types of partition walls: the bearing, and the non-bearing types. The bearing type supports ceiling joists. The nonbearing type supports only itself. This type may be put in at any time after

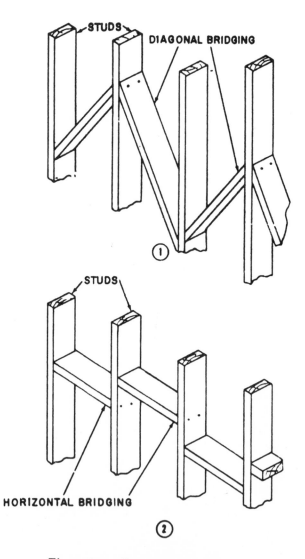

Figure 7–29. Types of wall bridging.

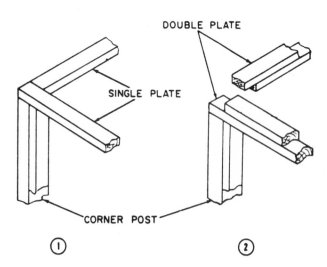

Figure 7–28. Plate construction.

the other framework is installed. Only one cap or plate is used. A sole plate should be used in every case, as it helps to distribute the load over a larger area. Partition walls are framed the same as outside walls, and door openings are framed as outside openings. Where there are corners or where one partition wall joins another, corner posts or T-posts are used as in the outside walls; these posts provide nailing surfaces for the inside wall finish. Partition walls in the theater of operations one-story building may or may not extend to the roof. The top of the studs has a plate when the wall does not extend to the roof; but when the wall extends to the roof, the studs are joined to the rafters.

7–12. Methods of Plumbing Posts and Straightening Walls

a. General. After the corner post, T-post, and intermediate wall studs have been nailed to the plates or girts, the walls must be plumbed and straightened so that the permanent braces and rafters may be installed. This is done by using a level or plumb bob and a chalkline.

b. Plumbing Posts.

(1) To plumb a corner with a plumb bob, first attach to the bob a string long enough to extend to or below the bottom of the post. Lay a rule on top of the post so that 2 inches of the rule extends over the post on the side to be plumbed; then hang the bob-line over the rule so that the line is 2 inches from the post and extends to the bottom of it, as shown in 1, figure 7–30. With another rule, measure the distance from the post to the center of the line at the bottom of the post; if it does not measure 2 inches, the post is not plumb. Move the post inward or outward until the distance from the post to the center of the line is exactly 2 inches. Then nail the temporary brace in place. Repeat this procedure from the other outside face of the post. The post is then plumb. This process is carried out for the remaining corner posts of the building. If a plumb bob or level is not available, a rock, a half-brick, or some small piece of metal may be used instead.

(2) An alternate method of plumbing a post is illustrated in 2, figure 7–30. Attach the plumb bob string securely to the top of the post to be plumbed, making sure that the string is long enough to allow the plumb bob to hang near the bottom of the post. Use two blocks of wood identical in thickness as gage blocks. Tack one block near the top of the post between the plumb bob string and the post (gage block No. 1), in-

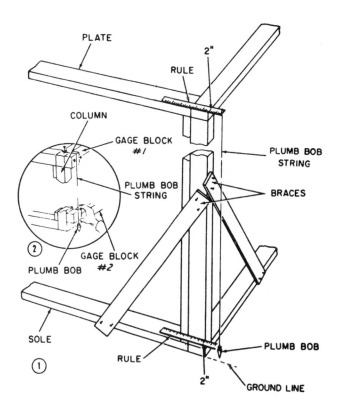

Figure 7–30. Plumbing a post.

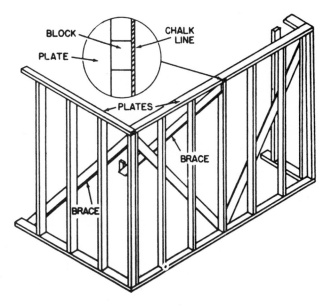

Figure 7–31. Straightening a wall.

serting the second block between the plumb bob string and the bottom of the post (gage block No. 2). If the entire face of the second block makes contact with the string, the post is plumb.

c. Straightening Walls (fig. 7–31). Plumb one corner post with the level or plumb bob and nail temporary braces to hold the post in place (*b* above). Repeat this procedure for all corner posts. Fasten a chalkline to the outside of one post at the top and stretch the line to the post the same as for the first post. Place a small 3/4-inch block under each end of the line as shown in figure 7–31 to give clearance. Place temporary braces at intervals small enough to hold the wall straight. When the wall is far enough away from the line to permit a 3/4-inch block to slide between the line and the plate, the brace is nailed. This procedure is carried out for the entire perimeter of the building. Inside partition walls should be straightened the same way.

7–13. Braces

Bracing is used to stiffen framed construction and make it rigid. The purpose of bracing may be to resist winds, storm, twist, or strain stemming from any cause. Good bracing keeps corners square and plumb and prevents warping, sagging, and shifts resulting from lateral forces that would otherwise tend to distort the frame and cause badly fitting doors and windows and the cracking of plaster. There are three commonly used methods of bracing frame structures:

a. Let-In Bracing (1, fig. 7–32). Let-in bracing is set into the edges of studs so as to be flush

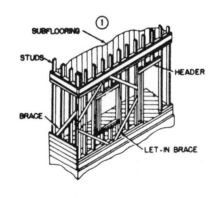

with the surface. The studs are always cut to let in the braces; the braces are never cut. Usually 1 by 4's or 1 by 6's are used, set diagonally from top plates to sole plates.

b. Cut-In Bracing (2, fig. 7–32). Cut-in bracing is toenailed between studs. It usually consists of 2 by 4's cut at an angle to permit toenailing, inserted in diagonal progression between studs running up and down from corner posts to sill or plates.

c. Diagonal Sheathing (3, fig. 7–32). The strongest type of bracing is sheathing applied diagonally. Each board acts as a brace of the wall. If plywood sheathing 5/8-inch thick or more is used, other methods of bracing may be omitted.

7–14. Exterior Walls

The exterior surfaces of a building usually consist of vertical, horizontal, or diagonal sheathing and composition, sheet-metal, or corrugated roofing. However, in theaters of operation the materials are not always available and substitutes must be provided. Concrete block, brick, rubble stone, metal, or earth may be substituted for wood in treeless regions. In the tropics, improvised siding and roofs can be made from bamboo and grasses. Roofing felt, sandwiched between two layers of light wire mesh, may serve for wall and roof materials where climate is suitable. Refer to TM 5–302 for details on substitute, expedient, and improvised construction.

a. Sheathing. Sheathing is nailed directly onto the framework of the building. Its purpose is to strengthen the building, to provide a base wall onto which the finish siding can be nailed,

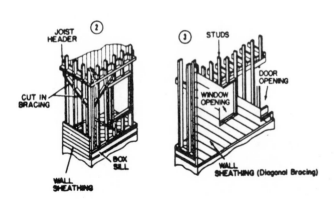

Figure 7–32. Common types of bracing.

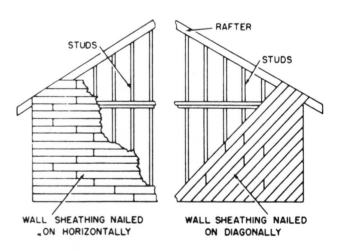

Figure 7–33. Diagonal and horizontal wooden sheathing.

to act as insulation, and in some cases to be a base for further insulation. Some of the common types of sheathing include—

(1) Wood, 11/16-inch thick by 6, 8, 10, or 12 inch wide of No. 1 common square or matched-edge material. It may be nailed on horizontally or diagonally (fig. 7–33).

(2) Gypsum board wall-sheathing, 1/2 inch thick by 24 inches wide and 8 feet long.

(3) Fiberboard, 25/32 inch thick by 24 by 48 inches wide and 8, 9, 10, and 12 feet long.

(4) Plywood, 5/16, 3/8, 1/2, 5/8 inches thick by 48 inches wide and 8, 9, 10, and 12 feet long.

b. *Application.*

(1) Wood wall sheathing comes in almost all widths, lengths, and grades. Generally, widths are from 6 to 12 inches, with lengths selected for economical use. Almost all solid wood wall sheathing used is 13/16 inches thick and either square or matched edge. This material may be nailed on horizontally or diagonally (fig. 7–33). Diagonal application adds much greater strength to the structure. Sheathing should be nailed on with three 8-penny common nails to each bearing if the pieces are over 6 inches wide. Wooden sheathing is laid on tight, with all joints made over the studs. If the sheathing is to be put on horizontally, it should be started at the foundation and worked toward the top. If it is to be put on diagonally, it should be started at the corners of the building and worked toward the center or middle of the building.

(2) Gypsum board sheathing (fig. 7–34) is made by casting a gypsum core within a heavy water-resistant fibrous envelope. The long edges of the 4- by 8-foot boards are tongued and grooved. Each board is a full 1/2 inch thick. Its

use is mostly with wood siding that can be nailed directly through the sheathing and into the studs. Gypsum sheathing is fireproof, water resistant, and windproof; does not warp nor absorb water; and does not require the use of building papers.

(3) Plywood as a wall sheathing (fig. 7–34) is highly recommended by its size, weight, stability, and structural properties, plus the ease and speed of application. It adds consider-

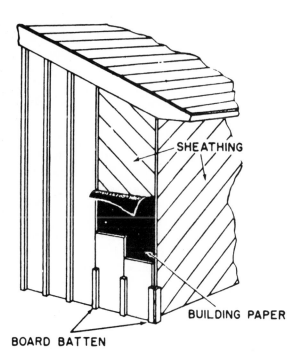

Figure 7–34. Gypsum and plywood sheathing.

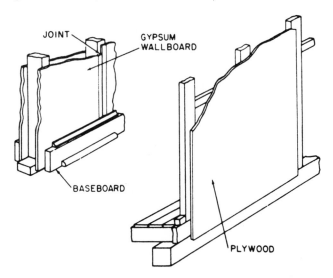

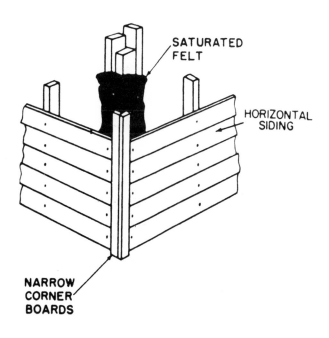

Figure 7–35. Vertical and horizontal wooden siding.

ably more strength to the frame than does diagonally applied wood boards. When plywood sheathing is used, corner bracing can be omitted. Large size panels save the time required for application and still provide a tight, draft-free installation of high insulation value. Minimum thicknesses of plywood wall sheathing is 5/16 inch for 16-inch stud spacing and 3/8 inch for 24-inch stud spacing. The panels should be installed with the face grain parallel to the studs. A little more stiffness can be gained by installing them across the studs, but this requires more cutting and fitting. Use 6-penny common nails for 5/16-, 3/8-, and 1/2-inch panels and 8-penny common nails for 5/8- and 13/16-inch panels. Space the nails not more than 6 inches on center at the edges of the panels and not more than 12 inches on center elsewhere.

c. *Vertical Wooden Siding.* This type of coverage is nailed to girts. The cracks are covered with wood strips called battens. The sheathing is nailed securely with 8- or 10-penny nails. The vertical sheathing requires less framing than siding since the sheathing acts as a support for the plate. To make this type of wall more weatherproof, some type of tar paper or light roll roofing may be applied over the entire surface and fastened with roofing nails and battens (fig. 7–35).

d. *Horizontal Wood Siding.* Wood siding is cut to various patterns and sizes to be used as the finished outside surface of a structure. The siding for outside wall coverings should be of a decay-resisting species that will hold tight at the joints and take and hold paint well. It should by all means be well seasoned lumber. Siding is made in sizes ranging from 1/2 inch to 3/4 inch by 12 inches. There are two principal types of siding (fig. 3–3): beveled siding and drop siding.

(1) *Beveled siding* (fig. 3–3). Beveled siding is made with beveled boards thin at the top edge and thick at the butt. It is the most common form of wood siding and comes in 1 inch for narrow widths, and 2 inches and over for the wide types. They are usually nailed at the butt edge and through the tip edge of the board below. Very narrow siding is quite often nailed near its thin edge like shingles. It is nailed to solid sheathing over which building paper has been attached. Window and door casings are first framed. The siding butts are put against the edges of these frames. Corners may be mitered, or the corner boards may be first nailed to the sheathing and then the siding is fitted against the edges.

(2) *Drop siding* (fig. 3–3). Drop siding is designed to be used as a combination of sheathing and siding, or with separate sheathing. It comes in a wide variety of face profiles and is either shiplapped or tongued and grooved. If used as a combined sheathing and siding material, tongue and grooved lumber is nailed directly to the studs with the tongue up. When sheathing is not used, the door and window casings are set after the siding is up. If sheathing is first used and then building paper is added, drop siding is applied like beveled siding, after the window and door casings are in place.

(3) *Corrugated metal sheets.* Corrugated metal is used extensively as a wall cover since little framing, time, and labor are required to install it. It is applied vertically and nailed to girts with the nails placed in the ridges. Sheathing can be used behind the iron with or without building paper. Since tar paper used behind metal will cause the metal to rust, a resin-sized paper should be used.

(4) *Building paper.*

(a) Building paper is of several types, the most common of which is the resin-sized. It is generally red or buff in color (sometimes black) and comes in rolls, usually 36 inches wide. Each roll contains 500 square feet and weighs from 18 to 50 pounds. Ordinarily, it is not waterproof. Another type is heavy paper saturated with a coaltar product, sometimes called sheathing paper. It is waterproof and protects against heat and cold.

(b) In wood-frame buildings to be covered with either siding, shingles, or iron, building paper is used to protect against heat, cold, or dampness. Building paper is applied horizontally along a wall from the bottom of the structure upward and nailed with roofing nails at the laps. Thus the overlapping of the paper helps water runoff. Care must be taken not to tear the paper. The waterproof type paper is used also in the built-up roof where the roof is nearly flat. Several layers are used with tar between each layer.

7–15. Interior Walls and Partitions

a. *Wall and Partition Coverings.* Wall and partition coverings are divided into two general types—wet wall material, generally plaster; and dry wall material including wood, plaster board, plywood, and fiberboard. Only dry wall material will be covered in this manual.

b. *Dry Wall Materials.* Dry wall material—

gypsumboard, fiberboard, or plywood, usually comes in sheets 1/2 inch thick and 4 x 8 feet in size, but may be obtained in other sizes. It is normally applied in either single or double thickness with panels placed as shown in figure 7–36. When covering both walls and ceilings, always start with the ceiling (para 7–17). Annular ringed nails should be used for applying finished-joint drywall to reduce nail popping.

(1) Apply dry wall as follows:

(a) Start in one corner and work around the room. Make sure that joints break at the centerline of a stud.

(b) Use 1/2-inch thick recessed-edge wallboard and span the entire height of the wall if possible.

(c) Use 13-gage nails, 1 5/8 inches long. Start nailing at the center of the board and work outward. Space the nails 3/8 inch in from the edge of the board and about 8 inches apart. Dimple nails below surface of panel with a ball-peen hammer. Be careful not to break the surface of the board by the blow of the hammer.

(d) Procedures for cutting and sealing wallboard are covered in (3) below.

(2) Fit dry wall materials to rough or uneven walls as follows:

(a) Place a piece of scrap material in the angle (fig. 7–37) and scribe (mark) it to indicate the surface peculiarities.

(b) Saw the scrap material along the scribed line.

(c) Place the scribed strip on the wallboard to be used. Keep the straight edge of the scrap material parallel with the edge of the wallboard. Scribe the good piece of wallboard.

(d) Saw the wallboard along the scribed line.

(3) Cut panels by sawing, or by scoring with an awl and snapping over a straight edge (fig. 7–38). *Cut with finish side up to avoid damaging surface.* Cut openings for pipe and electrical receptacles with a keyhole saw. Nail panels to wall studs with 13-gage nails, 8 inches on centers. *All panel end joints must center on studs.* Cover nails with cement. Joints may be left open, beveled, lapped, filled, covered with battens or moldings, or treated with cement and tape. The treatment of joints varies slightly with different materials. Generally, all cracks over 1/8 inch must be filled with special crack filler before joint cement is applied. The cement is spread over joints with a plasterer's trowel. Apply the cement evenly and thin (feather) edges on surface of wall panel. Fill channels in recessed edges with cement, carrying it 1 inch past channel edges. At corners, apply cement in a channel-wide band and feather edges. Press perforated tape into wet cement and smooth tape down with trowel. Clean off excess cement. At corners, fold tape down center before applying, and smooth each side of corner separately when applied. When cement is dry, apply a second coat of thinned cement to hide tape.

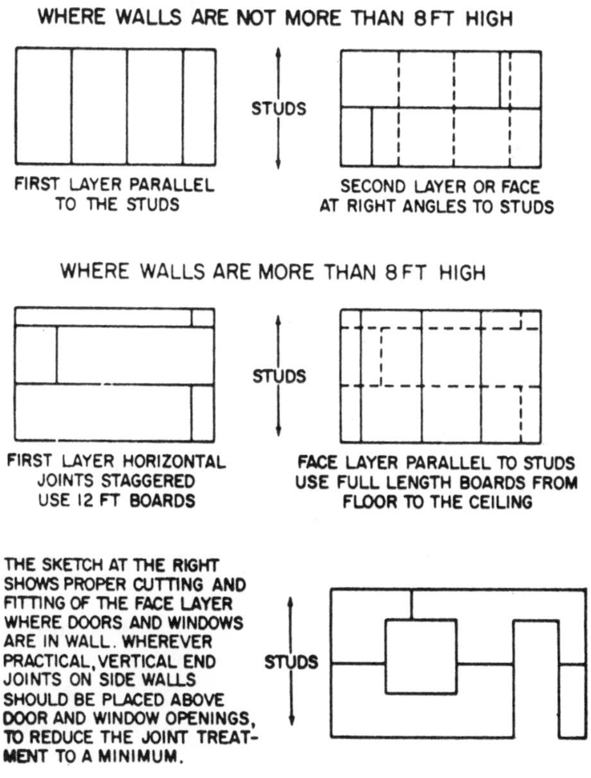

WHERE WALLS ARE NOT MORE THAN 8 FT HIGH

STUDS

FIRST LAYER PARALLEL TO THE STUDS

SECOND LAYER OR FACE AT RIGHT ANGLES TO STUDS

WHERE WALLS ARE MORE THAN 8 FT HIGH

STUDS

FIRST LAYER HORIZONTAL JOINTS STAGGERED USE 12 FT BOARDS

FACE LAYER PARALLEL TO STUDS USE FULL LENGTH BOARDS FROM FLOOR TO THE CEILING

THE SKETCH AT THE RIGHT SHOWS PROPER CUTTING AND FITTING OF THE FACE LAYER WHERE DOORS AND WINDOWS ARE IN WALL. WHEREVER PRACTICAL, VERTICAL END JOINTS ON SIDE WALLS SHOULD BE PLACED ABOVE DOOR AND WINDOW OPENINGS, TO REDUCE THE JOINT TREATMENT TO A MINIMUM.

STUDS

Figure 7–36. Placing wallboard.

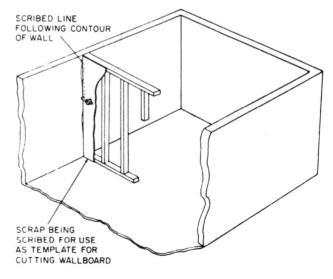

SCRIBED LINE FOLLOWING CONTOUR OF WALL

SCRAP BEING SCRIBED FOR USE AS TEMPLATE FOR CUTTING WALLBOARD

Figure 7–37. Fitting single-piece wallboard to uneven walls.

Feather the edges carefully to preserve flat appearance of wall. When the final coat is dry, smooth the joint with sandpaper.

c. Sheetrock. Sheetrock sheets are very brittle and require careful handling to prevent breakage. Approximately 1 1/4 inches of a sheet's edge is made 1/16 inch thinner than the body of the sheet. When two sheets are placed side by side, their edges form a recess to receive perforated paper tape and gypsum cement which conceals the joints between the sheets. A 1/8-inch space between the edges of the sheets helps to hold the filler cement in place. The sheets are usually fastened in place with blued nails which have an oversize head and are 1 1/2 inches long. The nails along the edges are covered with perforated tape and cement. Nails are spaced about 5 inches apart and 3/8 inch from the edge. Those in the middle of the sheets are spaced 8 or 9 inches apart and are set below the surface to receive the filler cement. It is common prac-

TO CUT PLASTERBOARD:

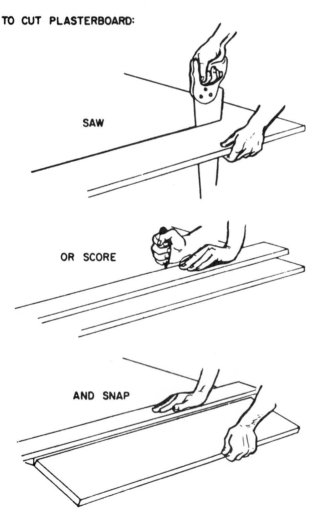

SAW

OR SCORE

AND SNAP

Figure 7-38. Cutting wallboard.

tice to strike the nailheads one extra blow for setting. This makes a slight depression (hammer mark) which holds the cement around the nailhead.

d. Wood Paneling. Plywood panels are used extensively as interior wall covering and can be obtained on the market in sizes from 1/4 to 3/4 inch thick; 36 to 48 inches wide; and 60, 72, 84, or 96 inches long. Plywood gives a wall a wood finish surface. If desired, the less expensive plywoods can be used and covered with paint or wallpaper or can be decorated in the same way as plastered surfaces. These panels are usually applied vertically from floor to ceiling and fastened with 4d finishing nails. Special strips or battens of either wood or metal may be used to conceal the joints when flush joints are used. Joints can also be treated with moldings, either in the form of battens fastened over the joints or applied as splines between the panels.

7–16. Moldings

The various interior trims of a building should have a definite architectural relationship in the design to that of the doors, windows, and the general architecture of the building.

a. Base Molding. Base molding serves as a finish between the finished wall and floor. It is available in several widths and forms. Two-piece base consists of a baseboard topped with a small base cap (A, fig. 7–39). When plaster is not straight and true, the small base molding will conform more closely to the variations than will the wider base alone. A common size for this type of baseboard is 5/8 by 3 1/4 inches or wider. One-piece baseboard is 5/8 by 3 1/4 inches or wider. One-piece base varies in size from 7/16 by 2 1/4 inches to 1/2 by 3 1/4 inches and wider (Band C, fig. 7–39). Although a wood member is desirable at the junction of the wall and carpeting to serve as a protective "bumper", wood trim is sometimes eliminated entirely. Most baseboards are finished with a base shoe, 1/2 by 3/4 inch in size (A, B, and C, fig. 7–39). A single-base molding without the shoe is sometimes placed at the wall-floor junction, especially where carpeting might be used.

b. Installation of Base Molding. Square-edged baseboard should be installed with a butt joint at inside corners and a mitered joint at outside corners (D, fig. 7–39). It should be nailed to each stud with two eightpenny finishing nails. Molded single-piece base, base moldings, and base shoe should have a coped joint at inside corners and

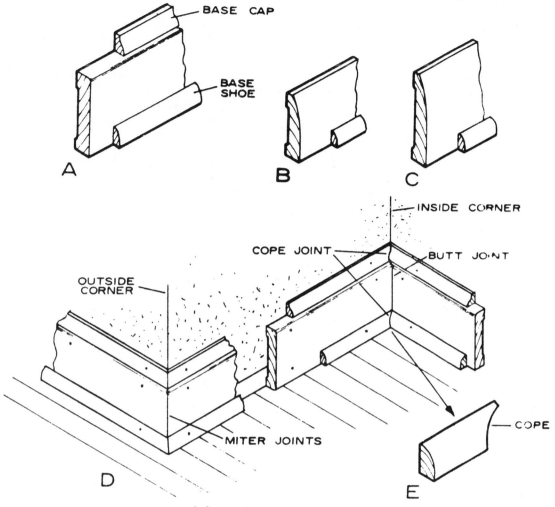

A, Square-edge base; B, narrow ranch base; C, wide ranch base;
D, installation; E, cope.

Figure 7-39. Base molding.

a mitered joint at outside corners. A coped joint is one in which the first piece is square-cut against the plaster or base and the second molding coped. This is done by sawing a 45° miter cut and with a coping saw trimming the molding along the inner line of the miter (E, fig. 7-39). The base shoe should be nailed into the subfloor with long slender nails and not into the baseboard itself. Thus, if there is a small amount of shrinkage of the joists, no opening will occur under the shoe.

7-17. Ceiling Covering

In present-day construction, dry, rigid wallboards are used instead of laths and plaster to cover ceilings, as well as walls (para 7-15). The most common drywall finishes are gypsumboard, fiberboard, and plywood. Sheets of gypsumboard and fiberboard are attached directly to the joists.

Smaller pieces of fiberboard (tiles) require furring strips (wooden strips nailed across joints) to which they are attached.

a. Gypsumboard.

(1) *Nailing to ceiling.* The 4-foot by 8-foot boards are nailed to the ceiling with 5-penny nails through 1/2-inch thick gypsum or 4-penny nails through 3/8-inch gypsum. The nails are spaced 5 to 7 inches apart, off center, and driven about 1/16 inch below the surface of the board.

(2) *Cutting panels and treatment of joints.* The cutting of the panels and the treatment of joints are the same as those of walls and partitions (para 7-15b(3).

(3) *Brace for paneling ceiling.* A brace is constructed and used (fig. 7-40) to raise and hold a panel in place to aid in fitting and nailing

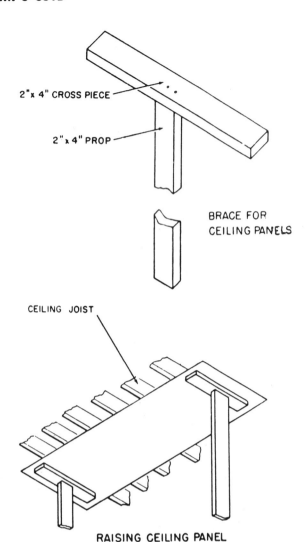

Figure 7–40. *Brace for raising and holding ceiling panels.*

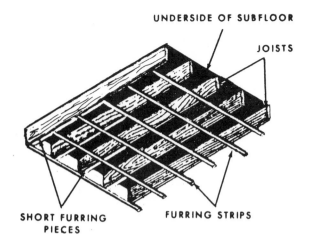

Figure 7–41. Furring strips on ceiling joists.

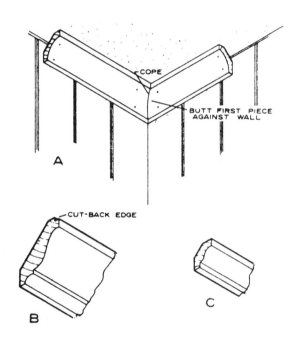

Ceiling moldings; A, Installation (inside corner); B, crown molding; C, small crown molding.

Figure 7–42. Ceiling molding.

the wallboard to the ceiling. Eight inch nail spacing is used in nailing the panels to the joists.

b. Fiberboard. Fiberboard sheets are obtained in thicknesses from 1/2 to 2 inches. The joints between the sheets may be covered with batten strips of either wood or fiberboard to further improve its appearance. When fiberboard sheets must be cut, a special fiberboard knife is recommended to obtain a smooth cut.

(1) *Tiles.* Fiberboard sheets are also made in small pieces called tiles which are often used for covering ceilings. These tiles may be square or rectangular to fit standard joist spacing. They may be made with a lap joint which permits blind nailing or stapling through the edge. They may also be of tongue-and-groove construction fastened in place with 2-penny box nails driven through special metal clips.

(2) *Furring strips.* For fiberboard tiles that need solid backing, furring strips are placed at right angles across the bottom of the joists and short furring pieces are placed along the joists between the furring strips, as shown in figure 7–41.

(3) *Tile installed in metal channels.* Metal channels are nailed to furring strips and the tiles are slid into them horizontally. In lowering ceilings, usually in older buildings, metal channels are suspended on wire to "drop" a ceiling below the original ceiling. Some large (2 x 4-ft) panels are installed in individual frames.

8. Ceiling Molding

Ceiling moldings are sometimes used at the junction of wall and ceiling for an architectural effect or to terminate dry-wall paneling of gypsumboard or wood (A, fig. 7–42). As in the base moldings, inside corners should also be copejointed. This insures a tight joint and retains a good fit if there are minor moisture changes. A cutback edge at the outside of the molding will partially conceal any unevenness of the plaster and make painting easier where there are color changes (B, fig. 7–42). For gypsum dry-wall construction, a small simple molding might be desirable (C, fig. 7–42). Finish nails should be driven into the upper wallplates and also into the ceiling joists for large moldings when possible.

Section III. DOOR FRAMES, WINDOW FRAMES, AND OTHER WALL OPENINGS

7–19. Doors

Door and window openings in exterior walls generally require headers. Regular studs are normally placed 16 inches on center apart. Extra studs are added at the sides of all such openings. Openings should allow 1/2 inch between the back at jambs and framing member for the plumbing and leveling of jambs.

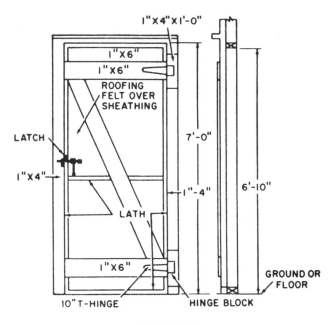

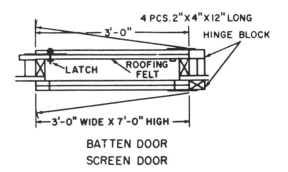

Figure 7–43. Single outside door.

a. *Door Frames.*

(1) Before the exterior covering is placed on the outside walls, the door openings are prepared for the frames. To prepare the openings, square off any uneven pieces of sheathing and wrap heavy building paper around the sides and top. Since the sill must be worked into a portion of the rough flooring, no paper is put on the floor. Position the paper from a point even with the inside portion of the stud to a point about 6 inches on the sheathed walls and tack it down with small nails.

(2) Outside door frames are constructed in several ways. In most hasty construction, the frames will be as shown in figure 7–43. This type requires no construction of frame because the studs on each side of the opening act as a frame. The outside finish is applied to the wall before the door is hung. The casing is then nailed to the sides of the opening which is set back the width of the stud. A 3/4- by 3/4-inch piece is nailed over the door to act as a support for the drip cap and is also set back the width of the stud. Hinge blocks are nailed to the casing where the hinges are to be placed. The door frame is now complete and ready for the door to be hung. Figure 7–43 shows the elevation of a single outside door.

(3) Inside door frames, like outside frames, are constructed in several ways. In most hasty construction, the type shown in figure 7–44 is used. The interior type is constructed like the outside type, except that no casing is used on inside door frames. Hinge blocks are nailed to the inside wall finish, where the hinges are to be placed, to provide a nailing surface for the hinge flush with the door. Figure 7–44 shows the elevation of a single inside door. Both the outside and inside door frames may be modified to suit climatic conditions.

b. *Door Jambs.* Door jambs (fig. 7–45) are the linings of the framing of door openings.

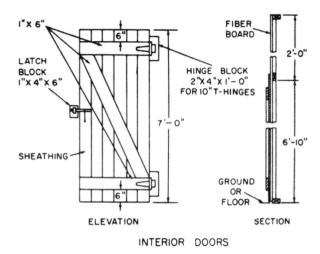

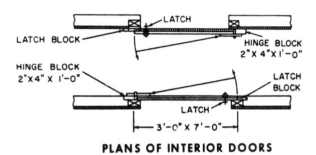

PLANS OF INTERIOR DOORS

Figure 7-44. Single inside door.

Casings and stops are nailed to the door jambs and the door is hung from them. Inside jambs are made of 3/4-inch stock and outside jambs of 1 3/8-inch stock. The width of the stock will vary with the thickness to the walls. Inside jambs are built up with 3/8- by 1 3/8-inch stops nailed to the jamb, while outside jambs are usually rabbeted out to receive the door. Jambs are made and set as follows:

(1) Regardless of how carefully rough openings are made, be sure to plumb the jambs and level the heads, when jambs are set.

(2) Rough openings are usually made 2 1/2 inches larger each way than the size of the door to be hung. For example, a 2-foot 8-inch by 6-foot 8-inch door would need a rough opening of 2 feet 10 1/2 inches by 6 feet 10 1/2 inches. This extra space allows for the jambs, the wedging, and the clearance space for the door to swing.

(3) Level the floor across the opening to determine any variation in floor heights at the point where the jambs rest on the floor.

(4) Now cut the head jamb with both ends square, having allowed width of the door plus the depth of both dadoes and a full 3/16 inch for door clearance.

(5) From the lower edge of the dado, measure a distance equal to the height of the door plus the clearance wanted under it. Mark and cut square.

(6) On the oposite jamb do the same, only make additions or subtractions for the variation in the floor, if any.

(7) Now nail the jambs and jamb heads together with 8-penny common nails through the dado into the head jamb.

(8) Set the jambs into the opening and place small blocks under each jamb on the subfloor just as thick as the finish floor will be. This is to allow the finish floor to go under.

(9) Plumb the jambs and level the jamb head.

(10) Wedge the sides with shingles between the jambs and the studs, to aline, and then nail securely in place.

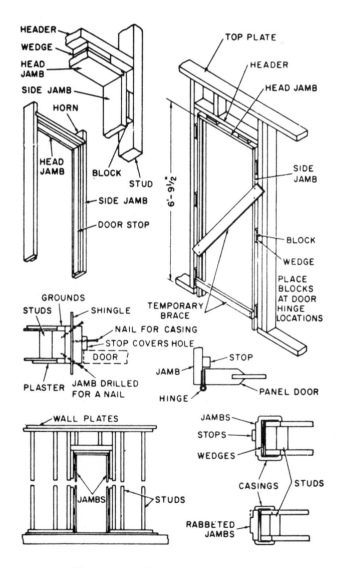

Figure 7-45. Door jamb and door trim.

(11) Take care not to wedge the jamb unevenly.

(12) Use a straightedge 5 or 6 feet long inside the jambs to help prevent uneven wedging.

(13) Check jambs and head carefully, because jambs placed out of plumb will have a tendency to swing the door open or shut, depending on the direction in which the jamb is out of plumb.

c. Door Trim. Door trim material is nailed onto the jambs to provide a finish between the jambs and the wall. It is frequently called "casing" (fig. 7–45). Sizes vary from 1/2 to 3/4 inch in thickness, and from 2 1/2 to 6 inches in width. Most trim has a concave back, to fit over uneven plaster. In mitered work, care must be taken to make all joints clean, square, neat, and well fitted. (If the trim is to be mitered at the top corners, a miter box, miter square, hammer nail set, and block plane will be needed.) Door openings are cased up as follows:

(1) Leave a margin of 1/4-inch from the edge of the jamb to the casing all around.

(2) Cut one of the side casings square and even at the bottom, with the bottom of the jamb.

(3) Cut the top or mitered end next, allowing 1/4-inch extra length for the margin at the top.

(4) Nail the casing onto the jamb and even with the 1/4-inch margin line, starting at the top and working toward the bottom.

(5) Use 4-penny finishing nails along the jamb side and 6-penny or 8-penny case nails along the outer edge of the casings.

(6) The nails along the outer edge will need to be long enough to go through the casing and into the studs.

(7) Set all nailheads about 1/8 inch below the surface of the wood with a nail set.

(8) Now apply the casing for the other side and then the head casing.

7–20. Windows

Windows are generally classified as sliding, double hung, and casement (fig. 7–46). All windows, whatever the type, consist essentially of two parts, the frame and the sash. The frame is made up of four basic parts: the head, the jambs (two), and the sill. The sash is the framework which holds the glass in the window. Where the openings are provided, studding must be cut away and its equivalent strength replaced by doubling the studs on each side of the opening to form trimmers and inserting a header at the top. If the opening is wide, the header should be doubled and trussed. At the bottom of the opening, the bottom header or rough sill is inserted.

a. Window Frames. These are the frames into which the window sashes are fitted and hung. They are set into the rough opening in the wall framing and are intended to hold the sashes in place. The rough window opening is made at least 10 inches larger each way (width and height) than the window glass (pane) size to be used. If the sash to be used is, for instance, a two-light window, 24 by 26 inches, add 10 inches to the width (24 inches) to obtain the total width of 34 inches for the rough opening. Add the upper and lower glasses (26 inches each) and an additional 10 inches for the total height of the rough opening, 62 inches. These allowances are standard and provide for weights, springs, balances, room for plumbing and squaring, and for regular adjustments.

b. Double-Hung Window. The double-hung window (fig. 7–47) is made up of two parts: an upper and a lower sash, which slide vertically past one another. Screens can be located on the outside of a double-hung window without interfering with its operation, and ventilators and window air conditioners can be placed with the window mostly closed. However, for full ventilation of a room, only one-half of the area of the window can be used, and any current of air

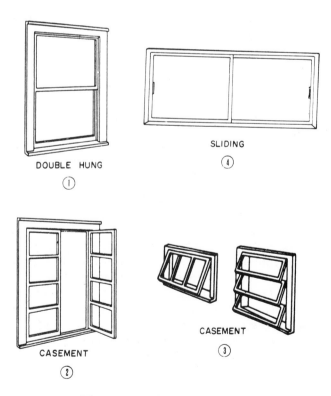

DOUBLE HUNG
①

SLIDING
④

CASEMENT
②

CASEMENT
③

Figure 7–46. Types of windows.

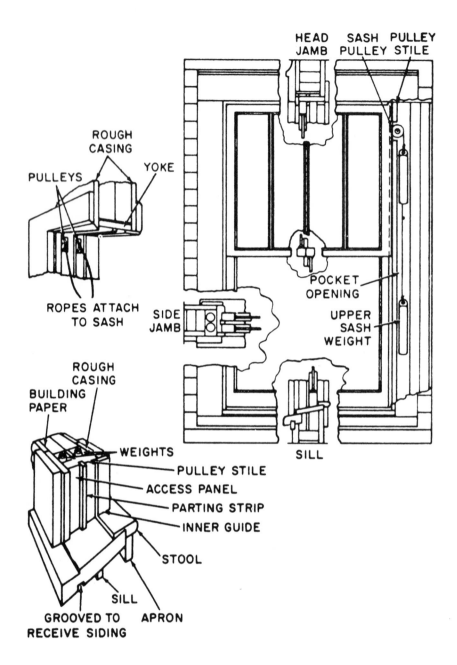

Figure 7-47. Double-hung window.

passing across its face is to some extent lost to the room.

(1) The box frame (fig. 7-47) consists of a top piece or yoke, two side pieces or jambs called pulley stiles, and the sill. The yoke and pulley stiles are dadoed into the inner and outer pieces (rough casing), forming an open box with the opening toward the studs and headers. The rough casing provides nailing surface to the studs and headers forming the plaster stop. The outside rough casing is also a blind stop for sheathing which should fit snugly against it, with building paper lapping the joint.

(2) The 2-inch space between the framing studs and the pulley stile forms the box for counterweights which balance the window sash. The weight box is divided by a thin strip known as the pendulum, which separates the weights for the two sash units. In the stiles near the sill is an opening for easy access to the weights. This opening has a removable strip which is part of the stile and channel for the lower sash (fig. 7-47).

(3) Yoke and stile faces are divided by a parting strip which is dadoed into them, but removable so that the upper sash can be taken out. The strip forms the center guide for the upper and lower sash, while the outerrough casing.

projecting slightly beyond the stiles and yoke, forms the outer guide. The inner guide for the sash is formed by a strip or stop, usually with a molding form on the inner edge. This stop is removable to permit the removal of the lower sash.

(4) At the upper parts of the stiles, two pulleys on each side (one for each sash) are mortised flush with the stile faces for the weight cord or chain.

(5) The sill is part of the box frame and slants downward and outward. It usually has one or two 1/4-inch brakes, one occurring at the point where the lower sash rests on the sill, and another near the outer edge to form a seat for window screens or storm sash. These brakes prevent water, dripping on the sill, from being blown under the sash. The underside of the sill, near its outer edge, is grooved to receive the edge of siding material to form a watertight seal.

(6) On the room side of the sill is another piece, the stool, which has a rabbet on its underside into which the sill fits. The stool edge projects from the will, forming a horizontal stop for the lower sash. The stool is part of the interior trim of the window, made up of side and top casings and an apron under the stool. The framed finished side and top casings are on the weather face. A drip cap rests on top of the outside head casing and is covered with metal flashing to form a watertight juncture with the siding material.

c. Hinged or Casement Windows. There are basically two types of casement windows, the outswinging and the inswinging types, and these may be hinged at the sides, top, or bottom. The casement window which opens out requires the window screen to be located on the inside with some device cut into its frame to operate the casement. Inswinging casements, like double-hung windows, are clear of screens, but they are extremely difficult to make watertight, particularly against a driving rainstorm. Casements have the advantage of their entire area being opened to air currents, with the added advantage of catching a parallel breeze and slanting it into a room.

(1) Casement windows are considerably less complicated in their construction, being simple frames and sash. The frames are usually made of planks 1 3/4 inch thick with rabbets cut in them to receive the sash. Usually there is an additional rabbet for screens or storm sash. The frames are rabbeted 1/2 inch deep and 1 1/2 or 1 7/8 inches wide for sash 1 3/8 or 1 3/4 inches

thick. The additional rabbet is usually 15/16 or 1 3/16 inches wide, depending on whether the screen or storm sash is 7/8 or 1 1/8-inch thick.

(2) Outswinging casement windows have the rabbet for the sash on the outer edges of the frame, the inner edge being rabbeted for the screen. Sill construction is like that for a double-hung window, with the stool much wider and forming a stop for the bottom rail. Casement-window frames are of a width to extend to the sheathing face on the weather side and to the plaster face on the room side (fig. 7-48).

(3) When there are two casement windows in a row in one frame, they may be separated by a vertical double jamb called a mullion, or the stiles may come together in pairs like a french door. The edges of the stiles may be a reverse rabbet; a beveled reverse rabbet with battens, one attached to each stile; or beveled astragals (T-shaped molding), one attached to each stile. The battens and astragals insure better weathertightness. The latter are more resistant to loosening through use. Two pairs of casement sash in one frame are hinged to a mullion in the center (fig. 7-48).

(4) Inswinging casement-window frames are like the outswinging type with the sash rabbet cut in the inner edge of the frame (fig. 7-48). The sill construction is slightly different, being of one piece (similar to that of a door sill) with

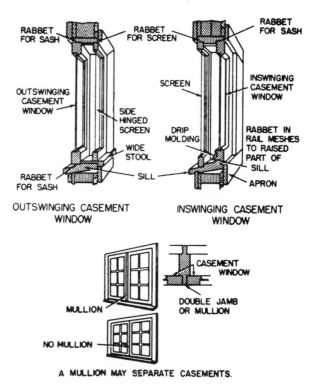

Figure 7-48. Casement windows.

a rabbet cut for a screen or storm sash toward the front edge, and the back raised where the sash rail seats. This surface is rabbeted at its back edge to form a stop for the rail which is also rabbeted to mesh.

(5) Sills in general have a usual slope of about 1 in 5 inches so that they shed water quickly. They are wider than the frames, extending usually about 1½ inches beyond the sheathing. They also form a base for the outside finished casing.

(6) The bottom sash rail of an inswinging casement window is constructed differently from the outswinging type. The bottom edge is rabbeted to mesh with the rabbet on the sill, and a drip molding is set in the weather face to prevent rain from being blown under the sash.

d. Window Frames In hasty construction, millwork window frames are seldom used. The window frames are mere openings left in the walls with the stops all nailed to the stud. The sash may be hinged to the inside or the outside of the wall or constructed so as to slide. The latter type of sash is most common in Army construction because it requires little time to install. Figure 7–49 shows the section and plan of a window and window frame of the type used in the field. After the outside walls have been finished, a 1 by 3 is nailed on top of the girt at the bottom of the window opening to form a sill. A 1 by 2 is nailed to the bottom of the plate and on the side studs which acts as a top for the window sash. One guide is nailed at the bottom of the opening flush with the bottom of the girt, and another is nailed to the plate with the top edge flush with the top of the plate. These guides are 1 by 3's, 8 feet long. Stops are nailed to the bottom girt and plate, between the next two studs, to hold the sash in position when open (fig. 7–49).

7–21. Other Wall Openings

a. Stovepipes. Stovepipes carried outside a building through a side wall eliminate the need for flashing and waterproofing around the pipe (fig. 7–50). The opening should be cut in an area selected to avoid cutting studs, braces, plates, and so on. Sheathing must be cut back in a radius 6 inches greater than that of the pipe. Safety thimbles or other insulation must be used on the inside and outside of the sheathing. Sheet metal insulation may be constructed and used as a single insulator on the outside. Make openings as follows:

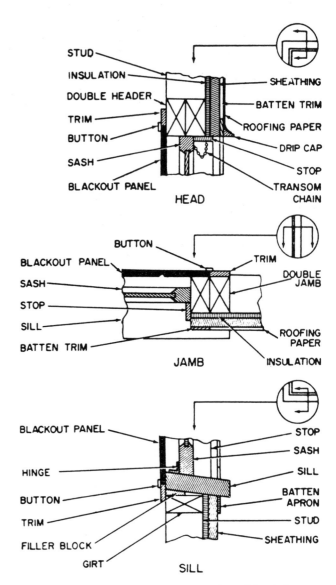

Figure 7–49. Detail of wall section with window frame and sash.

(1) Cut a hole through the sheet metal where the stovepipe is to penetrate.

(2) Mark a circle on the metal 1/2-inch larger in diameter than the pipe and then make another circle within this circle with a diameter 2 inches less than the diameter of the first.

(3) With a straightedge, draw lines through the center of the circle from the circumference. These marks should be from 1/2 to 3/4 inch apart along the outer circumference.

(4) Cut out the center circle, then cut to the outside of the circle along the lines drawn. After the lines have been cut, bend the metal strips outward at a 45° angle and force the pipe through the hole to the desired position. Very little water will leak around this joint.

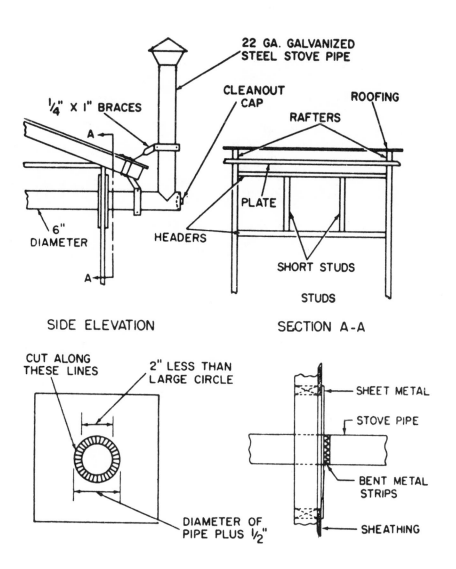

SIDE ELEVATION   SECTION A-A

METAL FLASHING

Figure 7-50. Preparation of wall opening for stovepipe.

b. *Ventilators.* Adequate ventilation is necessary to prevent condensation in buildings. Condensation may occur in the walls, in the crawl space under the structure, in basements, on windows, and so on. Condensation is most likely to occur in structures during the first 6 to 8 months after a building is built and in extreme cold weather when interior humidity is high. Proper ventilation under the roof allows moisture-laden air to escape during the winter heating season and also allows the hot dry air of the summer season to escape. The upper areas of a structure are usually ventilated by the use of louvers or ventilators.

(1) *Types of ventilators* (fig. 7-51). Types of ventilators used are as follows:

(a) Roof louvers (1).

(b) Cornice ventilators (2).

(c) Gable louvers (3).

(d) Flat-roof ventilators (4).

(e) Crawl-space ventilation (5).

(f) Ridge ventilators (6).

(2) *Upper structure ventilation.* One of the most common methods of ventilating is by the use of wood or metal louver frames. There are many types, sizes, and shapes of louvers. The following are facts to consider when building or installing the various kinds of ventilation:

(a) The size and number of ventilators are determined by the size of the area to be ventilated.

(b) The minimum net open area should be 1/4 square inch per square foot of ceiling area.

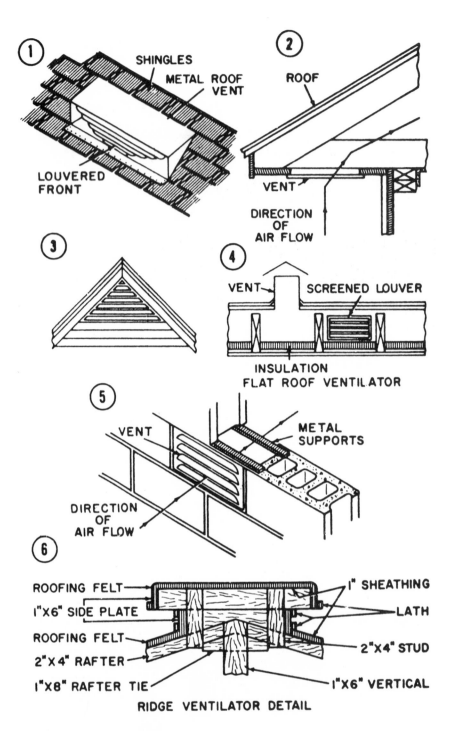

Figure 7-51. Types of ventilators.

(c) Most louver frames are usually 5 inches wide.

(d) Back edge should be rabbeted out for a screen or door, or both.

(e) Three-quarter-inch slats are used and spaced about 1 3/4 inches apart.

(f) Sufficient slant or slope to the slats should be provided to prevent rain from driving in.

(g) For best results, upper structure lou-vers should be placed as near the top of the gable as possible.

(3) *Crawl-space ventilation.* Crawl spaces under foundations of basementless structures should be well ventilated. Air circulation under the floors prevents excessive condensation that causes warping, swelling, twisting, and rotting of the lumber. These crawl-space ventilators are usually called "foundation louvers" (5, fig. 7-51). They are set into the foundation at the time it is

being built. A good foundation vent should be equipped with a copper or bronze screen and adjustable shutters for opening and closing the louver. The sizes for the louvers should be figured on the same basis as that used for upper structure louvers—1/4-inch for each square foot of under-floor space.

Section IV. STAIRWAYS

7-22. Steps and Stairs

Stairwork is made up of the framing on the sides, known as stringers or carriages, and the steps, known as treads. Sometimes pieces are framed into the stairs at the back of the treads; these pieces are known as risers. The stringers or carriages may consist of materials 2 or 3 inches thick and 4 or more inches wide which are cut to form the step of the stairs. Blocks (fig. 7-52) may also be nailed on to form the steps. There are usually three stringers to a stair, one at each of the two outer edges and one at the center. The floor joists must be properly framed around the stair well, or wellhole, in order to have enough space for the erection of the stair framing and the finished trim of the entire staircase.

a. The step or stair stringer may be made of 2 by 4's, with triangular blocks nailed to one edge to form the stringer. The blocks are cut from 2 by 6's and nailed to the 2 by 4, as shown in 1, figure 7-52. The step stringers are fastened at the top and bottom as shown in 2, figure 7-52. Figures 7-52 and 7-53 show the foundation and give the details of the sizes of the step treads, handrails, the methods of installing them, and the post construction. This type of step is most common in field construction.

b. When timbers heavier than 2 by 4's are used for stringers, they are laid out and cut as shown in figure 7-54.

7-23. Stairway Framing

a. To frame simple, straight string stairs, take a narrow piece of straight stock, called a story pole, and mark on it the distance from the lower

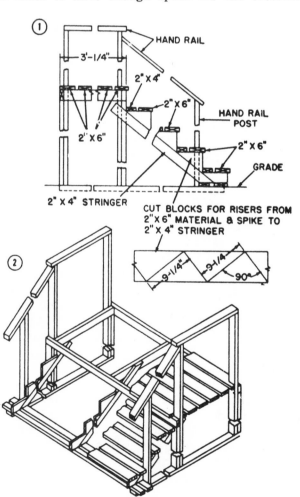

Figure 7-52. Step construction.

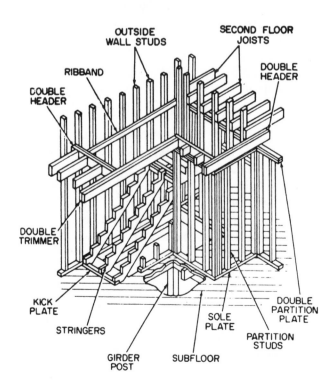

Figure 7-53. Details of complete stair construction.

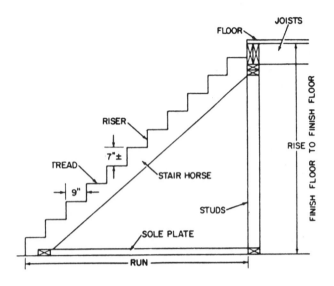

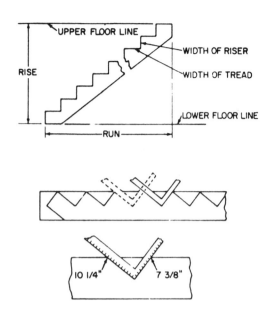

Figure 7-54. Method of laying out stair stringers.

floor to the upper floor level. This is the lower room height, plus the thickness of the floor joists, and the rough and finished flooring. It is also the total rise of the stairs. If it is kept in mind that a flight of stairs forms a right angled triangle (fig. 7-55), with the rise being the height of the triangle, the run being the base of the triangle, and the length of the stringers being the hypotenuse of the triangle, it will help in laying out the stair distances. Set dividers at 7 inches, the average distance from one step to another, and step off this distance on the story pole. If this distance will not divide into the length of the story pole evenly, adjust the divider span slightly and again step off this distance on the story pole. Continue this adjusting and stepping off until the story pole is marked off evenly. The span of the dividers must be near 7 inches and represents the rise of each step. Count the number of spaces stepped off evenly by the dividers, on the story pole. This will be the total number of risers in the stairs.

b. Measure the length of the wellhole for the length of the run of the stairs. This length may also be obtained from the details on the plans. The stair well length forms the base of a right-angled triangle. The height of the triangle and the base of the triangle have now been obtained.

c. To obtain the width of each tread, divide the number of risers, less one—since there is always one more riser than tread—into the run of the stairs. The numbers thus obtained are to be used on the steel square in laying off the run and rise of each tread and riser on the

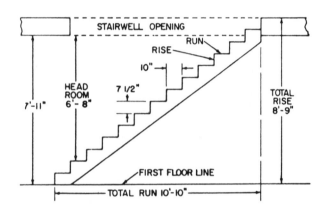

Figure 7-55. Principal parts of stair construction.

stringer stock (fig. 7-54). These figures will be about 7 inches and 10 inches, respectively, since the ideal run and rise totals 17 inches. Lay off the run and rise of each step on the stringer stock equal to the number of risers previously obtained by dividing the story pole into equal spaces. The distance of the height, base, and hypotenuse of a right-angled triangle are thus obtained.

7-24. Check on Design of Risers and Treads

a. Rules. The following are two rules of thumb that may be used to check the dimensions of risers and treads:

(1) Riser + tread = between 17 and 19 inches.

(2) Riser x tread = between 70 and 75 inches.

b. Check. If the sum of the height of the riser and the width of the tread ((1) above) falls between 17 and 19 inches, and the product of the height of the riser and the width of the tread equals between 70 and 75 inches, the design is satisfactory.

TABLE 7-1

SIZES OF BUILT—UP WOOD GIRDERS FOR VARIOUS LOADS AND SPANS

Based on Douglas Fir 4—SQUARE Guide—Line FRAMINIG

Deflection Not Over 1/360 Of Span—Allowable Fiber Stress 1600 lbs. per sq. in.

LOAD PER LINEAR FOOT OF GIRDER	LENGTH OF SPAN				
	6'-0''	7'-0''	8'-0''	9'-0''	10'-0''
	NOMINAL SIZE OF GIRDER REQUIRED				
750	6x8 in.	6x8 in.	6x8 in.	6x10 in.	6x10 in.
900	6x8	6x8	6x10	6x10	8x10
1050	6x8	6x10	8x10	8x10	8x12
1200	6x10	8x10	8x10	8x10	8x12
1350	6x10	8x10	8x10	8x12	10x12
1500	8x10	8x10	8x12	10x12	10x12
1650	8x10	8x12	10x12	10x12	10x14
1800	8x10	8x12	10x12	10x12	10x14
1950	8x12	10x12	10x12	10x14	12x14
2100	8x12	10x12	10x14	12x14	12x14
2250	10x12	10x12	10x14	12x14	12x14
2400	10x12	10x14	10x14	12x14	
2550	10x12	10x14	12x14	12x14	
2700	10x12	10x14	12x14		
2850	10x14	12x14	12x14		
3000	10x14	12x14			
3150	10x14	12x14			
3300	12x14	12x14			

The 6-in. girder is figured as being made with three pieces 2 in. dressed to 1-5/8 in. thickness

The 8-in. girder is figured as being made with four pieces 2 in. dressed to 1-5/8 in. thickness.

The 10-in. girder is figured as being made with five pieces 2-in. dressed to 1-5/8 in. thickness.

The 12-in. girder is figured as being made with six pieces 2 in. dressed to 1-5/8 in. thickness.

Note—For solid girders multiply above loads by 1.130 when 6-inch girder is used; 1.150 when 8-in. girder is used; 1.170 when 10-in. girder is used and 1.180 when 12-in. girder is used.

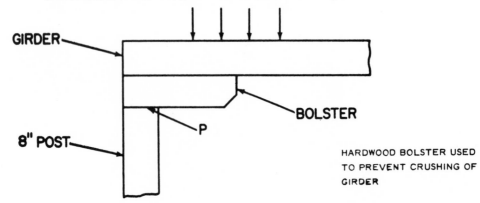

HARDWOOD BOLSTER USED TO PREVENT CRUSHING OF GIRDER

CHAPTER 8

ROOF SYSTEM AND COVERINGS

Section I. ROOFING

8-1. Ceilings

Ceiling joists form the framework of the ceiling of the room. They are usually lighter than floor joists, but large enough and strong enough to resist bending and buckling, and to remain rigid. Ceiling joists are generally installed 16 inches apart on centers, starting at one side of the building and continuing across. Extra joists, if needed, may be placed without affecting the spacing of the prime joists. The selection of the ceiling joists and their installation are much the same as those of floor joists. They are placed parallel with the rafters and extend in a continuous line across the structure. The ceiling joists are nailed to both the plates and the rafters, if possible, and lapped and spiked over bearing partitions. Joists that lie beside rafters on a plate are cut at the same slope as the pitch of the rafter, flush with the top of the rafter. They are installed crown or camber up. For details, see figure 8-1.

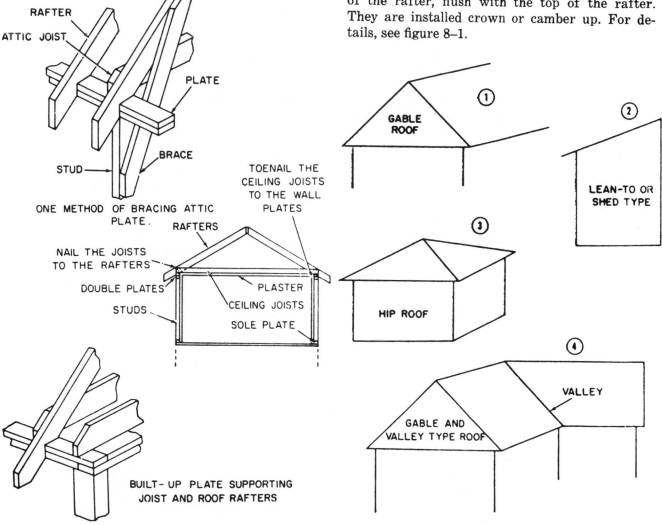

Figure 8-1. Ceiling joists.

Figure 8-2. Types of roofs.

8–2. Roofs

a. General. The primary object of a roof in any climate is to keep out the rain and the cold or heat. The roof must be sloped so as to shed water. In areas of heavy snows, roofs must be constructed more rigidly to bear the extra weight. They must also be strong enough to withstand high winds. The most commonly used types of roof construction are as follows:

(1) *Gable roof* (1, fig. 8–2). The gable roof has two roof slopes that meet at the center, or ridge, to form a gable. It is the most common roof because it is simple, economical and may be used on any type structure.

(2) *Lean-to or shed roof* (2, fig. 8–2). This near-flat roof is used where large buildings are framed under one roof, where hasty or temporary construction is needed, and where sheds or additions to buildings are erected. The pitch of the roof is in one direction only. The roof is held up by the walls or posts on four sides; one wall or the posts on one side are higher than those on the opposite side.

(3) *Hip roof* (3, fig. 8–2). The hip roof has four sides or slopes running toward the center of the building. Rafters at the corners extend diagonally to meet at the center, or ridge. Into these rafters, other rafters are framed.

(4) *Gable and valley roof* (4, fig. 8–2). This roof is a combination of two gable roofs intersecting each other. The valley is that part where the two roofs meet, each roof slanting in a different direction. This roof is seldom used, since it is complicated and requires much time and labor to construct.

b. Rafters. Rafters make up the main body of the framework of all roofs. They do for the roof what the joists do for the floor and what the studs do for the wall. Rafters are inclined members spaced from 16 to 48 inches apart which vary in size, depending on their length and the distance at which they are spaced. The tops of the inclined rafters are fastened in one of the various common ways determined by the type of roof. The bottoms of the rafters rest on the plate member which provides a connecting link between wall and roof and is really a functional part of both. The structural relationship between rafters and wall is the same in all types of roofs. The rafters are not framed into the plate but are simply nailed to it, some being cut to fit the plate while others, in hasty construction, are merely laid on top of the plate and nailed in place. Rafters may extend a short distance beyond the wall to form the eaves and protect the sides of the building.

c. Roofing Terms.

(1) *Basic triangle.* The basic principle involved in roof framing is the right triangle, shown in figure 8–3. When framing a roof, the basic right triangle is formed by the horizontal lines, or run, the rise (or altitude), and the length of the rafter (the hypotenuse). Any part of the triangle can be computed if the other two parts are known. Use the equation that states the square of the hypotenuse of a right triangle is equal to the sum of the squares of the two sides. Stating this formula in roofing terms, rafter length = $\sqrt{\text{run}^2 + \text{rise}^2}$.

(2) *Bird's mouth.* The bird's mouth is a cutout near the bottom of a rafter which fits over the top plate as shown at 2 of figure 8–4. This is the most common cut for fitting a rafter to the plate. The cut which fits the top of the plate

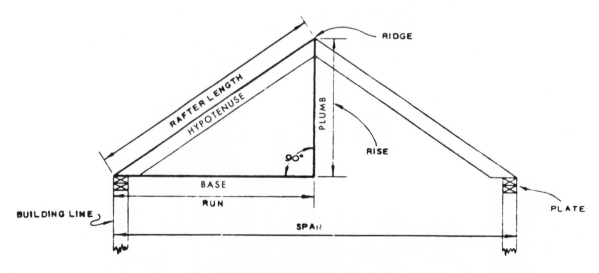

Figure 8–3. Right triangle.

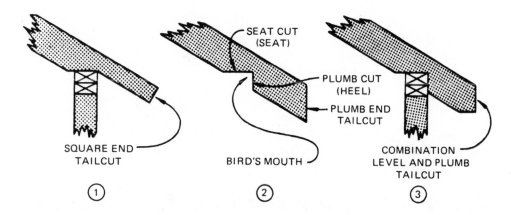

Figure 8-4. Cuts on bottom end of rafters.

is called the seat, while the cut for the side of the plate is called the heel.

(3) *Cut of roof.* The cut of a roof is the rise in inches and the unit of run (12 inches) (1, fig. 8-5).

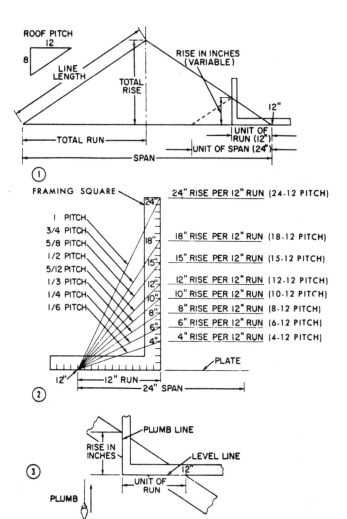

Figure 8-5. Pitch of roof.

(4) *Horizontal line.* A horizontal line is one level with the building foundation.

(5) *Line length.* Line length as used in roof framing is the hypotenuse of a triangle whose base is the total run and whose altitude is the total rise (1, fig. 8-5).

(6) *Overhang.* The overhang (8, fig. 8-6) is that portion of a rafter which extends beyond the outside edge of the plate or walls of a building. When laying out a rafter, this portion is an addition to what is considered the length of a rafter and is figured separately. The overhang is often referred to as the lookout, eave, or tailpiece.

(7) *Pitch.* Pitch signifies the amount that a roof slants. Units, or amount, of pitch are expressed as ratios. There are two methods of indicating pitch. Using the first method, the pitch is indicated as a ratio of the rise to the span of a roof. This ratio is stated as a fraction, as shown in 2, figure 8-5. The units of span and rise must be the same (inches or feet), and the fraction is reduced to its lowest common denominator. With the second method, pitch is stated as the ratio of rise (in inches) to (or per) 1 foot of span (12 inches). Using this method, 4, 6, or 8 inches rise per foot of span would give a pitch of 4-12, 6-12, or 8-12, as shown in 2, figure 8-5. Further examination of figure 8-5 shows that a roof with 1/2 pitch can also be said to have 12-12 pitch.

(8) *Plate.* This is the wall framing member (2, fig. 8-6) that rests on the top of the wall studs. It is sometimes called the rafter plate because it is the framing member upon which the rafters rest.

(9) *Plumb line.* A plumb line (3, fig. 8-5) is the line formed by the cord on which the plumb bob is hung.

(10) *Rafter types.* There are four types of rafters: common, hip, valley, and jack. The com-

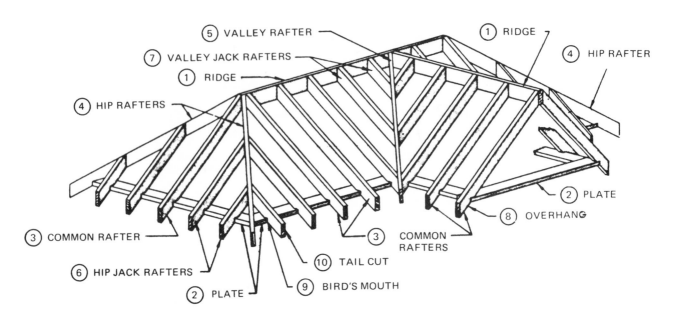

Figure 8-6. Identification of roof framing terms.

mon rafters (3, fig. 8-6) are the framing members which extend at right angles from the plate line to the ridge of the roof. They are called *common rafters* because they are common to all types of roofs and are used as the basis for laying out other types of rafters. *Hip rafters* are roof members which extend diagonally from the corner of the plate to the ridge as shown in 4, figure 8-6. *Valley rafters* (5, fig. 8-6), extend from the plate to the ridge along the lines where two roofs intersect. *Jack rafters* are a part of a common rafter. There are three kinds of jack rafters: the hip jack (6, fig. 8-6), the valley jack (7, fig. 8-6), and the cripple jack. The hip jack rafter extends from the plate to the hip rafter, while the valley jack rafter extends from the ridge to the valley rafter. A cripple jack rafter is placed between a hip and valley rafter. This rafter is also part of a common rafter but touches neither the ridge of the roof nor the rafter plate.

(11) *Ridge*. The ridge (1, fig. 8-6) is the highest horizontal roof member which helps to aline the rafters and tie them together at the upper end.

(12) *Rise*. The rise of a rafter is the vertical, or plumb, distance that a rafter extends upward from the plate (fig. 8-3).

(13) *Span*. The span of any roof (fig. 8-3) is the shortest distance between the two opposite rafter seats.

(14) *Total rise*. The total rise (1, fig. 8-5) is the vertical distance from the plate to the top of the ridge.

(15) *Total run*. Total run (1, fig. 8-5) always refers to the level distance over which any rafter passes. For the ordinary rafter, this would be one-half the span distance.

(16) *Unit of run*. The unit of measurement, 1 foot or 12 inches, is the same for the roof as for any other part of the building. By the use of this common unit, the framing square is employed in laying out large roofs (fig. 8-5).

8-3. Rafter Layout

Rafters must be laid out and cut with slope, length, and overhang exactly right so that they will fit when placed in the roof.

a. Scale or Measurement Methods. The carpenter first determines the length of the rafter and the length of the piece of lumber from which the rafter may be cut. If he is working from a roof plan, he learns the rafter lengths and the width of the building from it. If no plans are available, the width of the building must be measured with a tape.

(1) To determine the rafter length, first find one-half of the distance between the outside plates. This distance (total run) is the horizontal distance which the rafter will cover. The amount of rise per foot has yet to be considered. If the building to be roofed is 20 feet wide, half the span will be 10 feet. For example, the rise per foot is to be 8 inches. To determine the approximate overall length of a rafter, measure on the steel carpenter square the distance between 8 on the tongue and 12 on the blade, because 8 is

the rise and 12 is the unit of run. This distance is 14 5/12 inches, and represents the line length of a rafter with a total run of 1 foot and a rise of 8 inches. Since the run of the rafter is 10 feet, multiply 10 by the line length for 1 foot. The answer is 144 2/12 inches, or 12 feet and 1/6 inch. The amount of overhang, normally 1 foot, must be added if an overhang is to be used. This makes a total of 13 feet for the length of the rafter, but since 13 feet is an odd length for timber, a 14-foot timber is used.

(2) After the length has been determined, the timber is laid on sawhorses, ("saw benches"), with the crown or bow (if it has any) as the top side of the rafter. If possible, select a straight piece for the pattern rafter. If a straight piece is not available, have the crown toward the person laying off the rafter. Hold the square with the tongue in the right hand, the blade in the left, the heel away from the body, and place the square as near the upper end of the rafter as possible. In this case, the figure 8 on the tongue and 12 on the blade are placed along the edge of timber which is to be the top edge of the rafter as shown in 1, figure 8–7. Mark along the tongue edge of the square, which will be the plumb cut at the ridge. Since the length of the rafter is known to be 12 feet and 1/6 inch, measure the distance from the top of the plumb

cut and mark it on the timber. Hold the square in the same manner with the 8 mark on the tongue directly over the 12-foot and 1/6 inch mark. Mark along the tongue of the square to give the plumb cut for the seat (2, fig. 8–7). Next measure off, perpendicular to this mark, the length of overhang along the timber and make a plumb cut mark in the same manner, keeping the square on the same edge of the timber (3, fig. 8–7). This will be the tail cut of the rafter; often the tail cut is made square across the timber.

(3) The level cut or width of the seat is the width of the plate, measured perpendicular to the plumb cut, as shown in 4, figure 8–7. Using the try square, square lines down on the sides from all level and plumb cut ilnes. Now the rafter is ready to be cut (5, fig. 8–7).

b. Step-Off Method. If a building is 20 feet 8 inches wide, the run of the rafter would be 10 feet 4 inches, or half the span. Instead of using the above method, the rafter length may be determined by "stepping it off" by successive steps with the square as shown in figure 8–8. Stake the same number of steps as there are feet in the run, which leaves 4 inches over a foot. This 4 inches is taken care of in the same manner as the full foot run; that is, with the square at the last step position, make a mark on the rafters at the 4-inch mark on the blade, then move the square along the rafter until the tongue rests at the 4-inch mark (1, fig. 8–8). With the square held for the same cut as before, make a mark along the tongue. This is the line length of the rafter. The seat-cut and hangover are made as

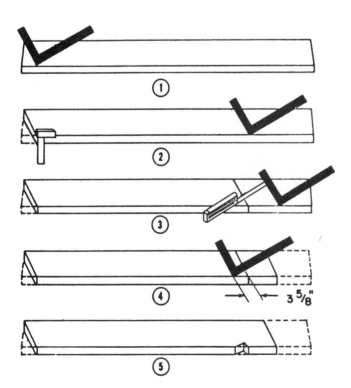

Figure 8–7. Rafter layout—scale or measurement method.

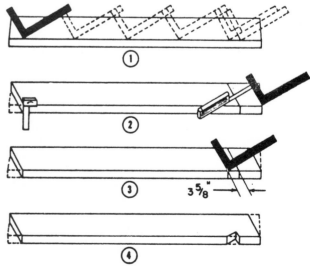

Figure 8–8. Rafter layout—step-off method.

described in *a* above (2, 3 and 4, fig. 8–8). When laying off rafters by any method, be sure to recheck the work carefully. When two rafters have been cut, it is best to put them in place to see if they fit. Minor adjustments may be made at this time without serious damage or waste of material.

(2) To use the table for laying out rafters, the width of the building must first be known. Suppose the building is 20 feet 8 inches wide and the rise of the rafters is to be 13 inches per foot of run. The total run of the rafter will be 10 feet 4 inches. Look in the first line of figures; under the 13-inch mark appears the number 17.69, which is the length in inches of a rafter with a run of 1 foot and a rise of 13 inches. To find the line length of a rafter with a total run of 10 feet 4 inches, multiply 17.69 inches by 10 1/3 and divide by 12 so as to get the answer in feet. The 17.69 inches times 10 1/3 equals 182.79 inches, which is divided by 12 to equal 15 3/12 feet. Therefore 15 feet 3 inches is the line length of the rafter. The remaining procedure for laying out the rafters after the length has been determined is described in *a* above.

(3) The second type of rafter table (fig. 8–10) appears on the back of the blade of some squares. This shows the run, rise, and the pitch of rafters of the seven most common pitches of roof. The figures are based on the length of the

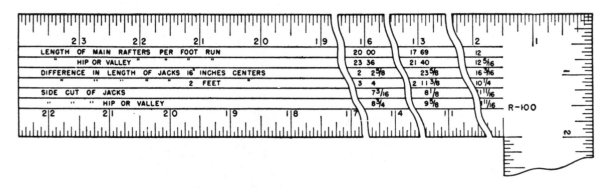

Figure 8–9. Rafter table method (type 1).

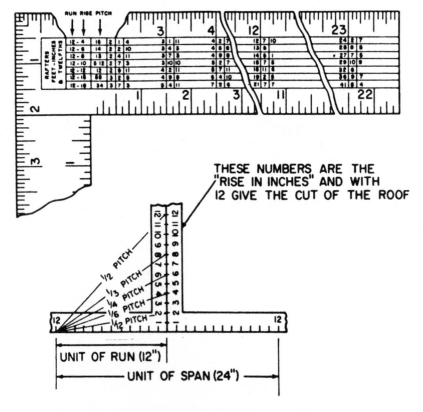

Figure 8–10. Rafter table method (type 2).

horizontal measurement of the building from the center to the outside. The rafter table and the outside edge of the back of the square, both the body and tongue, are in twelfths. The inch marks may represent inches or feet, and the twelfth marks may represent twelfths of an inch or twelfths of a foot. The rafter table is used in connection with the marks and figures on the outside edge of the square, At the left end of the table are figures representing the *run*, the *rise*, and the *pitch*. In the first column, the figures are all 12. These may be used as 12 inches or 12 feet as they represent the *run* of 12. The second column of figures represents various rises. The third column of figures, in fractions, represents the various pitches.

c. *Table Method, Using Rafter Table on Framing Square.* The framing square may have one or two types of rafter tables on the blade. One type gives both the line length of any pitch or rafter per foot of run and the line length of any hip or valley rafter per foot of run. The difference in length of the jack rafter spaced 16 or 24 inches (on center) is also shown in the table. Where the jack rafter, hip, or valley rafter needs side cuts, the cut is given in the table. The other type of table gives the actual length of rafter for a given pitch and span.

(1) The first type of table (fig. 8–9) appears on the face of the blade. It is used to determine the length of the common, valley, hip, and jack rafters, and the angles at which they must be cut to fit at the ridge and plate. To use the table, the carpenter first must know what each figure represents. The row of figures in the first line represents the length of common rafters per foot of run, as the title indicates at the lefthand end of the blade. Each set of figures under each inch division mark represents the length of rafter per foot of run with a rise corresponding to the number of inches over the number. For example, under the 16-inch mark apears the number 20.00 inches. This number equals the length of a rafter with a run of 12 inches and a rise of 16 inches. Under the 13-inch mark appears the number 17.69 inches which is the rafter length for a 12-inch run and a 13-inch rise. The other five lines of figures in the table will not be discussed as they are seldom used in the theater of operations.

(a) These three columns of figures show that a rafter with a run of 12 and a rise of 4 has one-sixth pitch, 12 and 6 has one-fourth pitch, and 12 and 12 has one-half pitch. To use this scale for a roof with one-sixth pitch (or the rise of one-sixth the width of the building) and

a run 12 feet, find 1/6 in the table, and follow the same line of figures to the right until directly beneath the figure 12. Here appear the numbers 12, 7, 10, which is the rafter length required and which represents 12 feet 7 inches, and 10/12 of an inch. They are written as follows: 12 feet, 7 10/12 inches. For a pitch of one-half (or a rise of one-half the width of the building) and a run of 12 feet, the rafter length is 16, 11, 6, or 16 feet, 11 6/12 inches.

(b) If the run is over 23 feet, the table is used as follows: using a run of 27 feet, find the length for a run of 23 feet, then find the length for 4 feet and add the two. The run for 23 feet with a pitch of one-fourth is 25 feet, 8 5/12 inches. For 4 feet, the run is 4 feet, 5 8/12 inches. The total run for 27 feet is 30 feet, 2 1/2 inches. When the run is in inches, the rafter table reads inches and twelfths instead of feet and inches. For example, if the pitch is one-half and the run is 12 feet, 4 inches, add the rafter length of a 12-foot run to that of a rafter length of 4-inch run, as follows: for a run of 12 feet and one-half pitch, the length is 16 feet, 11 6/12 inches. For a run of 4 inches and one-half pitch, the length is 5, 7, 11. In this case the 5 is inches, the 7 is twelfths, and the 11 is 11/12 of 1/12, which is nearly 1/12. Add it to the 7 to make it 8, making a total of 5 8/12 inches, then add the two lengths together. This sum is 17 feet, 5 2/12 inches. The lengths that are given in the table are the line lengths; the overhang must be added. After the length of the rafter has been found, the rafter is laid out as explained in (a) above.

(c) When the roof has an overhang, the rafter is usually cut square to save time. When the roof has no overhang, the rafter cut is plumb, but no notch is cut in the rafter for a seat. The level cut is made long enough to extend across the plate and the wall sheathing. This type of rafter saves material, although little protection is given to the side wall.

8–4. Timber Trusses

a. *Definition.* A truss is a framed or jointed structure composed of straight members connected only at their intersections in such a way that if the loads are applied at these intersections the stress in each member is in the direction of its length.

b. *Types.* The web members of a truss divide it into triangles. The various types of trusses used in building construction are shown in figure 8–11. The members indicated by heavy lines normally carry tensile stresses for vertical loads.

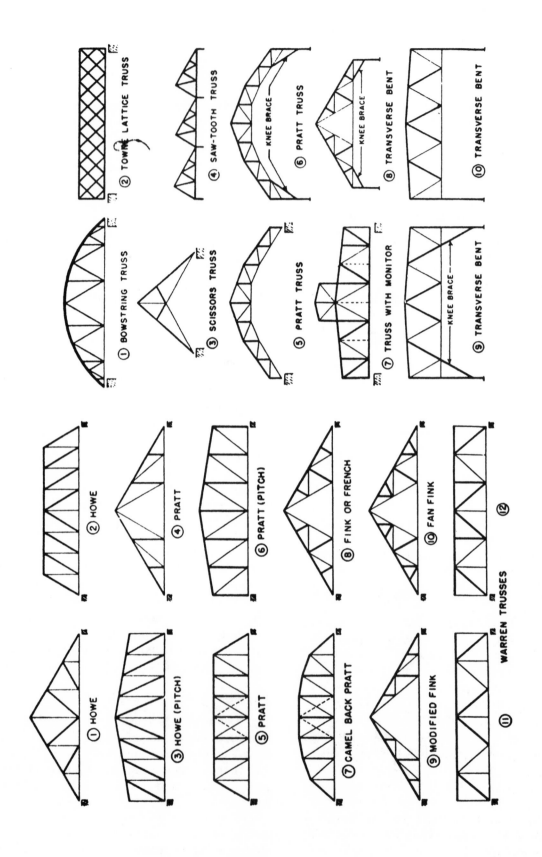

Figure 8–11. Types of trusses.

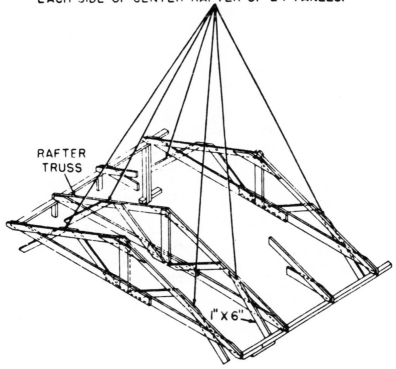

KNEE BRACES WILL BE ON RAFTERS AT EACH
PANEL JOINT, ON TWO RAFTERS AT CENTER
OF EACH 20' PANEL AND ON RAFTERS AT
EACH SIDE OF CENTER RAFTER OF 24' PANELS.

RAFTER
TRUSS

1" X 6"

Figure 8–12. Truss and knee braces.

Sometimes the top chords of these trusses are slightly sloping in one or two directions for roof drainage, but this does not change the type of truss. The necessary number of subdivisions or panels depends upon the length of the span and the type of construction.

c. Truss Terms.

(1) *Bottom chord* is a member which forms the lower boundary of the truss.

(2) *Top chord* is a member which forms the upper boundary of the truss.

(3) *Chord member* is a member which forms part of either the top or bottom chord.

(4) *Member* is the component which lies between any adjacent joints of a truss; it can be of one or more pieces of structural material.

(5) *Web member* is a member which lies between the top and bottom chords.

(6) *Joint* is any point in a truss where two or more members meet and is sometimes called a "panel point".

(7) *Panel length* is the distance between any two consecutive joint centers in either the top or bottom chords.

(8) *Pitch* is the ratio of the height of truss to the span length.

(9) *Height of truss* is the vertical distance at midspan from the joint center at the ridge of a pitched truss, or from the centerline of the top chord of a flat truss, to the centerline of the bottom chord.

(10) *Span length* is the horizontal distance between the joint centers of the two joints located at the extreme ends of the truss.

d. Use. Timber trusses are used for large spans to provide wide unobstructed floor space for such large buildings as shops and hangars. The Howe and Fink trusses (fig. 8–11) are most commonly used. Sometimes small buildings are trussed to save material; these small trusses act as rafters and give the roof rigidity.

e. Support. Trusses are supported by bearing walls, posts, or other trusses. To brace a truss to a wall or post, knee braces are used as shown in figure 8–12. These braces tend to make a truss of the entire building by tying the wall to the roof.

f. Layout. In laying out a truss (fig. 3–13), first get the material to a level spot of ground where workbenches will be approximately level. Obtain from the blueprints the measurement of all pieces that are to be used in the truss. Lay out the length on the different sizes of timber and cut them accurately. After all the lengths of different sizes of material for truss have been cut, lay the pieces in their correct position to form a truss and nail them together temporarily. After the truss is assembled in this way, lay out the location of all holes to be bored, then recheck the measurements to be sure that they are correct; after this is done, bore the holes to the size called for on the print, using a brace and bit or the woodborer which accompanies the air compressor. They should be bored perpendicular to the face of the timber. After the holes have been bored, the truss is dismantled and the nails withdrawn.

g. Assembly. The assembling of a truss after it has been cut and bored is simple. In most cases, timber connectors are used where the different members of the truss join. The truss is again assembled as it was for boring holes, with the timber connectors in place. The bolts are then placed in the holes and tightened, a washer being placed at the head and nut ends of each bolt. Straight and sound timber should be used in trusses to avoid weak places.

h. Purlins. Purlins are used in roof construction to support the sheet metal where corrugated sheet metal is used, or to support the sheathing when roofs are framed with trusses. In small roofs, short purlins are inserted between the rafters and nailed through the rafters as shown in figure 7–2. Where heavy trusses are used, the purlins are continuous members which rest on the trusses and support the sheathing. This type of purlin is used only in large buildings. In small buildings, such as barracks, mess halls, and small warehouses, 2 by 4's are used for purlins, with the narrow side up.

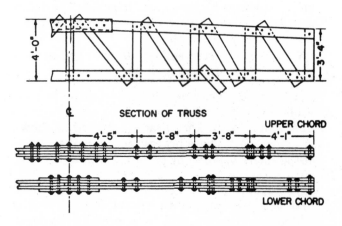

Figure 8–13. Selection of truss.

8–5. Roof Trusses

a. Assembling Rafters Into Trusses. Rafters are usually assembled into trusses, as shown in 1, 2, and 3, figure 8–14. Two rafters are connected at the top by using a collar tie well nailed into both rafters. Before any ties or chords are nailed, the rafters should be spread at the lower end to equal the width of the building. This is done by using a template, or by measuring the distance between the seat cuts with a tape. A 1- by 6-inch or 2- by 4-inch chord is nailed across the rafters at the seat cut to tie them together. This chord forms a truss with the two rafters. A hanger or vertical member (4, fig. 8–14) of 1 by 6 is nailed to the rafter joint and extends to the chord at midpoint, thus tying the rafter to the chord. If no additional bracing is needed, the truss is set in place on the plates. If additional bracing is needed, a knee brace is nailed to the chord. The knee brace forms an angle of 45° with the wall stud. For easier erection, the knee brace may be omitted until the rafter truss is set in place.

b. Use of Template. Rafter framing constructed without the use of ridgeboards may be rapidly completed by use of a truss assembly jig or template. The template is laid out (5 and 6, fig. 8–14) to form a pattern conforming to the exact exterior dimensions of the truss. Lay out a template as follows: (5, fig. 8–14).

(1) Measure and mark a straight line on a selected surface, the exact length of the joists which will form the chord of the truss. This is the baseline A.

(2) From the center of the baseline and at right angles to it, lay out a line the length required to form the leg of a right triangle, the base of which is half the length of the baseline, A, and the hypotenuse, B, which is the length of the rafter measured as indicated. This is the centerline C.

(3) Nail 2- by 4- by 8-inch blocks flush with the ends of baseline A and centerline C as shown. Mark centerline on center jig blocks.

(4) Start assembly by setting a rafter in the jig with plate cut fitted over jig block at one end of baseline. Peak is flush with centerline on peak jig block. Nail a holding block outside rafter at point D.

(5) Assemble trusses in the following order: lay one 2- by 4-inch joist or chord in place across base blocks. Lay two 2- by 4-inch rafters in place over joist. Center one end of a 1- by 6-inch hanger under rafter peak. Center rafters against peak block. Nail through rafters into hanger with six

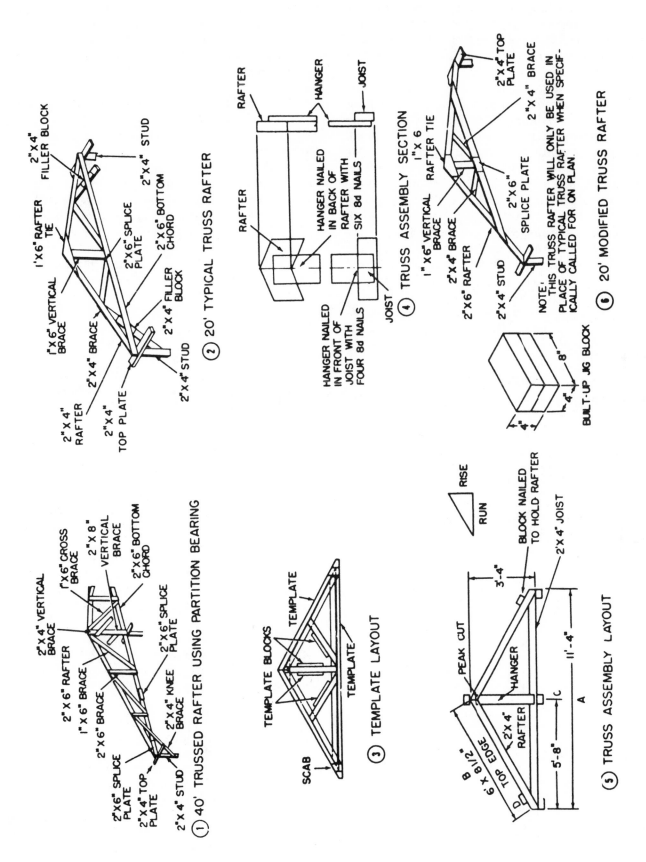

① 40' TRUSSED RAFTER USING PARTITION BEARING

2"X 4" VERTICAL BRACE
1"X 6" CROSS BRACE
2"X 8" VERTICAL BRACE
2"X 6" BOTTOM CHORD
1"X 6" BRACE
2"X 6" RAFTER
2"X 6" BRACE
2"X 6" SPLICE PLATE
2"X 4" TOP PLATE
2"X 4" KNEE PLATE
2"X 6" SPLICE PLATE
2"X 4" STUD

② 20' TYPICAL TRUSS RAFTER

2"X 4" FILLER BLOCK
1"X 6" RAFTER TIE
2"X 4" STUD
2"X 6" SPLICE PLATE
2"X 6" BOTTOM CHORD
1"X 6" VERTICAL BRACE
2"X 4" FILLER BLOCK
2"X 4" BRACE
2"X 4" STUD
2"X 4" RAFTER
2"X 4" TOP PLATE

③ TEMPLATE LAYOUT

TEMPLATE BLOCKS
TEMPLATE
TEMPLATE
SCAB

④ TRUSS ASSEMBLY SECTION

RAFTER
RAFTER
HANGER
JOIST
HANGER NAILED IN BACK OF RAFTER WITH SIX 8d NAILS
HANGER NAILED IN FRONT OF JOIST WITH FOUR 8d NAILS
JOIST

BUILT-UP JIG BLOCK
8"
4"
4"

⑥ 20' MODIFIED TRUSS RAFTER

2"X 4" TOP PLATE
2"X 4" BRACE
1"X 6 RAFTER TIE
1"X 6" VERTICAL BRACE
2"X 6" RAFTER
2"X 4" STUD
2"X 6" SPLICE PLATE
2"X 4" BRACE

NOTE: THIS TRUSS RAFTER WILL ONLY BE USED IN PLACE OF TYPICAL TRUSS RAFTER WHEN SPECIFICALLY CALLED FOR ON PLAN.

⑤ TRUSS ASSEMBLY LAYOUT

RISE
RUN
PEAK CUT
BLOCK NAILED TO HOLD RAFTER
2"X 4" JOIST
3'-4"
11'-4"
A
C
HANGER
2"X 4" RAFTER
5'-8"
B 81/2"
6' X TOP EDGE
D

Figure 8-14. Rafter trusses.

8-penny nails. Line up one end of chord. Nail through rafter with 16-penny nails. Line up other end of chord. Nail as above. Center bottom of hangers on top of chord and nail with 8-penny nails.

c. Placement of Trusses. After the rafters have been assembled into trusses, they must be placed on the building. The first set of rafters may be assembled in the end section of the building or at the center as shown in figure 8–15. The rafter trusses are raised by hand into position and nailed into place with 16-penny nails. These trusses are temporarily braced to the end section of the building until the sheathing is applied. Temporary workbenches may be built for the workers to stand on while erecting these trusses; this will save time. The knee braces are not used on every rafter truss unless needed. The trusses are installed as follows:

(1) Mark proper positions of all truss assemblies on top plate. The marks must show the exact position on the face of all rafters (south or north, etc.).

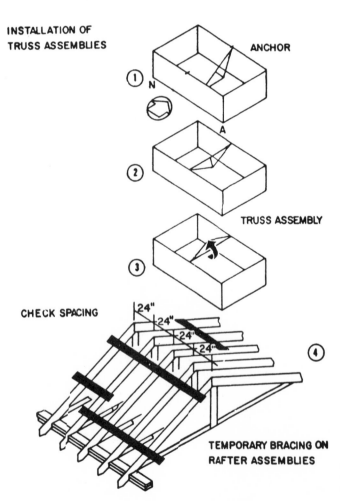

Figure 8–15. Erection of rafter trusses.

(2) Rest one end of a truss assembly, peak down, on an appropriate mark on top plate on one side of structure (1, fig. 8–15).

(3) Rest other end of truss on opposing mark on top plate on other side of structure (2, fig. 8–15).

(4) Rotate assembly into position by means of a pole or rope (3, fig. 8–15).

(5) Line up rafter faces flush against marks and secure.

(6) Raise, aline, and nail three assemblies into position. Nail temporary 1- by 6-inch braces across these three assemblies (4, fig. 8–15) and other assemblies as they are brought into position. Check rafter spacing at peaks as braces are nailed on.

(7) Braces may be used as a platform when raising those trusses for which there is too little room to permit rotation.

8–6. Bracing of Rafters

a. General. In small roofs which cover only narrow buildings and in which the rafters are short, there is no need for interior support or bracing. In long spans, the roof would sag in the middle if it were not strengthened in some way. To support long rafters, braces or other types of supports must be installed.

b. Types.

(1) *Collar beams.* A collar beam or tie is a piece of stock (usually 1 by 4, 1 by 6, or 1 by 8) fastened to a pair of rafters in a horizontal position between the plate and the ridge of the roof. This beam tends to keep the building from spreading. The lower the collar beam or chord, the better it fulfills its purpose. This type of bracing is used on small roofs where no ceiling joists are used and the building is not wide enough to require a truss.

(2) *Truss.* In wide buildings, where the joists or chords must be spliced and there is no support underneath, the rafter and joists support one another as shown in figure 8–16.

8–7. Roof Openings

a. General. Major roof openings are those which interrupt the normal run of rafters or other roof framing. Such openings may be for ventilator, chimney, or trap door passage or for skylight or dormer windows.

b. Construction. Roof openings are framed by headers and trimmers (fig. 8–17). Double headers are used at right angles to the rafters, which are set into the headers in the same way as joists in floor opening construction. Trimmers are ac-

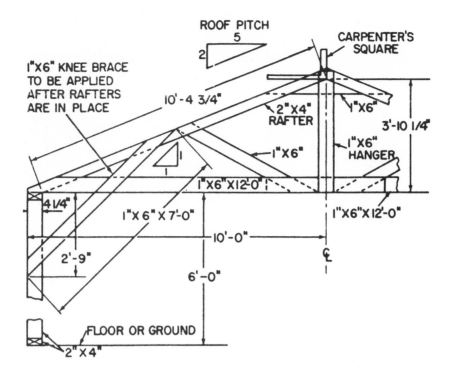

Figure 8-16. Truss or rafter support detail.

tually double rafter construction in roof openings. Nailing strips may be added if needed.

8-8. Roof Covering

a. General. Asphalt and asbestos-cement roof covering are the types most frequently used on

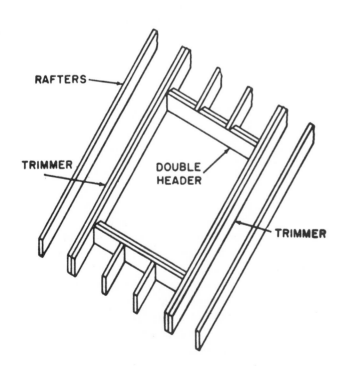

Figure 8-17. Roof opening construction.

pitched-roof structures. Built-up roofing is used mainly on flat or nearly flat roofs.

b. Asphalt and Asbestos-Cement Roofing. Asphalt roofing comes in rolls (usually 36 inches wide, called rolled roofing), in rolled strips (usually 15 inches wide), in flat strips (usually 12 inches wide and 36 inches long), and as individual separate shingles. The type most commonly used is the flat strip, often called a strip shingle. A 12 x 36 square-butt strip shingle is shown in figure 8-18. This shingle should be laid 5 inches to the weather, meaning that 7 inches of each course should be overlapped by the next higher course. The lower, exposed end of a shingle is called the butt. The shingle shown in figure 8-18 has a square butt, divided into three tabs. Various other butt shapes are manufactured. Asbestos-cement roofing usually consists of individual shingles, 12-inch by 24-inch which is the size most commonly used.

c. Laying Asphalt Roofing.

(1) The first essential in covering a roof is to erect a scaffold to a height which will bring the eaves about waist-high to a man standing on the scaffold.

(2) Before any roof covering is applied, the roof sheathing must be swept clean and carefully inspected for irregularities, cracks, holes, or any other defects. No roofing should be applied unless the sheathing boards are absolutely dry.

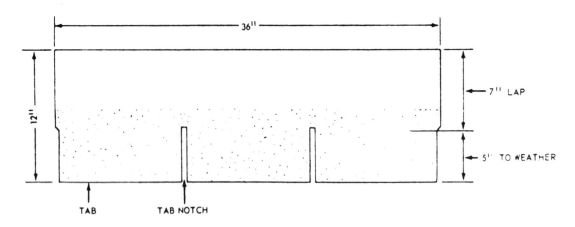

Figure 8–18. A 12 x 36 square-butt asphalt strip shingle.

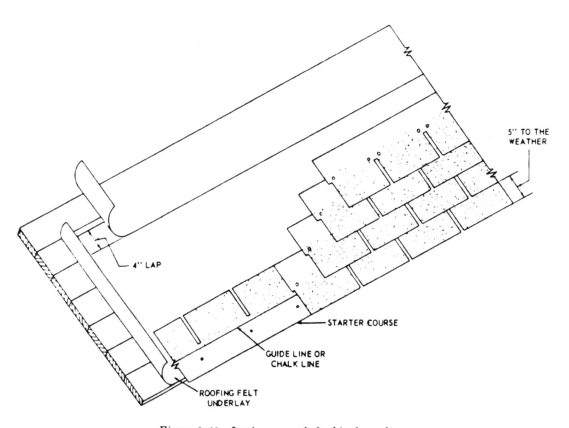

Figure 8–19. Laying an asphalt shingle roof.

(3) An underlay of roofing felt is first applied to the sheathing. Roofing felt usually comes in 3-foot-wide rolls, and it should be laid with a 4-in. lap as indicated.

(4) Before work begins, bundles of shingles should be distributed along the scaffold. There are 27 strips in a bundle of 12 x 36 asphalt strip shingles, and three bundles will cover 100 square feet.

(5) After the first course at the eaves (called the starter course) is laid by inverting the first course of shingles, each course which follows is begun by stretching a guide line or snapping a chalk line from edge to edge to position the course.

(6) Figure 8–19 shows the method of laying a 12 x 36 asphalt strip-shingle roof. Strip shingles should be nailed with 1-inch coppper or hot-dipped galvanized roofing nails, two to each tab; this means six nails to each full strip. Nails should be placed about 6 1/2 inches from the butt edges to insure that each nail will be covered

by the next course (blind nailing) and driven through two courses.

(7) An asbestos-cement roof is laid in about the same way as the asphalt strip shingles.

d. Shingles at Hips and Valleys. One side of a hip or valley shingle must be cut at an angle to obtain an edge line which will match the line of the hip or valley rafter. One way to cut these shingles is to use a pattern made as follows. Select a piece of 1 x 6 about 3 feet long. Determine the unit length of a common rafter in the roof. Set the framing square back up on the piece to the unit run of a common rafter on the tongue and the unit length of a common rafter on the blade, as shown in the top view of figure 8-20. Draw a line along the tongue. Saw the piece along this line, and use it as a pattern to cut the shingles as shown in the bottom view of figure 8-20.

e. Flashing.

(1) Places especially liable to leakage in roofs and outside walls are made watertight by the installation of flashing. Flashing consists of sheets or strips of a watertight, rustproof material (such as galvanized sheet or sheet copper alloy for valleys and felt for hips), installed so as to deflect water away from places that are liable to leakage. The places in a roof most liable to leakage are the lines along which adjoining roof surfaces intersect (such as the lines followed by ridges, hips, and valleys), and the lines of intersection between roof surfaces and the walls of dormers, chimneys, skylights, and the like.

(2) Ridge lines and hip lines tend naturally to shed water, and these lines are therefore only moderately subject to leakage. A strip of felt paper, applied as shown in figure 8-21 usually makes a staisfactory flashing for a ridge or hip. The ridge or hip is then finished as shown in figure 8-21. Squares are made by cutting shingles into thirds. The squares are then blind-nailed to the ridge or hip as shown.

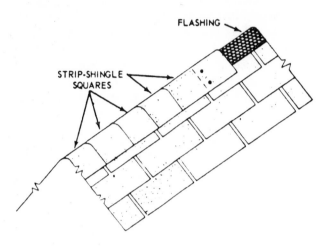

Figure 8-21. Hip or ridge flashing and finish on asphalt strip-shingle roof.

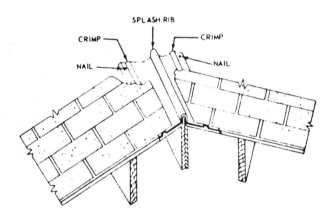

Figure 8-22. Open valley flashing.

(3) Since water gathers in the valleys of a roof they are highly subject to leakage. Valley flashing varies with the manner in which the valley is to be finished. There are two common types of valley finish, known as the open valley and the closed valley.

(a) Figure 8-22 shows part of an open valley. The roof covering does not extend across the valley. The flashing consists of a prefabricated piece of galvanized iron, copper, zinc, or some similar metal, with a splash rib or ridge down

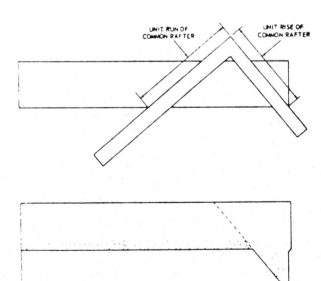

Figure 8-20. Laying out pattern for cutting hip and valley shingle.

the center and a smaller crimp along each of the edges. The flashing is nailed down to the valley with nails driven in the edges, outside the crimps, as shown. Great care must be taken not to drive any nails through the flashing inside of the crimps. Puncturing the flashing inside the crimps is very likely to cause leakage.

(b) In the closed valley the roof covering extends across the valley. Sheet metal flashing is cut into small sheets measuring about 18 inches x 10 inches, called shingle tins. This flashing is laid under each course of shingles, along the valley, as the course is laid. After the first course of the double course at the eaves is laid, the first sheet of flashing is placed on top of it. The second course is laid over the first course, and a sheet of flashing is then laid over this one so that the metal is partly covered by the next course. This procedure is continued all the way up the valley.

(4) Shingle tins measuring about 5 inches x 7 inches are used in a similar way to lay flashing up the side walls of dormers, chimneys, skylights, and the like (fig. 8-22). Each tin is bent at a right angle so that part of the tin extends up the side wall and the rest lies flat on the roof covering. Flashing of this type is called side flashing. In addition to the side flashing, a dormer, chimney, or skylight has a strip of flashing called an apron (fig. 8-23) along the bottom of the outer wall or face. A chimney or skylight has a similar strip, called the saddle flashing, along the bottom of the inner wall or face.

f. Built-Up Roofing Material.

(1) The following building papers are used on a built-up roof. Their purpose is to prevent the seepage of bitumen through roof sheathing on which a built-up roof has been applied (fig. 8-24).

Figure 8-23. Vertical wall flashing.

Figure 8-24. Applying built-up roofing.

(a) Rosin paper is a felt paper filled with rosin compound. It usually is pale red.

(b) Kraft paper is a light brown paper which is usually glazed.

(c) Sisal kraft consits of two layers of glazed kraft with a center section of sisal and embedded in a black bituminous compound and laminated by heat and pressure.

(2) Roofing felt is a felt paper that has been saturated with a bituminous compound (heavy pitch or asphalt oils) and is used as a roof covering. The basic ingredients are usually either asbestos or rag felts. The size of roll may vary from 32 to 36 inches wide. Weights for built-up roofing vary from 15 to 55 pounds per square. The 15-pound felt is most commonly used because of its light weight.

(3) A binder is used to bond the roofing felt together and form a watertight seal (fig. 8-24). Asphalt and coal tar are the two main types of bituminous binders used. Deterioration of built-up roofs is caused by the drying out of the binder. If this did not happen, a built-up roof would last indefinitely. Asphalt, the preferred of the two binders, is used on roofs which have up to 6 inches of slope per foot (1/4 pitch). It has a melting point of 350 to 400° F. A roof covered with asphalt should be protected with a covering of slag, gravel, or other protective material. Tar has a lower melting point (300 to 350° F.) than as-

phalt and thus will move more easily. Therefore, it is not recommended for roofs having a slope of more than 3 inches per foot (1/8 pitch).

(4) Aggregate, crushed stone, or gravel from 1/4 to 5/8 inch in diameter is embedded in a coat of asphalt or tar to hold the roof covering down. It also prevents the binding from disintegrating under the effects of the sun.

(5) *Gravel stops and metal edge strips.* Gravel stops (slag or gravel surfaced roofs) and metal edge strips (smooth-surfaced built-up roofs) finish off all exposed edges and eaves to prevent wind from getting under the edges and causing blowoffs. The gravel stop also prevents the loss of gravel or slag from areas near the edge of the roof. The flashing flange of the gravel stop or edge strip is placed over the last ply of felt and should extend at least 4 inches on the roof. It should be nailed securely to the roof deck and double-felt stripped, and then the finished coat of bitumen and surfacing or cap sheet should be applied. The lip of the gravel stop should extend a minimum of 3/4 inch above the roof deck and the lip of the edge strip should be a maximum of 1/2 inch above the deck. Both should be securely fastened to the fascia board.

Section II. REROOFING

8-9. Asphalt-Shingle Roofs

a. Material. The following two types of asphalt-strip shingles are used for reroofing hospitals and mobilization type buildings with pitched roofs. These shingles are applied directly over the existing roll roofings.

(1) *Standard-weight shingles.* The shingles should be four-tab, 10 by 36 inches in size, intended for a 4-inch maximum exposure. Weight per square (100 square feet) applied should be approximately 210 pounds. They are fastened with 1 1/4- or 1 1/2-inch nails with heads having a minimum diameter of 3/8-inch. Zinc-coated nails are best.

(2) *Thick-butt shingles.* Thick-butt shingles should be three-tab, 12 by 36 inches in size, intended for a 5-inch maximum exposure. The entire surface of the shingles should be covered with mineral granules. The bottom part of each shingle, including the part intended to be exposed and a section at least 1 inch above the cutout sections, should be thicker than the remainder of the shingle. Weight per square applied should be approximately 210 pounds. The shingles should be fastened with 1 1/2- or 1 3/4-inch nails with heads having a minimum diameter of 3/8 inch. Zinc-coated nails are best.

b. Preparation of Roof Decks. These instructions assume that the roof decks are covered with smooth or mineral-surfaced asphalt-prepared roofing and that the shingles will be applied directly over the existing roofing.

(1) Drive all loose and protruding nails in flush with the existing roll roofing.

(2) Cut out all vertical and horizontal buckles or wrinkles in the existing roofing and nail down the edges with 3/4-inch or 1-inch roofing nails so the entire roof deck is smooth (fig. 8-25).

(3) Where shingles are applied over smooth-surfaced roofings or over mineral-surfaced roofing which does not match the shingles, apply an 18-inch starting strip of mineral-surfaced roll roofing at the eaves. Use roofing surfaced with granules of the same type and color as the shingles. Before they are applied unroll the strips carefully and lay them on a smooth, flat surface until they lie perfectly flat. In applying starter strips, nail them at the top at about 18-inch intervals so the lower edge, when bent down and nailed to the edge of the sheathing board, extends about 3/4 inch beyond the edge of the board to form a drip edge. Space nails in the edge of the sheathing board 6 inches apart. A starter strip need not be used if the shingles are the same color as the existing roofing and the existing roofing is not buckled.

c. Detailed Instructions for Applying Shingles.

(1) *Standard-weight, four-tab, 10- by 36-inch shingles.*

(a) Start the first course with a full shingle placed so one edge, which is cut off flush with the tab, is flush with the side of the roof. The bottoms of the tabs are placed flush with the eaves. Place nails about 3/4 inch above each cutout section (fig. 8-26) and in the same relative position at each end of the shingle. Use two nails at every cutout. Nail at the center first, then above the cutout sections nearest the center, and finally, at the ends. Nailing may start at one end and proceed regularly to the other. Complete the first course with full width shingles applied so the ends barely touch each other.

Figure 8–25. Flattening surface and nailing down roofing to be repaired.

(b) Start the second course with a shingle from which half a tab has been cut. Place it so the bottoms of the tabs are flush with the tops of the cutout sections of the shingle in the first course. Complete this course with full-width shingles.

(c) Start the third course with a shingle from which one tab has been cut; the fourth with one from which one and one-half tabs have been cut, and so on, until eventually a full shingle is used again.

(2) *Thick-butt, three-tab shingles.* Follow the same method described for standard shingles. Always nail these shingles through the thick part about 3/4 inch above the cutout sections (fig. 8–26). The importance of nailing through the thick part of asphalt shingles cannot be emphasized too strongly, because practically all difficulties experienced with asphalt shingles on Army buildings have resulted from nailing the shingles too high.

(3) *Hips and ridges.*

(a) Finish hips and ridges with individual shingles furnished especially by the manufacturer or with shingles cut from strip shingles. Hips and ridges may also be finished with a strip of mineral-surfaced roofing 9 inches wide bent equally on each side and nailed on 2-inch centers 3/4 inch from the edges.

(b) Apply individual hip shingles as on the roof, starting at the lowest point and bending the shingle equally across the hip. Place one nail on each side, about 3/4 inch above the section to be exposed and about 3/4 inch from the edge. The shingles used to finish the hips should be kept in line with the main roof courses. Expose standard-weight shingles 4 inches and thick-butt shingles 5 inches.

(c) Finish ridges the same as hips, always working in the direction opposite that of the prevailing winds.

(d) *Valleys.* Construct valleys from two layers of mineral-surfaced roll roofing surfaced with granules of the same type and color as the shingles. Apply the first layer, 18 inches wide, with the mineral surfacing down. Lay the second layer the full width of the roll with the weather side up. Lay each sheet so it is smooth, conforming to the contour of the roof. Nail valley sheets at approximately 18-inch intervals to hold them in place until the remainder of the roofing is applied. Follow manufacturers' instructions for cutting the shingles at valleys.

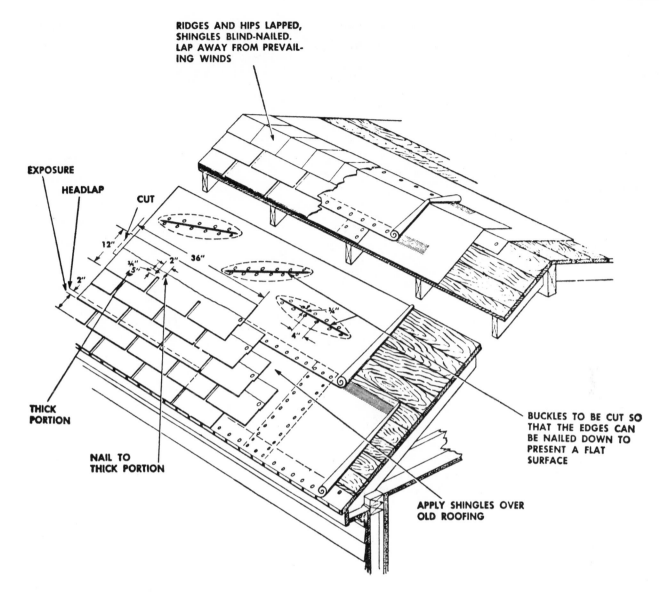

RIDGES AND HIPS LAPPED, SHINGLES BLIND-NAILED. LAP AWAY FROM PREVAILING WINDS

EXPOSURE

HEADLAP

CUT

12"

2"

36"

2"

3"

4"

THICK PORTION

NAIL TO THICK PORTION

BUCKLES TO BE CUT SO THAT THE EDGES CAN BE NAILED DOWN TO PRESENT A FLAT SURFACE

APPLY SHINGLES OVER OLD ROOFING

Figure 8–26. Replacement of roofs.

8–10. Asphalt-Prepared Roll Roofings

a. Mineral-Surfaced Roll Roofings. Mineral-surfaced, asphalt-prepared, two-ply roofing should consist of a layer of 15-pound asphalt-saturated felt and two plies of roll roofing, cemented together with hot asphalt. Cut roll roofing material into lengths of 18 or 20 feet, stacked free from wrinkles and buckles in protected piles, and maintain it at a temperature of at least 50° F. for 24 hours before laying. First, cover the roof areas with a layer of 15-pound asphalt-saturated felt, with all joints lapped 2 inches, and nail as required to prevent blowing off during the application of roofing. Next, lay either plain unsurfaced roofing or mineral-surfaced roofing as a starter sheet. Lay this upside down, in dry condition, parallel to and at the eaves, and nail through tin or fiber disks on 12-inch staggered centers; that

is, with one row of nails on 12-inch centers, placed not more than 2 inches from the lower edge, and with a second row on 12-inch centers, staggered with respect to the first and about 8 inches above the first. Over the lower half of this sheet, apply a uniform coating of hot asphalt at the rate of 30 pounds per square (100 square feet) and place the first sheet of roll roofing in the asphalt. Cover the entire roof area. Lap each successive sheet in such a way as to obtain a two-ply roofing, with a 2-inch headlap. Cement the lower or mineral-surfaced portion of each sheet with hot asphalt to the preceding sheet. Nail the edge through tin or fiber disks on 12-inch staggered centers. Use two rows of nails. Place the first row on 12-inch centers not more than 2 inches above the mineral surfacing, and the second row on 12-inch centers staggered with respect

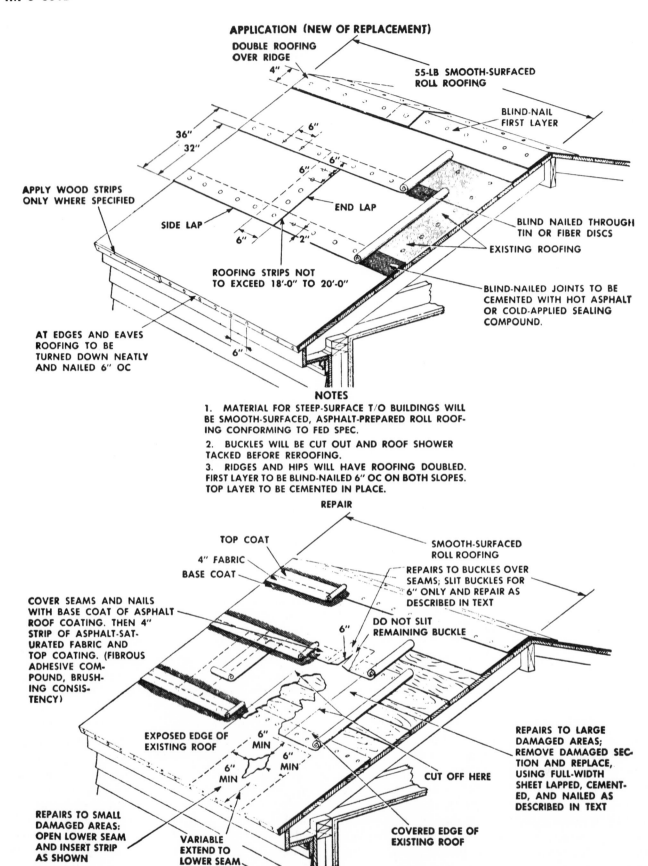

APPLICATION (NEW OF REPLACEMENT)

DOUBLE ROOFING OVER RIDGE

4"

55-LB SMOOTH-SURFACED ROLL ROOFING

BLIND-NAIL FIRST LAYER

36"

32"

6"

6"

APPLY WOOD STRIPS ONLY WHERE SPECIFIED

SIDE LAP

END LAP

6"

2"

6"

ROOFING STRIPS NOT TO EXCEED 18'-0" TO 20'-0"

BLIND NAILED THROUGH TIN OR FIBER DISCS

EXISTING ROOFING

BLIND-NAILED JOINTS TO BE CEMENTED WITH HOT ASPHALT OR COLD-APPLIED SEALING COMPOUND.

AT EDGES AND EAVES ROOFING TO BE TURNED DOWN NEATLY AND NAILED 6" OC

6"

NOTES

1. MATERIAL FOR STEEP-SURFACE T/O BUILDINGS WILL BE SMOOTH-SURFACED, ASPHALT-PREPARED ROLL ROOFING CONFORMING TO FED SPEC.

2. BUCKLES WILL BE CUT OUT AND ROOF SHOWER TACKED BEFORE REROOFING.

3. RIDGES AND HIPS WILL HAVE ROOFING DOUBLED. FIRST LAYER TO BE BLIND-NAILED 6" OC ON BOTH SLOPES. TOP LAYER TO BE CEMENTED IN PLACE.

REPAIR

TOP COAT

4" FABRIC

BASE COAT

SMOOTH-SURFACED ROLL ROOFING

REPAIRS TO BUCKLES OVER SEAMS; SLIT BUCKLES FOR 6" ONLY AND REPAIR AS DESCRIBED IN TEXT

DO NOT SLIT REMAINING BUCKLE

COVER SEAMS AND NAILS WITH BASE COAT OF ASPHALT ROOF COATING. THEN 4" STRIP OF ASPHALT-SATURATED FABRIC AND TOP COATING. (FIBROUS ADHESIVE COMPOUND, BRUSHING CONSISTENCY)

6"

EXPOSED EDGE OF EXISTING ROOF

6" MIN

6" MIN

6" MIN

REPAIRS TO SMALL DAMAGED AREAS: OPEN LOWER SEAM AND INSERT STRIP AS SHOWN

VARIABLE EXTEND TO LOWER SEAM

CUT OFF HERE

COVERED EDGE OF EXISTING ROOF

REPAIRS TO LARGE DAMAGED AREAS; REMOVE DAMAGED SECTION AND REPLACE, USING FULL-WIDTH SHEET LAPPED, CEMENTED, AND NAILED AS DESCRIBED IN TEXT

Figure 8-27. Smooth surface roll roofing.

to the first and about 8 inches above the first. Perform the work in such a way that no fastenings or asphalt will show on the finished surface. Apply the asphalt immediately before unrolling the sheet of roofing. Do not apply the asphalt more than 3 feet ahead of the roll. Step the edge of each sheet into the asphalt so that all laps are securely sealed. Place the end laps 6 inches in width, with the underlying edges nailed on 6-inch centers, and asphalt-cement the overlying edges thereto and step down firmly. Place one ply of roofing at eaves and edges, turn down neatly, and secure it with a wood member nailed on 8-inch center.

b. Smooth-Surfaced Roll Roofing. Apply single-ply roll roofing for theater of operations construction horizontally with at least 4-inch side laps and 6-inch end laps (fig. 8–27). Nail the underlying edges of laps through tin or fiber disks on 6-inch centers, and cement overlying laps with hot asphalt or an approved cold-applied sealing compound. Step down firmly on the edges to provide proper adhesion. Double the roofing over the ridge, with at least 4-inch laps. Turn roofing down neatly at eaves and edges and nail it in place on 6-inch centers. Before laying the roll-roofing material, cut it into 18- or 20-foot lengths, stack them free of wrinkles and buckles in protected piles, and maintain them at a temperature of at least 50° F. for 24 hours.

8–11. Built-Up Roofs

a. Asphalt-Prepared Rolled Roofs. Reroof buildings with roofs of relatively low pitch (less than 2 inches per foot), that were originally roofed with asphalt-prepared roll roofings, with smooth-surfaced asphalt built-up roofing, or with coal-tar-pitch built-up roofing, as described below.

(1) Use smooth-surfaced asphalt built-up roofing to reroof buildings with original smooth-surfaced roll roofing.

(2) Mobilization type buildings with roofs of relatively low pitch (usually 1/2 inch per foot), originally roofed with wide-selvage mineral-surfaced roll roofing, should be reroofed with asphalt built-up roofing, or with coal-tar-pitch built-up roofing. If the roof is nearly flat so water collects and stands, the latter type of roofing is best. Asphalt roofs may be smooth or mineral-surfaced. Coal-tar-pitch roofs *must* be mineral-surfaced.

b. Asphalt Built-Up Roofs. Prepare the roof deck by driving in all loose and protruding nails

and cutting out all buckles and wrinkles. Then apply a three-ply smooth-surfaced asphalt built-up roof as follows:

(1) Lay one layer of 15-pound, asphalt-saturated felt over the entire surface. Lap each sheet 3 inches horizontally and vertically and nail the laps on 12-inch centers. Also nail through the center of each sheet on 12-inch centers staggered with respect to the nails at the horizontal laps. Use nails long enough to penetrate into the sheathing at least 3/4 inch. They should be driven through tin or hard fiber disks.

(2) Mop the entire surface with a uniform coating of hot asphalt, using 25 pounds per 100 square feet.

(3) Over this coating of asphalt, lay two additional layers of 15-pound, 36-inch, asphalt-saturated felt, lapping each sheet 19 inches. Lap the ends of the sheets not less than 6 inches. Nail these felts 1 inch from the back edge on 12-inch centers through tin or hard fiber disks. Use nails long enough to penetrate into the wood sheathing at least 3/4 inch.

(4) Mop each of these sheets the full width of the lap with hot asphalt, using 25 pounds per 100 square feet.

(5) Apply a uniform mopping of hot asphalt over the entire surface, using 30 pounds per 100 square feet of roof surface. If a slag or gravel-surfaced roof is desired for mobilization type buildings, pour the surface coating on, using 45 pounds per 100 square feet. Into this coating, while hot, place 300 pounds of roofing slag or 400 pounds of roofing gravel per 100 square feet of roof surface.

(6) Materials needed per 100 square feet of roof surface:

(a) Asphalt—80 pounds.

(b) Asphalt-saturated felt—45 pounds.

(7) Do not heat asphalt above 400°F. Lay felt while asphalt is hot.

(8) Apply layers of felt so they are free from wrinkles or buckles.

(9) If the existing roofing is so rough that it is impossible to obtain a smooth surface by the method outlined above, remove the original roofing and apply a three-ply smooth-surfaced, asphalt built-up roof; but substitute 30-pound asphalt-saturated felt for 15-pound felt.

c. Coal-Tar Pitch Built-Up Roofs. Prepare the roof surface as described in paragraph 8–9b(1) and (2) and apply a three-ply coal-tar-pitch built-up roof as follows:

(1) Apply one layer of 15-pound, coal-tar-saturated felt over the entire roof surface and

prepare it as described in b(1) above.

(2) Mop the entire surface with a uniform coating of hot coal-tar pitch, using 30 pounds per 100 square feet.

(3) Over this coating of coal-tar pitch lay two additional layers of 15-pound coal-tar-saturated felt 36 inches wide, lapping each sheet 19 inches over the preceding sheet. If 32-inch felt is used, lap each sheet 17 inches. Nail the felt 1 inch from the back edge on 12-inch centers through tin or hard fiber disks. Use nails long enough to penetrate into the wood sheathing at least 3/4 inch. Lap the ends of the sheets at least 6 inches.

(4) Mop each of these sheets the full width of the lap with hot coal-tar pitch, using 25 pounds per 100 square feet.

(5) Apply over the entire surface a uniform pouring of hot coal-tar pitch, using 55 pounds per 100 square feet. While the pitch is hot, place over it 300 pounds of roofing slag or 400 pounds of roofing gravel per 100 square feet.

(6) Materials required per 100 square feet of roof surface:

Coal-tar pitch:	110 pounds.
Coal-tar-saturated felt:	45 pounds.
Roofing slag:	300 pounds.
or	
Roofing gravel:	400 pounds.

(7) Do not heat the coal-tar pitch above 375° F. and lay felt while it is still hot.

(8) Apply the layers of felt so they are free from wrinkles or buckles.

8–12. Slate Roofs

a. Very old slate roofs sometimes fail because of failure of the nails used to fasten the slates. In such cases, remove and replace the entire roof, including the felt underlay materials. Remove or drive in any protruding nails. Make every effort to obtain a smooth, even deck similar to the original one. Apply 30-pound asphalt-saturated felt horizontally over the entire roof deck. Lap the sheets not less than 3 inches; turn them up on vertical surfaces not less than 6 inches and over ridges and hips not less than 12 inches. Secure the sheets along laps and exposed edges with large-head roofing nails spaced about 6 inches.

b. Re-lay all original slates that are in good condition. Replace defective slates with new slates of the same size, matching the original as nearly as possible in color and texture.

c. Recommended slate sizes for large new

buildings are 20 or 22 inches long; for small new buildings, 16 or 18 inches long. Use slates of uniform length, in random widths, and punched for a head lap of not less than 3 inches.

d. Lay roof slates with a 3-inch head lap and fasten each slate with two large-head slating nails. Drive the slating nails so their heads just touch the slate. Do not drive the nails "home." The opposite is true of wood shingles; therefore, workmen accustomed to laying wood shingles must nail slate carefully. Bed all slates on each side of hips and ridges within 1 foot of the top and along gable rakes within 1 foot of the edge in an approved elastic cement. Match slate courses on dormer roofs with those on the main roof. Lay slate with open valleys.

8–13. Tile Roofs

a. Preparation. Before reroofing with tiles, restore the roof deck as nearly as possible to its original condition by replacing defective boards and applying asphalt-saturated felt (30-pound type) or prepared roofing. Lap the sheets not less than 3 inches; turn them up on vertical surfaces not less than 6 inches and over ridges and hips not less than 12 inches. Secure the sheets along laps and exposed edges with large-head roofing nails spaced about 6 inches.

b. Roof Tiles. Tiles must be free from fire cracks or other defects that will impair the durability, appearance, or weather tightness of the finished roof. Special shapes are provided for eaves starters, hips, ridges, top fixtures, gable rakes, and finials. Special shapes for field tile at hips and valleys may be factory-moulded before burning or may be job-cut from whole tile and rubbed down to clean, sharp lines. Roof tiles for use on Army buildings are generally furnished in one or more of the following types.

(1) Mission tiles are straight-barrel type, moulded to a true arc of a circle, and machine-punched for one nail and a 3-inch head lap. Use regular cover tile for ridges and hips and finish with plain mission finials. Eaves closures and hip starters are available. Approved sizes are generally 8 inches wide by 14 to 18 inches long.

(2) Spanish tiles are S-shaped and machine-punched for two nails and a 3-inch head lap. Eaves closures and hip starters are available. Use mission-type cover tiles for hips and ridges. Approved sizes are generally 9 1/2 to 12 inches wide by 12 to 18 inches long.

(3) Slab shingle tiles are flat, noninterlocking type, punched for two nails and a 2-inch head

lap. **Approved** sizes are 6 to 10 inches wide, 15 inches long, and 1/2 inch thick.

  c. Laying Tile Roofs.

   (1) *Mission and Spanish tiles.*

    (*a*) Before starting to lay tiles, mop the wood nailing strips with hot asphalt and fill spaces back of cant strips with asphaltic cement. Lay tiles with open valleys. Set eaves closures back 3 inches from the lower edge of eaves tiles. Lay pan tiles with uniform exposures to the weather. Lay cover tiles in a uniform pattern, except where otherwise necessary to match existing roofs. Give all tiles a minimum lap of 3 inches and extend pan tiles 1 inch over rear edge of gutter. Cut tiles so they meet projections with finished joints and point up with roofer's cement. Waterproof the spaces between field tiles and wood nailing strips at ridges and hips with a fill of roofer's cement. Fit all tiles properly and then secure them with nails long enough to penetrate at least 1 inch into the wood base. Fill spaces between pan and cover tiles in first row at eaves solid with cement mortar composed of 1 part portland cement, 3 parts fine sand, and enough clean water to form a plastic mix. Wet all tiles before applying mortar, and then press them firmly into the mortar bed. Match the tile courses on dormer roofs with those on the main roof. Cut surplus mortar off neatly. Point up all open joints. Remove loose mortar from exposed surfaces.

    (*b*) Where hurricane winds can be expected, consider reinforcing tile roofs by laying all field tiles in portland cement mortar. To do this, fill the ends of tiles at eaves, hips, ridges, rakes, and spaces beneath ridges solid with cement mortar and fill the full width of laps between the tiles, both parallel and perpendicular to the eaves, with cement mortar.

   (2) *Slab shingle tiles.* Lay slab shingle tiles with a 2-inch head lap and secure each tile with two large-head roofing nails. Double the tiles at the eaves and project them 1 inch over the rear edge of gutters. Lay all tiles within 1 foot of hips, ridges, and abutting vertical surfaces in roofer's cement. Lay 10- or 12-inch tiles with 1-inch head lap on sides of dormers. Match the tile courses on dormer roofs with those on the main roof. Lay tile roofs with open valleys.

8–14. Cement-Asbestos Roofs

  a. Preparation. Before reroofing with cement-asbestos shingles, restore the roof deck as nearly as possible to its original condition by replacing defective boards and applying new 30-pound

asphalt-saturated felt or prepared roofing. Lay this covering in horizontal courses. Lap the sheets not less than 3 inches; turn them up on vertical surfaces not less than 6 inches and over ridges and hips not less than 12 inches. Secure the sheets along laps and exposed edges with large-head roofing nails spaced about 6 inches.

  b. Laying Cement-Asbestos Shingles.

   (1) Re-lay all cement-asbestos shingles that are in good condition. Replace defective shingles with new shingles of the same size and matching the originals as nearly as possible in color and texture.

   (2) Lay each shingle with a 2-inch head lap and secure it with two large-head slating nails. Drive the nails so their heads just touch the shingles. Do not drive the nails "home" as in laying wood shingles. Bed all shingles on each side of hips and ridges within 1 foot of the top and along gable rakes within 1 foot of the edge in an approved elastic slater's cement. Project the shingles 1 inch over the rear edges of gutters. Lay shingles with 1-inch head lap on sides of dormers. Match the shingle courses on dormer roofs with those on the main roof. Lay shingles with open valleys.

8–15. Metal Roofs
To conserve critical materials, replace metal roofs with nonmetallic roofing materials.

8–16. Wood Shingles
  a. When old roofing is removed:

   (1) Restore the roof deck as nearly as possible to its original condition by replacing all rotted boards and pulling out or driving down all protruding nails.

   (2) Install flashings and apply new shingles.

  b. Apply new wood shingles directly over weathered wood-shingle roofs, if the existing shingle roofs can be made smooth and can be nailed properly. Reroof over existing wood shingles as follows:

   (1) Nail down or cut off curled and warped shingles, nail loose shingles securely, and remove or drive down protruding nails.

   (2) Cut off the old first-course shingles at the eaves just below the butts of the second course and replace them with a 1- by 3-inch or a 1- by 4-inch strip nailed flush with the eaves line.

   (3) Cut back the shingles at the gable ends about 3 inches and replace them with a 1- by

2-inch, 1- by 3-inch, or 1- by 4-inch strip nailed flush with the gable end.

(4) Remove weathered shingles at the ridge and replace them with a strip of beveled siding, thin edge down, to provide a solid base for nailing the ridge shingles. Treat hips the same as ridges.

(5) Fill open valleys with wooden strips level with the old shingle surface, or with a narrow strip placed across the "V" of the valley to act as a support for new flashings.

(6) Inspect flashings carefully, including valley flashings. Replace terne and galvanized flashings. Reuse old flashings if they are in good condition.

(7) Use the following nails in applying shingles over an existing roof: 5d box or special overroofing nails, 14-gage, 1 3/4 inches long for 16- and 18-inch shingles; and 6d, 13-gage, 2 inches long for 24-inch shingles. One square of roofing will need about 3 1/2 pounds of nails.

(8) Apply new shingles as recommended by their manufacturer.

CHAPTER 9

ACCESSORIES

Section I. DOORS

9-1. Job-Built Doors

a. Types. Doors, both exterior and interior, are classified as batten, panel, and flush (fig. 9-1). The batten door is the most commonly used and most easily constructed type of job-built door. It can be made in several ways, one of the simplest consisting of diagonal boards nailed together as two layers, each layer at right angles to the other. This type of door frequently is used as the core for metal-sheathed fire doors. Another type of batten door is made up of vertical boards tongued and grooved or shiplapped and held rigid by two to four crosspieces, ledgers, which may or may not be diagonally braced. If two additional pieces forming the sides of the door and corresponding to the ledgers are used, these are known as the frames.

b. Construction. In hasty construction, the carpenter makes a batten door from several 2 by 6 boards with ledgers and braces as shown in 1, figure 9-1. The ledgers are nailed with their edge 6 inches from the ends of the door boards. A diagonal is placed between the ledgers, beginning at the top ledger end opposite the hinge side of the door and running to the lower ledger diagonally across the door. If it is an outside door, roofing felt is used to cover the boards on the weather side. The ledgers are nailed over the felt. Wooden laths are nailed around the edges and across the middle of the door to hold the roofing felt in place. In hanging these doors, one-quarter of an inch clearance should be left around the door to take care of expansion. T-strap hinges are fastened to the ledgers of the door and to the hinge blocks on the door casing or post (1, fig. 9-1).

9-2. Mill-Built Doors

a. Exterior Doors. The usual exterior door is the panel type (1, fig. 9-2). It consists of stiles (solid vertical members), rails (solid cross members), and filler panels.

b. Interior Doors. The two general interior types are the panel and the flush doors (fig. 9-3). The louvered doors (fig. 9-3) are also popular and are used as hinged or as sliding doors. Any hinged interior door should not open or swing in the direction of a natural entry, or swing into hallways, against a blank wall, or be obstructed by other swinging doors.

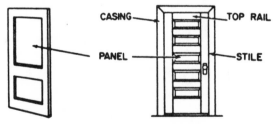

① BATTEN DOOR

DIAGONALLY CONSTRUCTED DOOR

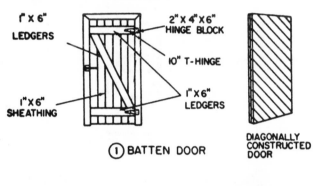

② PANEL DOOR

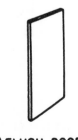

③ FLUSH DOOR

Figure 9-1. Types of doors.

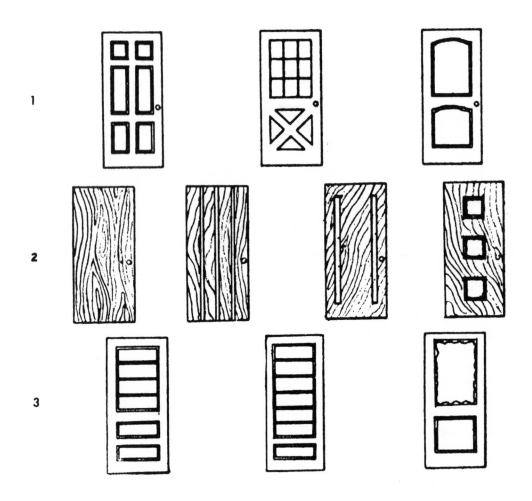

1   TRADITIONAL PANEL

2   FLUSH

3   COMBINATION

Figure 9–2. Exterior doors.

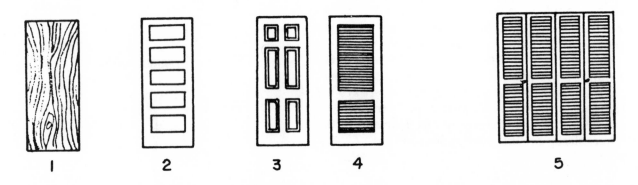

1, FLUSH; 2, PANEL (FIVE CROSS); 3, PANEL (COLONIAL); 4, LOUVERED; 5, FOLDING (LOUVERED).

Figure 9–3. Interior doors.

9–3. Exterior Door Frames

a. Before the exterior covering is placed on the outside walls, the door openings are prepared for the frames. To prepare the openings, square off any uneven pieces of sheathing and wrap heavy building paper around the sides and top. Since the sill must be worked into a portion of the rough flooring, no paper is put on the floor. Position the paper from a point even with the inside portion of the stud to a point about 6 inches on the sheathed walls and tack it down with small nails.

b. In most hasty construction, the outside doors will be as shown in figure 9–4. This type requires no frame, since the studs on each side of the opening act as a frame. The outside finish is applied to the wall before the door is hung. The casing is then nailed to the sides of the opening, set back the width of the stud. A 3/4- by 3/4-inch piece is nailed over the door to support the drip cap and is also set back the width of the stud. Hinge blocks are nailed to the casing

where the hinges are to be placed. The door frame is now complete and ready for the door to be hung.

c. The principal parts of a door frame are shown in figure 9–5. On an outside door, the outside casings and the sill are also considered as parts of the door frame. A prefabricated outside door frame, delivered to the site assembled, looks like the right-hand view in figure 9–5.

d. The starting point for door frame layout calculations is the size of the door (height, width, and thickness) as given on the door schedule. Construction information on door frames is usually given in detail drawings like those shown in figure 9–6 and the left-hand view of figure 9–7. In the type of frame shown in figure 9–6 the door jambs (linings of the framing of door openings) are rabbeted to a depth of 1/2 inches. The rabbet prevents the door from swinging through the frame when it is closed. Other types of frames instead of a rabbet use a strip of wood, nailed to the inner faces of the jamb and called a stop. The stop also serves as a basis for weatherproofing the door. Most project drawings call for exterior door jambs to be of the rabbeted type.

e. The side jambs of an entrance door are cut to the height of the door, less the depth of the head jamb rabbet (if any), plus the following:

(1) The diagonal thickness of the sill, plus the sill bevel allowance (the sill bevel allowance is shown in figure 9–5).

(2) The thickness of the threshold, if any (the distinction between the sill and the thres-

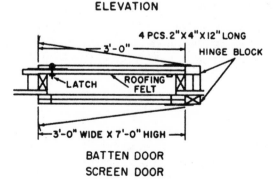

Figure 9–4. Single outside door.

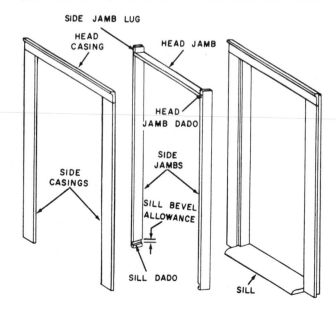

Figure 9–5. Principal parts of a door frame.

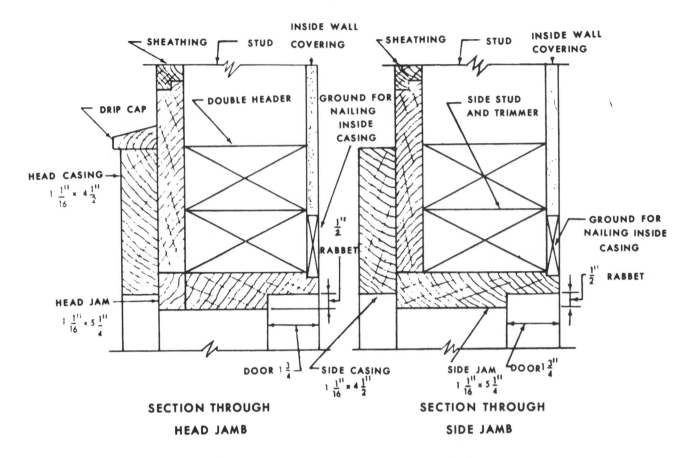

Figure 9-6. Typical door frame detail drawings.

hold is shown in the left-hand view of figure 9-7).

(3) The thickness of the head jamb.

(4) The height of the side jamb lugs.

f. The head jamb is cut to the width of the door, less the combined depths of the side jamb rabbets (if any), plus the combined depths of the head jamb dadoes (grooves).

g. The casing layout depends on the way the side and head casings are to be joined at the corners. The casings are usually set back about 3/8 inch from the faces of the jambs.

9-4. Interior Door Frames

Inside door frames, like outside frames, are constructed in several ways. In most hasty construction, the type shown in figure 9-8 is used. The interior type is constructed like the outside type except that no casing is used on inside door frames. Hinge blocks are nailed to the inside wall finish, where the hinges are to be placed, to provide a nailing surface for the hinge flush with the door. Figure 9-8 shows the elevation of a single inside door. Both the outside and inside

door frames may be modified to suit a climatic condition.

9-5. Door Jambs

Casings and stops are nailed to the door jambs (fig. 9-9) and the door is hung from them. Inside jambs are made of 3/4-inch stock and outside jambs of 1 3/8-inch stock. The width of the stock will vary with the thickness of the walls. Inside jambs are built up with 3/8- by 1 3/8-inch stops nailed to the jamb, while outside jambs are usually rabbeted out to receive the door. Jambs are made and set as follows:

a. Regardless of how carefully rough openings are made, be sure to plumb the jambs and level the heads, when jambs are set.

b. Rough openings are usually made 2 1/2 inches larger each way than the size of the door to be hung. For example, a 2-foot 8-inch by 6-foot 8-inch door would need a rough opening of 2 feet 10 1/2 inches by 6 feet 10 1/2 inches. This extra space allows for the jambs, the wedging, and the clearance space for the door to swing.

c. Level the floor across the opening to deter-

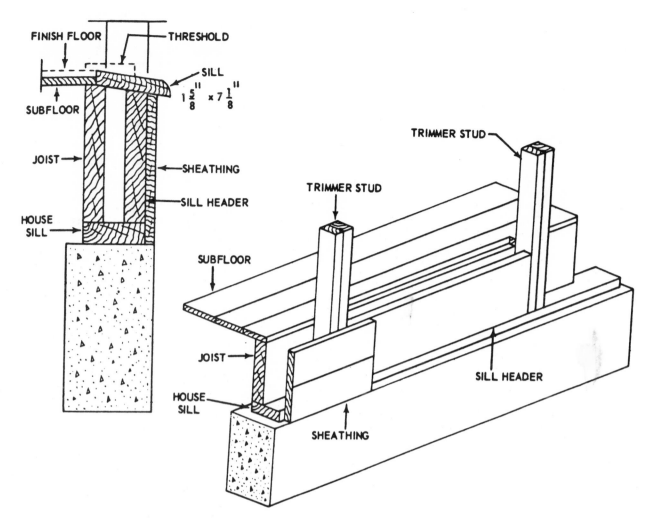

Figure 9-7. Sill installation.

mine any variation in floor heights at the point where the jambs rest on the floor.

d. Now cut the head jamb with both ends square, having allowed width of the door plus the depth of both dadoes and a full 3/16 inch for door clearance.

e. From the lower edge of the dado, measure a distance equal to the height of the door plus the clearance wanted under it. Mark and cut square.

f. On the opposite jamb do the same, only make additions or subtractions for the variation in the floor, if any.

g. Now nail the jambs and jamb heads together with 8-penny common nails through the dado into the head jamb.

h. Set the jambs into the opening and place small blocks under each jamb on the subfloor just as thick as the finish floor will be. This is to allow the finish floor to go under.

i. Plumb the jambs and level the jamb head.

j. Wedge the sides with shingles between the jambs and the studs, to aline, and then nail securely in place.

k. Take care not to wedge the jamb unevenly.

l. Use a straightedge 5 or 6 feet long inside the jambs to help prevent uneven wedging.

m. Check jambs and head carefully, because jambs placed out of plumb tend to swing the door open or shut, depending on the direction in which the jamb is out of plumb.

9-6. Door Trim

Door trim material is nailed onto the jambs to provide a finish between the jambs and the plastered wall. It is the edge trim around interior door openings and the interior side of exterior doors and windows, frequently called "casing" (fig. 9-9). Sizes vary from 1/2 to 3/4 inch in thickness, and from 2 1/2 to 6 inches in width. Most trim has a concave back, to fit over uneven plaster. In mitered (beveled edges) work, care must be taken to make all joints clean, square, neat, and well fitted. (If the trim is to be mitered

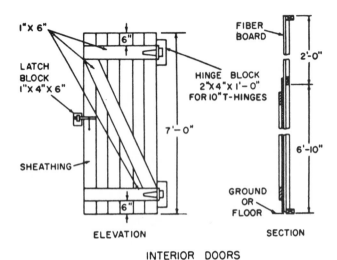

INTERIOR DOORS

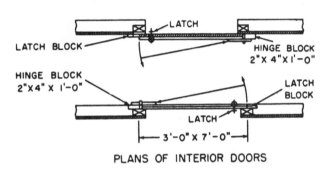

PLANS OF INTERIOR DOORS

Figure 9–8. Single inside door.

at the top corners, a miter box, miter square, hammer, nail set, and block plane will be needed.) Door openings are cased up as follows:

a. Leave a margin of 1/2 inch from the edge of the jamb to the casing all around.

b. Cut one of the side casings square and even at the bottom with the bottom of the jamb.

c. Cut the top or mitered end next, allowing 1/4-inch extra length for the margin at the top.

d. Nail the casing onto the jamb and even with the 1/4-inch margin line, starting at the top and working toward the bottom.

e. Use 4-penny finish nails along the jamb side and 6-penny or 8-penny case nails along the outer edge of the casings.

f. The nails along the outer edge must be long enough to go through the casing and plaster and into the studs.

g. Set all nailheads about 1/8 inch below the surface with a nail set.

h. Now apply the casing for the other side and then the head casing.

9–7. Door Stops

In fitting doors, the stops are usually temporarily nailed in place until the door has been hung. Stops for doors in single-piece jambs are generally 7/16 inch thick and may be 3/4 to 2 1/2 inches wide. They are installed with a mitered joint at the junction of the side and head jambs. A 45° bevel cut at the bottom of the stop, about 1 to 1 1/2 inches above the finish floor, will eliminate a dirt pocket and make cleaning or refinishing of the floor easier (fig. 9–9).

9–8. Hanging Mill-Built Doors

If mill-built doors are used, install them in the finished door frames as described below.

a. Cut off the stile extensions, if any, and place the door in the frame. Plane the edges of the stiles until the door fits tightly against the hinge side and clears the lock side of the jamb about 1/16 inch. Be certain the top fits squarely into the rabbeted recess and that the bottom swings free of the finished floor about 1/2 inch. The lock stile of the door must be beveled slightly so that the edge of the stile will not strike the edge of the door jamb.

b. After proper clearances have been made, tack the door in position in the frame and wedge at the bottom (fig. 9–10). Mark positions of hinges with a sharp pointed knife on the stile and on the jamb. The lower hinge must be placed slightly above the lower rail of the door and the upper hinge slightly below the top rail of the door in order to avoid cutting out part of the tenons of the door rails which are housed in the stile. Three measurements are to be marked—the location of the butt on the jamb; the location of the butt on the door; and the thickness of the butt on both jamb and door.

c. Door butts or hinges are mortised into door and frame as shown in figure 9–11. Butt sizes indicate the height of each leaf and the width of the pair when open. Use three butt hinges on all full length doors, to prevent warping and sagging. Place butts and mortise them with the utmost accuracy so the door will open and close properly and so the door, when open, will not strike the casing. The butt pin must project more than half its thickness from the casing.

d. Using the butt as a pattern, mark the dimensions of butts on the door edge and the face of the jamb.

e. Cut the marked areas, called gains, on the door jambs and door to fit the butts. Use a 1-inch chisel and mallet.

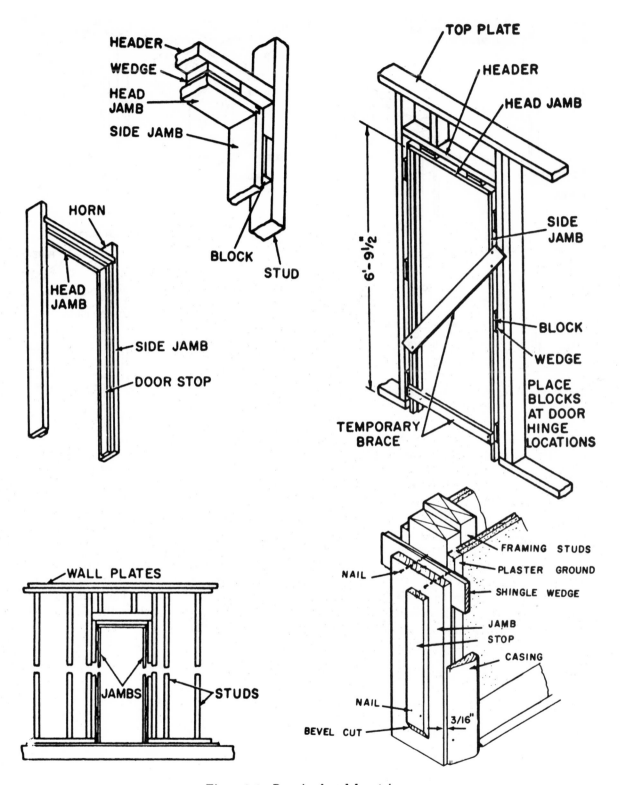

Figure 9-9. Door jamb and door trim.

f. Test the gains. The butts must fit snugly and exactly flush with the edge of the door and the face of the jamb.

g. Screw three halves of the butt joints on the door and the other three halves on the jamb. Place butts so that pins are inserted from the top when the door is hung.

h. Set the door against the frame so the two

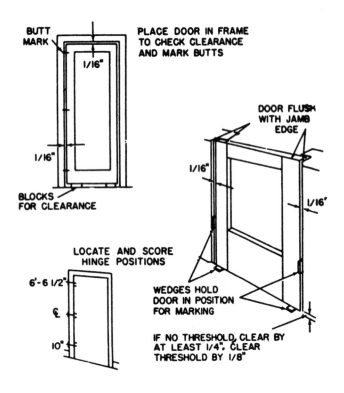

Figure 9–10. Wedging door, locating and scribing hinge positions.

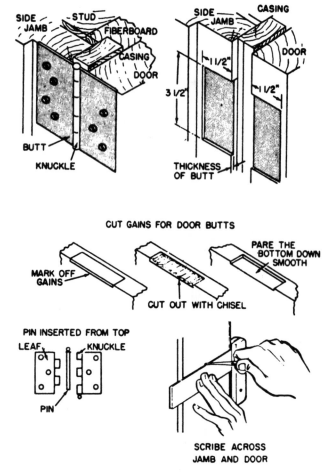

Figure 9–11. Installing door butts.

halves of the top butt engage. Insert the top pin. Engage and insert pins in bottom and center butts.

9–9. Lock Installation

Since types of door locks differ, follow the installation instructions that come with lock sets. After placing hinges in position, mark off the position of the lock (fig. 9–12) on the lock stile, about 36 inches from the floor level. Hold the case of the mortise lock on the face of the lock stile and mark off, with a sharp knife, the area to be removed from the edge of the stile which

is to house the entire case. Next, mark off the position of the door knob hub and the position of the key. Then mark off the position of strike place on the jamb. Bore out the wood to house the lock and strike chisel and mortises, clean, and then install the lock set. The strike plate should be flush or slightly below the face of the door jamb (fig. 9–13).

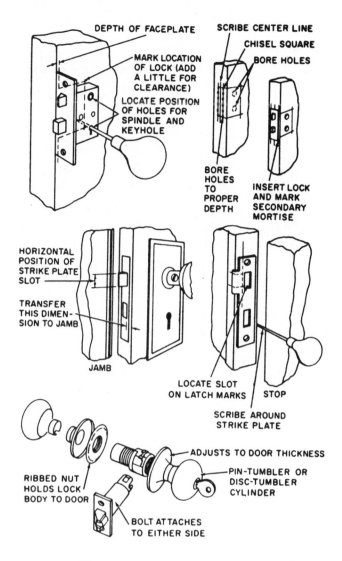

Figure 9-12. Installation of lock.

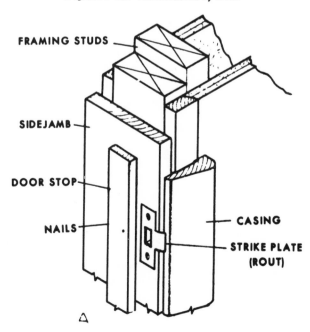

Figure 9-13. Installation of strike plate.

Section II. WINDOWS

9-10. Types of Windows

Windows are generally of the double hung and casement type (fig. 9–14). All windows, whatever the type, consist essentially of two parts, the frame and the sash. The frame is made up of four basic parts: the head, the jambs (two), and the sill. Where openings (window) are desired, studding must be cut away and its equivalent strength replaced by doubling the studs on each side of the opening to form trimmers and inserting a header at the top. If the opening is wide, the header should be doubled and trussed. At the bottom of the opening, the bottom header or rough sill is inserted.

9-11. Window Frames

a. These are the frames into which the window sashes are fitted and hung. They are set into the rough opening in the wall framing and are intended to hold the sashes in place. The rough window opening is made at least 10 inches larger each way (width and height) than the window glass size to be used. If the sash to be used is, for instance, a two-light window, 24 by 26 inches, add 10 inches to the width (24 inches) to obtain the total width of 34 inches for the rough opening. Add the upper and lower glasses (26 inches

each) and an additional 10 inches for the total height of the rough opening, 62 inches. These allowances are standard and provide for weights, springs, balances, room for plumbing and squaring, and for regular adjustments.

b. In hasty construction, millwork window frames are seldom used. The window frames are mere openings left in the walls with the stops all nailed to the stud. The sash may be hinged to the inside or the outside of the wall or constructed so as to slide. The latter type of sash is most common in Army construction because it requires little time to install. Figure 9–15 shows the section and plan of a window and window frame of the type used in the field. After the outside walls have been finished, a 1 by 3 is nailed on top of the girt at the window opening to form a sill. A 1 by 2 is nailed to the bottom of the plate and on the side studs and acts as a top for the window sash. One guide is nailed at the bottom of the opening flush with the bottom of the girt, and another is nailed to the plate with the top edge flush with the top of the plate. These guides are 1 by 3's. Stops are nailed to the bottom girt and plate, between the next two studs, to hold the sash in position when open (fig. 9–15).

9-12. Double-Hung-Windows

The double-hung window (fig. 9–16) is made up of an upper and a lower sash, which slide vertically past one another. Its frame construction and operation are more involved than that of casement windows. The double-hung window consists of the following:

a. The box frame consists of a top piece or yoke; two side pieces or jambs called pulley stiles, and the sill. The yoke and pulley stiles are dadoed into the inner and outer pieces (rough casing), forming an open box with the opening toward the studs and headers. The rough casing provides nailing surface to the studs and headers forming the plaster stop. The outside rough casing is also a blind stop for sheathing which should fit snugly against it, with building paper lapping the joint.

b. The 2-inch space between the framing studs and the pulley stile forms the box for counterweights which balance the window sash. The weight box is divided by a thin strip known as the pendulum, which separates the weights for the two sash units. In the stiles near the sill is an opening for easy access to the weights. This opening has a removable strip which is **part of**

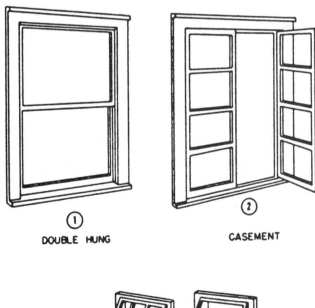

① **DOUBLE HUNG** ② **CASEMENT**

③

CASEMENT

Figure 9–14. Double hung and casement windows.

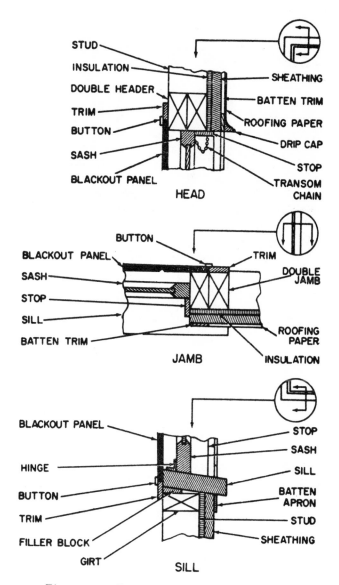

Figure 9-15. *Detail of wall section with window frame and sash.*

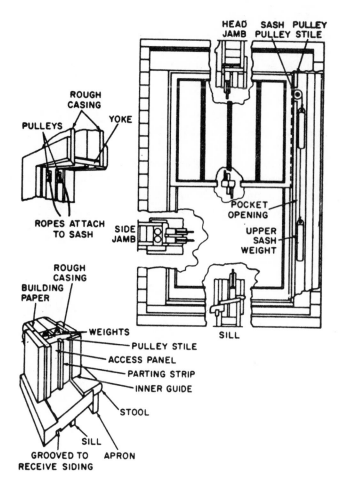

Figure 9-16. *Double-hung windows.*

the stile and channel for the lower sash (fig. 9-16).

c. Yoke and stile faces are divided by a parting strip which is dadoed into them, but removable so that the upper sash can be taken out. The strip forms the center guide for the upper and lower sash, while the outer rough casing, projecting slightly beyond the stiles and yoke, forms the outer guide. The inner guide for the sash is formed by a strip or stop, usually with a molding form on the inner edge. This stop is removable to permit the removal of the lower sash.

d. At the upper parts of the stiles, two pulleys on each side (one for each sash) are mortised flush with the stile faces for the weight cord or chain.

e. The sill is an integral part of the box frame and slants downward and outward. It usually has one or two 1/4-inch brakes, one at the point where the lower sash rests on the sill, and another near the outer edge to form a seat for window screens or storm sash. These brakes prevent water dripping on the sill from being blown under the sash. The underside of the sill, near its outer edge, is grooved to receive the edge of siding material to form a watertight seal.

f. On the room side of the sill is another piece, the stool, which has a rabbet on its underside into which the sill fits. The stool edge projects from the sill, forming a horizontal stop for the lower sash. The stool is part of the interior trim of the window, made up of side and top casings and an apron under the stool. The framed finished side and top casings are on the weather face. A drip cap rests on top of the outside head casing and is covered with metal flashing to form a watertight juncture with the siding material.

9-13. Hinged or Casement Windows

There are basically two types of casement windows, the outswinging and the inswinging types, and these may be hinged at the sides, top, or bottom. The casement window which opens out requires the window screen to be located on the inside with some device cut into its frame to operate the casement, otherwise the window screen must be hinged and swung up to operate the window. Inswinging casements, like double-hung windows, are clear of screens, but they are extremely difficult to make watertight, particularly against a driving rainstorm. This is why most casement windows are constructed to swing out. The following explains the construction of casement window frames.

a. The casement window frames (fig. 9-17) are usually made of planks 1 3/4 inch thick with rabbets cut in them to receive the sash. Usually there is an additional rabbet for screens or storm sash. The frames are rabbeted 1/2-inch deep and 1 1/2 or 1 7/8 inches wide for sash 1 3/8 or 1 3/4 inches thick. The additional rabbet is usually 15/16 or 1 3/16 inches wide, depending on whether the screen or storm sash is 7/8 or 1 1/8 inch thick.

b. Outswinging casement windows have the rabbet for the sash on the outer edges of the frame, the inner edge being rabbeted for the screen. Sill construction is very much like that for a double-hung window, with the stool much wider and forming a stop for the bottom rail. Casement-window frames are wide enough to extend to the sheathing face on the weather side and to the plaster face on the room side (fig. 9-17).

c. When there are two casement windows in a row in one frame, they may be separated by a vertical double jamb called a mullion, or the stiles may come together in pairs like a french door. The edges of the stiles may be a reverse rabbet; a beveled reverse rabbet with battens, one attached to each stile; or beveled astragals (T-shaped molding), one attached to each stile. The battens and astragals insure better weather-tightness. The latter are more resistant to loosening through use. Two pairs of casement sash in one frame are hinged to a mullion in the center (fig. 9-17).

d. Inswinging casement-window frames are like the outswinging type with the sash rabbet cut in the inner edge of the frame. The sill construction is slightly different, being of one piece (similar to that of a door sill) with a rabbet cut for a screen or storm sash toward the front edge,

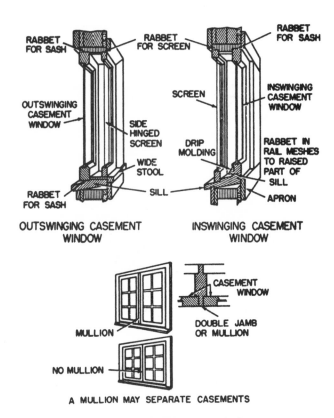

Figure 9-17. Casement windows.

and the back raised where the sash rail seats. This surface is rabbeted at its back edge to form a stop for the rail which is also rabbeted to mesh.

e. Sills in general have a usual slope of about 1 in 5 inches so that they shed water quickly. They are wider than the frames, extending usually to the plaster line and about 1 1/2 inches beyond the sheathing. They also form a base for the outside finishing casing.

f. The bottom sash rail of an inswinging casement window is constructed differently than the outswinging type. The bottom edge is rabbeted to mesh with the rabbet on the sill, and a drip molding is set in the weather face to prevent rain from being blown under the sash.

9-14. Window Sashes

a. Types of Job-Built Sashes. A window normally is composed of an upper and a lower sash. These sashes slide up and down, swing in or out, or may be stationary. There are two general types of wood sash—fixed or permanent; and movable. Fixed sashes are removable only with the aid of a carpenter. Movable sash may slide up and down in channels in the frame (double-hung), or swing in or out and be hinged at the side (casement type). Sliding sashes are counterbalanced by sash weights whose actual weight is one-half that of each sash. Sashes are classified according to the number of pieces of glass, or lights—single or divided.

b. Construction. A sash can be made of 1- by 3-inch material with Cel-O-glass or an equivalent. Cel-O-glass comes in rolls and can be cut to any desired size. Two frames are made with the glass substitute installed on one; the two frames are then nailed together. The side pieces are cut to a length equal to the height of the sash less the width of one piece of material. The top and bottom pieces are cut the same length as the window, less the width of the material. They are fastened at the joints with corrugated metal fasteners. When the two frames are nailed together, they should be turned so that the joints are not over each other. This staggers the joints and strengthens the sash. If the sash is too large for the glass substitute to cover, a muntin may be placed in the sash to hold the glass substitute and should be fastened with corrugated metal fasteners. Where long sashes are made, a muntin should be placed in the center to give added strength. Figure 9–18 shows the window frame and sash detail.

c. Window Sash Installation.

(1) *Double-hung windows.* Place the upper sash in position and trim off a slight portion of the top rail of the sash to insure a good fit. Then tack the upper sash in position. Fit the lower sash in position by trimming off the stiles. Place the lower sash in the opening and trim off, from the bottom rail, enough to permit the meeting rails (lower rail of supper sash and top rail of bottom sash) to meet on the level.

(2) *Sash weights.* If sash weights are used, remove each sash after it has been properly fitted and weight each one. Select sash weights equal to half the weight of each sash and place in position in the weight pocket. Measure proper length of sash cord for lower sash and attach to the stile and weight on both sides. Adjust length of cord so that sash moves up and down easily and the weight does not strike the pulley or rest on the frame. Install the cords and weights for the upper sash and adjust the cord and weight so that each cord and weight runs smoothly. Close the pockets in the frame and install the blind stop, parting stop, and bead stop (fig. 9–18).

(3) *Sliding windows.* Details of installation of sliding windows and the typical side wall section are shown in figure 9–19.

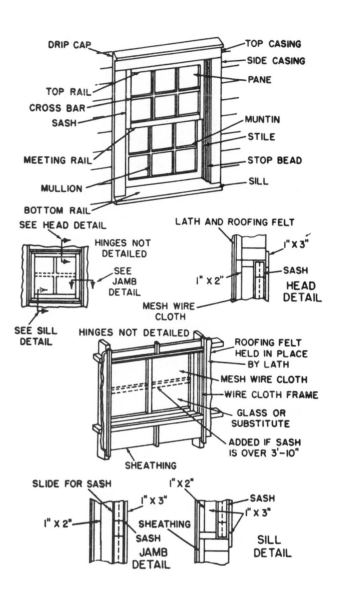

Figure 9–18. Window frame and sash detail.

9–15. Mill-Built-Sashes

a. Types. Sashes are mill built of wood or steel. They are made for fixed or movable emplacement and may be casement or doublehung as desired. The sash size is determined by the size of the glass (fig. 9–20). Overall dimensions are generally standard and made to fit standard construction frames. The thickness of sash is usually 1 1/8, 1 3/8, or 1 3/4 inches. The 1 3/8 inch sash generally is used in frame construction. In giving the size of a sash, the width of the glass is always given first, then the height, then the number of pieces of glass, or lights. Thus a sash might be spoken of as a 24 by 26 by 1 light. This means that the glass itself is 24 by 26 inches and that there is only one piece of glass. However, the sash would be larger than 24 by 26

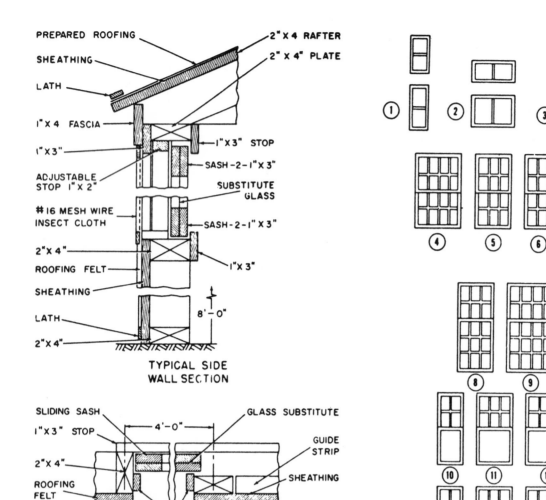

TYPICAL SIDE WALL SECTION

SLIDING WINDOW

Figure 9–19. Window sash installation.

Figure 9–20. Types and sizes of milled sashes.

inches because of the frame around the glass. For the frame of a two-light window with a 1 3/8-inch check rail, add 4 inches to the width and 6 inches to the length.

Example: A two-light window has a glass size of 24 by 26. Find the size of the window frame.

Solution: 24 inches + 4 inches = 28 inches, or 2 feet 4 inches, the width. 26 inches x 2 = 52 inches, 52 inches + 6 inches = 58 inches, or 4 feet 10 inches, the length. Therefore, the window frame size for these sashes would be 2 feet 4 inches by 4 feet 10 inches.

b. Installation.

(1) Prepare the sash cords, chains, or balances that are to be used. If cords are used, tie them to the weights, run them through the pulleys at the top, and tie a knot in the end of each. This knot will be set in the side of the sash in a recess made to receive it.

(2) Adjust the length of the cord. The length can be determined by placing the sash in its position and measuring. When the inside sash is down in place, the weight for that sash should be near the top pulley. When the outside sash is up in place, the weight for it should be down, not quite touching the bottom.

(3) Fit the outside top sash first. Do not fit it too tightly; allow for swelling. Use a sharp plane for squaring.

(4) Remove the parting bead on one side of the frame to put the sash into place. This is the strip about 1/2 by 3/4 inch which is grooved into the frame on each side separating the two sashes.

(5) Notch out each end of the check rail as far as the parting bead extends beyond the frame.

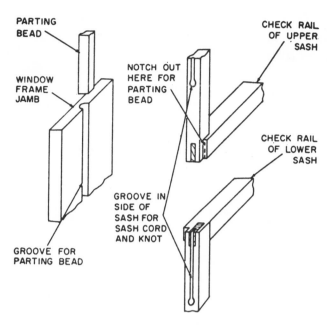

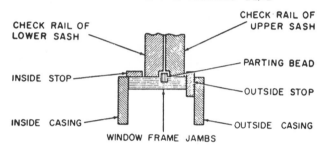

DETAIL OF JAMB AND PARTING BEAD

CROSS SECTION OF WINDOW SASH AND JAMB

Figure 9–21. Details of check rails for double-hung window sash.

This should be done accurately to prevent bad fitting, which would either let in wind and cold or, if too tight, cause the sash to slide with difficulty (fig. 9–21).

(6) When the sash is fitted, put it in place, replace the parting beads, and attach sash cords to the sides.

(7) Plane and fit the inside bottom sash next for easy operation. Fit the sides of it first.

(8) After the sides have been fitted, set the sash in place and determine how much, if any, need come off the bottom, other than the bevel

that is always planed on to match the slant of the window sill. The two check rails must come together and be even at the middle of the window. If not, the window locks will not meet or be workable.

(9) If the rails do not match, scribe off the necessary amount at the bottom, taking care to keep the same bevel on the bottom edge of the sash.

(10) When the lower sash is fitted, put it in place, secure the sash cords, and check both sashes for each operation.

Section III. SCREENS

9–16. Window Screens

Screen sash is usually 3/4-inch stock, but for large windows and doors 1 1/8-inch material frequently is used or 3/4-inch lumber is braced with a horizontal member.

a. Construction. Window-screen sash is usually 1 3/4 or 2 1/4 inches wide. Screen may be attached by stapling or tacking. Cut screen about 1 inch wider and longer than the opening; cover the edges with molding; then rabbet the inside

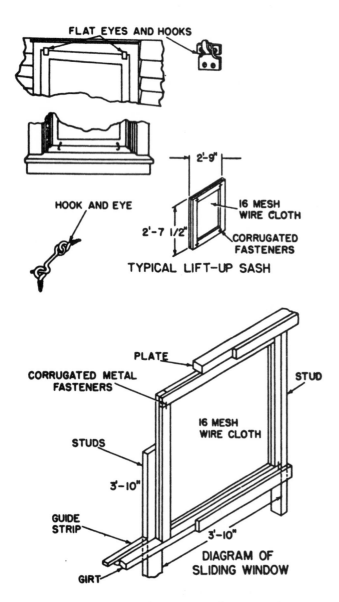

Figure 9–22. Window-screen sash construction.

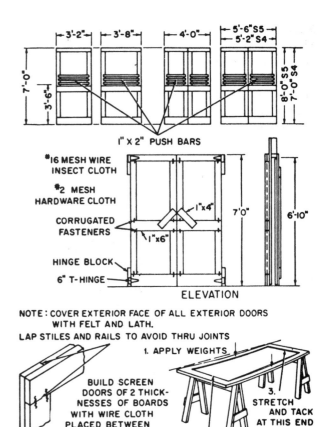

Figure 9–23. Door screen construction.

edges about 3/8 by 1/2 inch, attach the screen in the rabbet, and nail 3/8 by 1/2 inch molding flush with face of sash. Figure 9–22 illustrates the construction of screen sashes using mesh wire cloth.

b. Joints. Window sashes may be made with open mortise, four tenons, with rails tenoned into stiles; with half-lap corners; or with butt joints or corrugated fasteners. In either of the first two cases, the joints may be nailed or glued.

c. Attaching Screen Material. When attaching screen material, start at one end and tack or staple it with copper staples, holding the material tightly. Then, hand-stretch the screen along the side, working toward the other end and attach, making sure that the weave is parallel to the ends and sides. Tack the sides and apply the

molding. Copper staples should be used for bronze or copper screen, and cadmium staples for aluminum screens.

9–17. Door Screens

Door screens are made as shown in figure 9–23. Two separate frames are made of 1 by 4 material for the sides and top and of 1 by 6 material for the bottom and middle pieces. The first frame is made of two side pieces the full length of the door; the crosspieces are the width of the door less the width of the two side pieces. This frame is put together with corrugated metal fasteners, then the screen wire is applied. The second frame is made with the crosspiece the full width of the door. The side pieces are cut to correspond with the distance between the crosspieces. The second frame is placed over the first frame and nailed securely. For push-and-pull plates, two short braces of 1 by 4 are nailed to the side opposite the hinge side.

9–18. Hood or Canopy

The hood or canopy is used in tropical climates to protect the screened opening at the ends of the buildings. It is framed to the end walls with short rafters which are nailed to the building with knee braces, as shown in figure 9–24. The rafters are nailed to the wall, the bottom edge flush with the bottom of the end plate. The rafters and braces are of 2 by 4's nailed with 8- or 10-penny nails. The sheathing is of the same material as the roof sheathing and is covered with roll roofing. The hood should extend about 2 1/2 or 3 feet from the building.

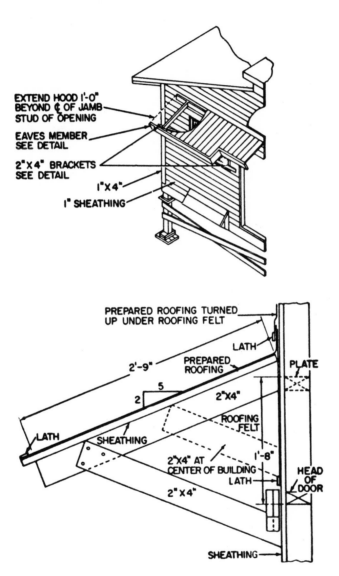

Figure 9-24. Hood or canopy.

CHAPTER 10

NONSTANDARD FIXED BRIDGE

Section I. INTRODUCTION

10–1. Definitions

a. Bridge. A bridge is a structure that carries a roadway over a depression or an obstacle. A bridge completely supported by its two end supports (abutments) is called a single-span bridge. A bridge having one or more intermediate supports (between the abutments is a multispan bridge. Bridges may be classified in different ways. Two general classifications, for example, are highway and railroad bridges. All supports of a fixed bridge transmit the load directly to the ground.

b. Nonstandard Fixed Highway Bridge. **This is a semipermanent bridge constructed from local materials or class IV materials drawn from a depot. It differs from standard bridges in that the latter are prefabricated bridges assembled at the site. The most common nonstandard fixed highway bridges are the simple stringer type (the stringers being natural logs), structural**

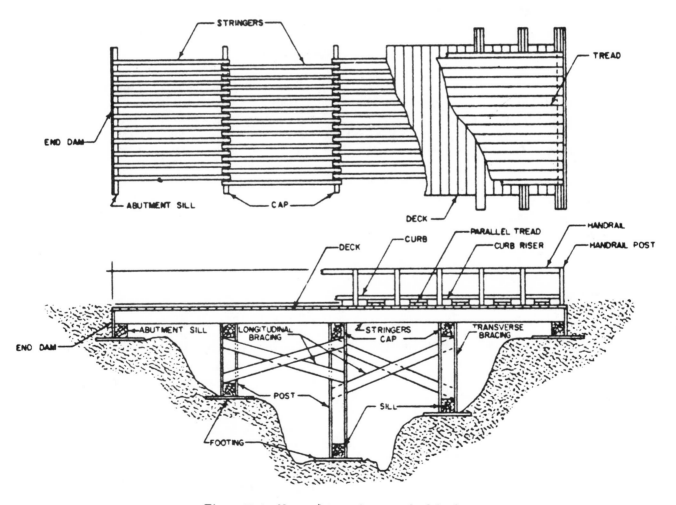

Figure 10–1. Nomenclature of nonstandard fixed highway bridge.

grade timber, and structural steel. They may also be constructed of any other suitable materials.

10-2. Nomenclature

A military bridge is generally considered as having two principal parts: the lower part or substructure, and the upper part or superstructure (fig. 10-1).

a. *Substructure.* The substructure consists of the transverse supports for the superstructure; that is, the supports which are built crosswise to the direction of traffic. These supports are either abutments (end supports) or intermediate supports (bents and piers). The substructure takes the load directly from the stringers, which are the lowermost members of the superstructure.

b. *Superstructure.* The superstructure consists of the stringers, flooring (decking and trends), curbing, walks, handrails, and other items forming that part of the bridge above the substructure.

(1) *Stringers.* Stringers rest on the span the distance between the intermediate supports or abutments. Stringers are the main load-carrying members of the superstructure; they receive the load from the flooring and transmit it to the substructure.

(2) *Flooring.* The flooring system consists of two parts: decking and tread. The decking is laid directly over the stringers at right angles to the centerline of the bridge. Often, every fifth plank is extended to provide a bearing surface for handrail knee braces. The tread is laid parallel to the centerline of the bridge and between the inside faces of the curbs.

(3) *Curbs.* Curbs are wood members placed at both edges of the roadway to guide the wheels of the vehicles. Curbs shown in figure 10-1 are installed on risers to permit surface water to drain easily from the bridge floor.

(4) *Handrails.* Railings supported by posts along the sides of the bridge roadway guide vehicle drivers and serve as a protective measure for both vehicular and foot traffic.

(5) *Scabbing.* Scabbing consists of short pieces used to join or splice structural members together.

Section II. SUBSTRUCTURE

10-3. Abutments

There are two types of end supports or abutments: footing type and pile type.

a. *Footing Type.* The footing type abutment consists of footings, sill, and end dam.

(1) *Footings.* The footings transmit the load to the ground. They receive the load from the sill and distribute it over a sufficient area to keep the support from sinking into the ground.

(2) *Sill.* The sill receives the load from the stringers and transmits it to the footings.

(3) *End dam.* The end dam, or bulkhead, is a wall of planks at the end of the bridge to keep the approach road backfill from caving in between the stringers.

b. *Pile Type.* The pile type abutment has three main parts: piles driven into the ground transmitting the load to the soil, a cap on top of the piles to receive the load from the stringers, and sheeting fastened to the piles to hold the backfill in place.

10-4. Intermediate Supports

The most common intermediate supports are bents and piers. Table 10-1 is a general guide for selecting types of piers to be used for various conditions.

a. *Pile Bent.* The pile bent (fig. 10-2) consists of the following members: the bent cap which provides a bearing surface for the stringers and transmits the load to the piles, and the piles which transmit the load to the soil. Such piles are known as bearing piles because they carry superimposed loads. The support for the loads may come either from column action, when the tip of the pile bears on a firm stratum such as rock or hard clay, or from friction between the pile and the soil into which it is driven. In both cases, earth pressure must provide some lateral support, but transverse bracing is often used to brace the bent laterally.

b. *Trestle Bent.* The trestle bent (fig. 10-3) is similar to the pile bent except that the posts, taking the place of piles, transmit the load from the cap to the sill, the sill transmits the load to the footings, and the footings transmit the load to the soil. The length of the posts will vary with the height of the bridge above the gap to be spanned. Transverse bracing similar to that used with the pile bent is provided.

c. *Pile-Bent Pier.* The pile pier (fig. 10-4) is composed of two or more pile bents. The common cap in this case transmits the load to the corbels. Corbels are the short, stringer-like members that, in turn, transmit the load to the individual bent

Table 10–1. Guide to Selection of Pier Type for Various Conditions

Type	Combined span length	Ground to grade height	Remarks
Timber crib pier	To 50'	To 12'	Highway bridges only. Designed for vertical load only. Steel or timber stringers.
Timber trestle bent	To 30'	To 12'	Highway bridges only. Designed for vertical loads only. Steel or timber stringers.
Timber trestle pier	To 60'	To 18'	Highway bridges only. Designed for vertical loads only. Steel or timber stringers.
Timber pile bent	To 50'	Governed by unbraced length.	Highway bridges only. Designed for vertical and lateral loads. Steel or timber stringers.
Timber pile pier	To 200'	Governed by unbraced length.	Highway and RR bridges. Designed for vertical and lateral loads. Steel or timber stringers.
Steel pile bent	To 70'	Governed by unbraced length.	Highway bridges only. Designed for vertical, and lateral loads. Steel or timber stringers.
Steel pile pier	Any length	Governed by unbraced length.	Highway and RR bridges. Designed for vertical and lateral loads. Steel or timber stringers.
Framed timber tower	Any length	To 60'	Highway and RR bridges. Designed for vertical and lateral loads. Steel or timber stringers.
Framed steel tower	Any length	To 80'	Highway and RR bridges. Designed for vertical and lateral loads. Steel or timber stringers.
Concrete pier	Any length	To 25'	Highway and RR bridges. Designed for vertical and lateral loads. Steel or timber stringers.

caps. Piers are usually provided with cross bracing that ties the individual bents together and gives them rigidity in a longitudinal direction.

d. Trestle Bent Pier. The trestle-bent pier (timber trestle pier) (fig. 10–5) is the same as the pile-bent pier, except that it has sills and footings which transmit the load to the soil.

e. Crib Pier. The crib pier (fig. 10–6) is quite different from pile and trestle piers. It is com-posed of logs or dimensioned timber fitted together in log cabin style and is usually filled with rock or other stable fill material. The crib pier should be constructed so that it needs no exterior bracing for stability. As an expedient, crib piers may be constructed to the height of the stringers, thus eliminating the trestle bents.

10–5. Bracing

a. Longitudinal Bracing. Longitudinal bracing (fig. 10–3) is used to provide stability in the direction of the bridge centerline.

b. Transverse Bracing. Transverse bracing (fig. 10–3) provides stability at right angles to the centerline. It is sometimes called sway bracing or lateral bracing.

c. Diaphragms. Diaphragms are braces placed between stringers to prevent them from deflecting laterally (buckling) under load. In spacing these diaphragms, the L/b ratio should not exceed 30 for timber (L = distance between diaphragms; b = width of top of stringer). Thus, for example, diaphragms should be used every 15 feet between stringers 6 inches wide.

10–6. Substructure Construction Procedure

a. Layout of Centerline. The first task in constructing a trestle-bent bridge is the layout of the centerline. Stretch a line or tape representing the centerline across the stream or ravine. Attach the line to stakes driven into the ground at least 15 feet behind the proposed location of the abutment sills. For defiles wider than 100 feet, use intermediate stakes as required to prevent

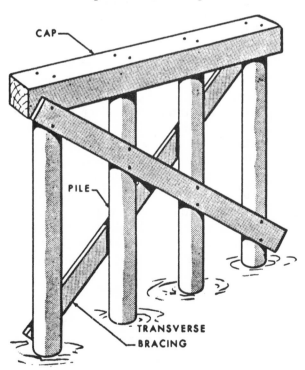

CAP

PILE

TRANSVERSE BRACING

Figure 10–2. Pile bent.

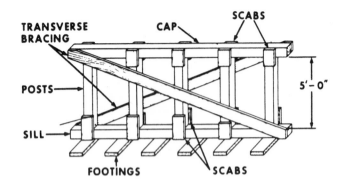

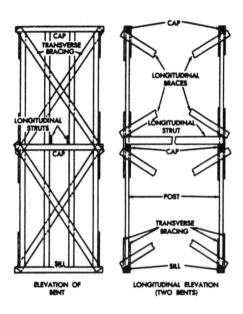

Figure 10–3. Trestle bent.

sag in the line. Place the line at the level of the intended top of the flooring or at some known distance above or below it (fig. 10–7).

b. Construction of Abutments. Time saving in abutment construction is especially important on relatively short bridges, because abutment and approach preparation ofter require as much time as the rest of the bridge. Use the simplest type of abutment possible; often a timber sill with timber footings is adequate (fig. 10–8). The end dam is installed AFTER the stringers and planks.

(1) *Layout.* After the centerline is fixed, place the abutment sill at approximately its correct location under the tape. See that it is at right angles to the centerline by using a line from the centerline stake (15 feet behind the sill (fig. 10–7)) to each end of the sill. Both distances must be the same.

(2) *Construction.* Once the sill is properly

located, mark its position and remove it to construct the foundation. Observe the following in construction:

(*a*) Remove earth as needed to provide a level surface for footings. The sill must be level and supported equally by each footing when installed.

(*b*) See that the surface which supports the footings is about 2 inches higher than its final desired position to allow for settlement.

(*c*) Do not dig too deeply. If this is done by mistake, DO NOT BACKFILL with earth. Instead, raise the level with planking.

(*d*) Place the two outside footings so that their outer edges are under the ends of the sill. Place the long dimension of the footings parallel to the bridge centerline.

(*e*) Place the remaining footings between and in line with the outside footings. Position them so that there is equal spacing between all footings.

(*f*) Place sill on the footing centerline so that the load comes in the middle of each footing. Place sill with the largest dimension vertical, as shown in figure 10–5.

(*g*) Provide for drainage of the abutment area.

c. Retaining Walls. Retaining walls and revetments, when needed, are a part of the abutment construction (fig. 10–9).

(1) *Retaining walls.* The simplest type of retaining wall is built of planks or logs supported by piles or posts (fig. 10–10). Wingwalls are used to prevent the earth from washing out behind the retaining wall. Piles or posts are driven 4 feet into the ground, and anchor cables are fastened from the top of the piles to a deadman behind the retaining wall or to the end of the wingwall. These deadmen and anchors can be eliminated if two or three rows of piles driven as far as they will go (to refusal) are used.

(2) *Combination abutment and retaining wall.* For long spans and heavy loads, the abutment and retaining wall are often constructed as a unit. This may also be necessary where steep banks and poor soil conditions exist. A typical abutment of this type is shown in figure 10–11.

10–7. Construction of Trestle Bent

a. Layout. After the position of the near-shore abutment sill is established, locate the position of the first trestle bent. Measure the length of the first span from the abutment sill along the centerline. Drive a small stake under the centerline where the center of the trestle bent is to be,

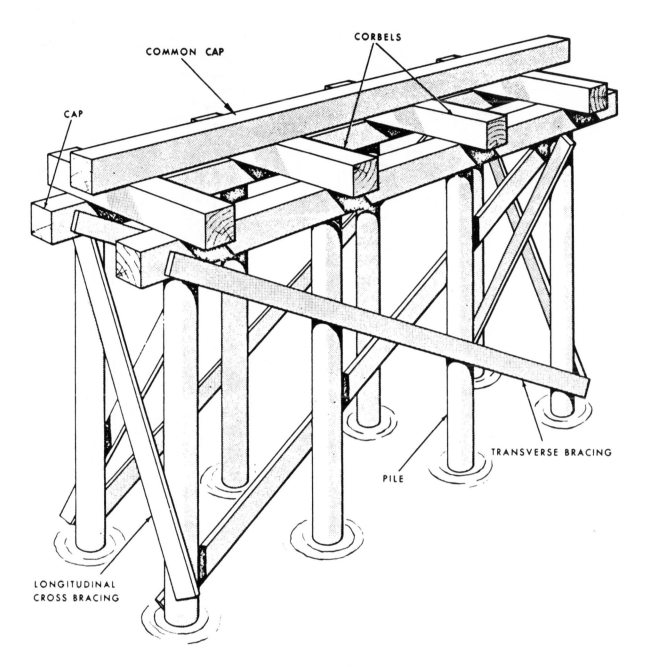

Figure 10–4. Pile pier.

using a plumb bob if necessary. Continue this procedure until all trestle bents and the far-shore abutment sill are located.

b. *Placing Footings.* Excavation for and placement of footings under the trestle bent is the same as for the abutment. The outside footings under the trestle sill are centered under the outside posts of the bent.

c. *Height of Trestle Bent.* Measure the vertical distance from the centerline down to the top of the footings (fig. 10–12). If the centerline was placed at the intended top of the flooring, this distance, minus the thickness of the tread, deck, and stringers, gives the height of the trestle bent. If steel stringers are to be used, allow also for the thickness of the nailing strips.

d. *Height of Trestle Bent Posts.* To obtain the correct height of the trestle bent posts, subtract the thickness of the cap and sill from the height of the trestle bent (fig. 10–3).

e. *Additional Construction Procedures.*

(1) Make the length of the cap and sill equal to roadway width plus 2 feet.

(2) Center the outside posts under the roadway edges (1 foot from the ends of the cap and

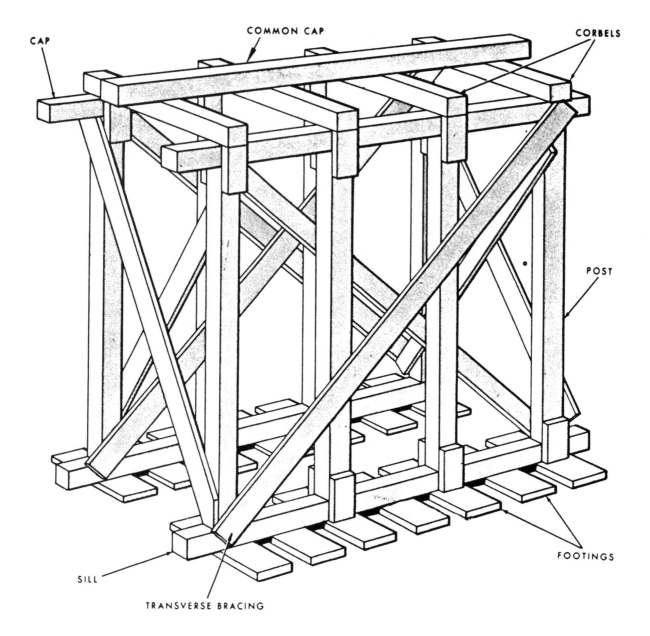

CAP

COMMON CAP

CORBELS

POST

FOOTINGS

SILL

TRANSVERSE BRACING

Figure 10-5. Timber trestle pier.

sill). Space all other posts evenly between the outside posts.

(3) Use driftpins or bolts to fasten the sill and cap to the posts. Use scabbing instead of driftpins when fast erection is required.

(4) Nail transverse bracing across both sides of the bent (usually 3- by 12-inch planks are used). Fasten bracing to each post that it passes over. Cut bracing so the ends extend enough beyond where they are nailed to prevent splitting.

(5) Put the bent into position, using a plumb bob to insure that it is straight. Hold it in place with temporary braces nailed to stakes driven into the ground. Use these temporary braces until the permanent logitudinal bracing can be nailed to the outside posts of adjacent trestle bents.

Figure 10–6. Crib pier.

Figure 10–8. Timber sill abutment.

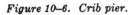
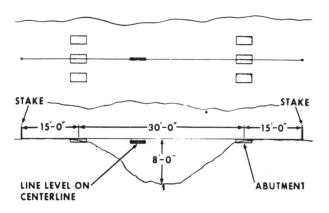

Figure 10–7. Layout of bridge centerline.

Figure 10–9. Abutment and retaining wall.

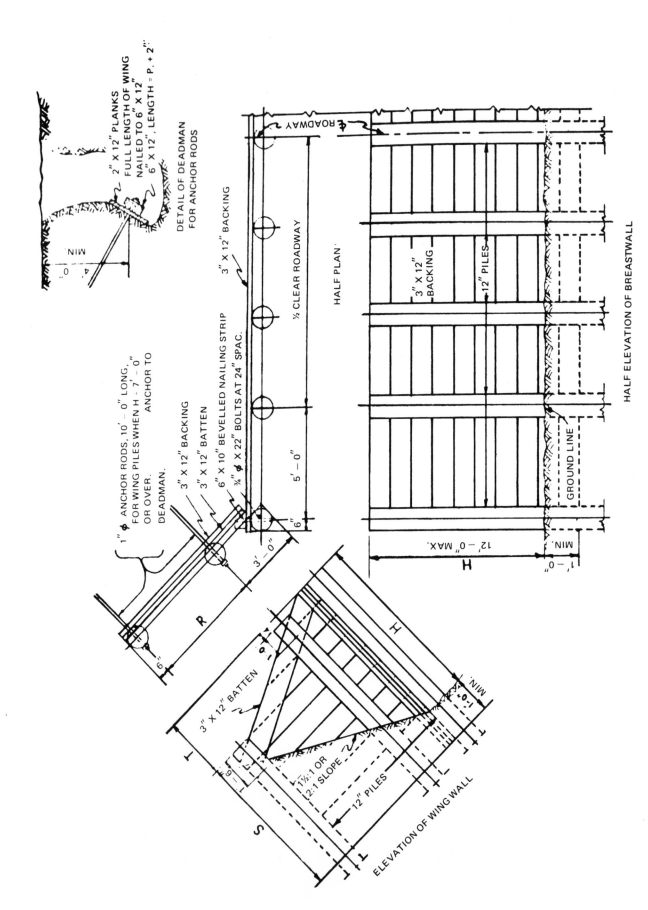

Figure 10–10. Retaining wall.

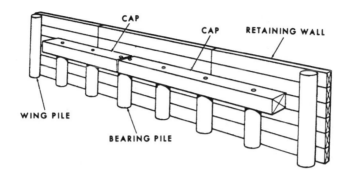

*Figure 10–11. Combination pile abutment and
retaining wall.*

Figure 10–12. Determining height of trestle bent.

Section III. SUPERSTRUCTURE

10–8. Superstructure of a Timber Trestle Bridge

The superstructure is the spanning structure of girders and decks. It consists of stringers, the flooring (decking and tread), and other features such as curbs, handrails, and sidewalks.

10–9. Stringers

After the abutment and trestle bents are in place, stringers are installed. When wood stringers are used, they are usually long enough to extend clear across the abutment sills and trestle caps on which they rest, which means that stringers of one span are lapped with those of the next span (fig. 10–13).

a. When stringers are LAPPED, place one outside stringer so that its INSIDE face is under the inside face of one curb and place the other outside stringer so that its OUTSIDE face is under the inside face of the other curb. Thus,

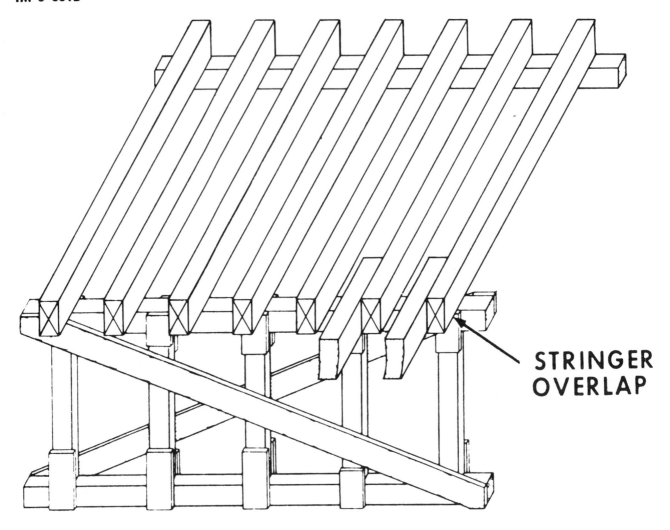

Figure 10–13. Stringers placed on abutment sill and bent.

STRINGER OVERLAP

stringers can be lapped with a similar spacing on the next span. Remaining stringers are usually spaced evenly between the outside stringers. On some narrow one-lane bridges, stringers may be grouped closer together directly under the vehicle tracks.

b. When stringers are BUTTED or continuous across the span, place the outside faces of BOTH outside stringers under the inside faces of the curbs.

c. Fasten wood stringers by nails driven diagonally through the side of the stringer into the cap or by driftbolts (fig. 10–14). When using driftbolts, bore a hole, smaller in diameter and 3 inches shorter than the driftbolt, through the stringer and into the cap.

d. Fasten steel stringers by driving railroad **spikes** into the cap beside the flange, by driving

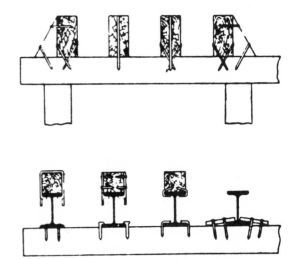

Figure 10–14. Methods of fastening stringers.

60d nails partially into the cap and bending them over the bottom flange, or by driving nails or driftbolts through prebored holes in the bottom flange (fig. 10-14). When steel stringers are not fastened through their flanges, frequent inspection is necessary to be sure that the stringers have not shifted. Fasten wood nail strips (fig. 10-14) to the top flange of steel stringers to provide a means of fastening the flooring. When a laminated deck (planks placed on edge, fig. 10-15) is to be installed, the planks may be fastened to steel stringers either by metal clips provided for the purpose or by driving nails partially into the deck and bending them around the stringer flange (D and F, fig. 10-15).

10-10. Flooring

The flooring system of a typical timber-stringer trestle bridge consists or two main parts, the decking and the tread.

a. Deck. The decking is the part of the structure that is laid on the stringers to form the roadway across the trestle bridge. Decking may be laminated (fig. 10-16) or solid plank (fig. 10-17). Laminated decks may be solid, or open with uniform spacing between members.

(1) For open laminated deck where the planks are long enough to reach completely across the width, use two space blocks between each lamination. Place spacers on the stringer nearest the one-third length of the lamination. Where the laminations are not long enough (usually true for two-lane bridges), lap the laminations on a central stringer and put a spacer block at each outside stringer (fig. 10-15).

(2) For solid laminated deck, place laminations solidly against one another.

(3) For a solid plank deck, lay planks horizontally and at right angles to the stringers. Leave a 1/4-inch space between planks to allow for swelling when wet.

(4) Extend decking about 2 feet at approximately 5-foot intervals to provide support for handrail posts (fig. 10-18).

b. Tread. The tread consists of planks placed over the decking and between (but NOT under) the curb. The planks are usually 2 or 3 inches thick and of varying length. They are laid parallel to the direction of traffic. On one-lane bridges the tread is limited to the path of the wheels or track, while two-lane bridges are fully covered with tread (fig. 10-16).

10-11. Curbs

A curb system on a timber trestle bridge is used to guide the traffic on the bridge. When assorted sizes of lumber are available make curbs of 6- by 6-inch timber supported on 6- by 12- by 30-inch curb risers (fig. 10-19), spaced on approximately 5-foot centers. The curb is usually bolted to the decking with 1/2-inch bolts, two per curb riser.

10-12. Handrails

Handrails mark the bridge route and provide a safety factor for pedestrians crossing the bridge. When available, make handrails of 2- by 4-inch or larger material. Over a laminated deck, make handrail posts and knee braces of the same material as the deck so that they can be fastened snugly between the laminations which are extended to receive them. For solid-plank decks, toenail 4- by 4-inch posts or two- 2 x 4's nailed together to the extended planks (fig. 10-19). Make posts 42 inches high and space them on 5-foot centers. Place posts so that the distance from the inside face of the curb to the inside face of the handrail is at least 10 inches.

10-13. Sidewalks

If sidewalks are necessary, form them by extending the decking an additional 36 inches. Place stiffening members underneath the outside edge and support them with braces attached to the stringers, where necessary.

10-14. End Dam

The end dam is the wall which withstands the earth pressure of the abutment of a bridge (figs. 10-1 and 10-8). After the stringers and flooring are in place, construct an end dam of flooring planks across the end of the stringers. The end dam should extend across the roadway and from the top of the footing to the top of the tread. After placement of the end dam, complete the approach up to the top of the bridge deck, then post the traffic control and classification signs. The bridge is now ready for traffic (fig. 10-20).

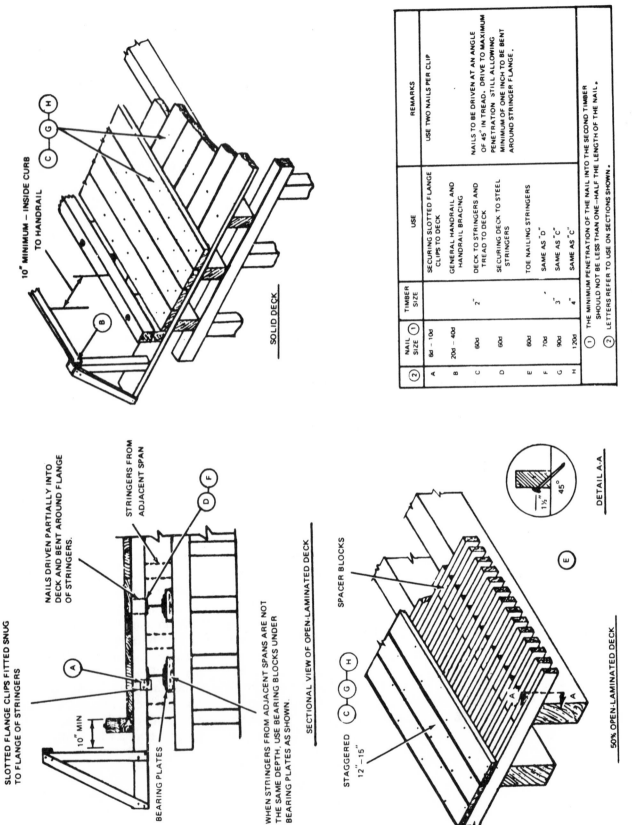

Figure 10-15. Bridge superstructure construction details.

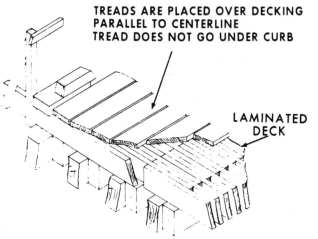

TREADS ARE PLACED OVER DECKING
PARALLEL TO CENTERLINE
TREAD DOES NOT GO UNDER CURB

LAMINATED DECK

HANDRAIL

KNEEBRACE

HANDRAIL POST
CURB
CURB RISER
TREAD
SOLID DECK
STRINGERS

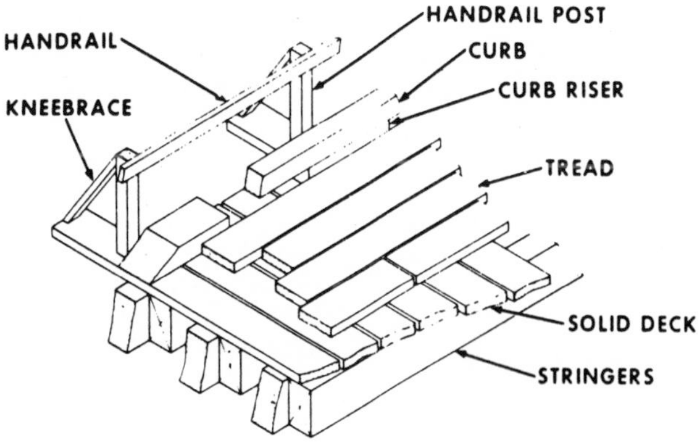

Figure 10–17. Tread, curb, and handrail constructed on solid deck.

Figure 10–16. Tread placement on a laminated deck.

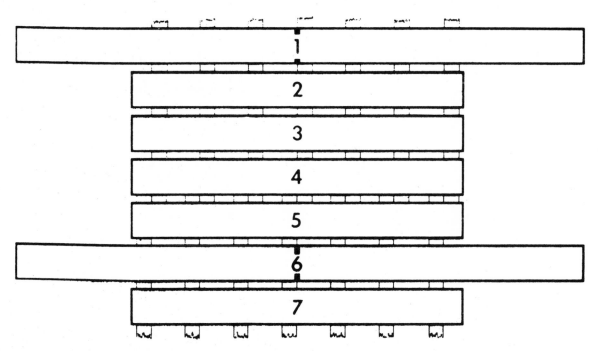

DECK PLANK ARE EXTENDED TO RIGHT AND LEFT AS
SHOWN TO PROVIDE FOR HANDRAIL KNEE BRACES.
SPACE PLANKS TO PERMIT WATER TO DRAIN.

Figure 10–18. Extended deck to provide handrail support.

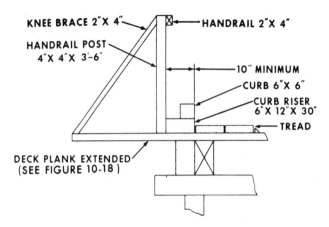

Figure 10-19. Standard curb and handrail.

KNEE BRACE 2″X 4″
HANDRAIL 2″X 4″
HANDRAIL POST 4″X 4″X 3′-6″
10″ MINIMUM
CURB 6″X 6″
CURB RISER 6″X 12″X 30″
TREAD
DECK PLANK EXTENDED (SEE FIGURE 10-18)

Figure 10-20. Completed timber trestle bridge.

CHAPTER 11

TIMBER PILE WHARVES

Section I. INSTALLATION OF PILES

11-1. Introduction

Wharves are used for loading and unloading ships. This chapter describes how a carpenter constructs a timber pile wharf used in loading and unloading ships. Section I discusses the layout, straightening, and bracing of piles for pile wharf construction. Section II deals with the construction of the wharf superstructure and the installation of docking hardware.

11-2. Wharf Structures

Wharf is an overall term which applies to any waterfront structure designed to make it possible for vessels to lie alongside for loading and unloading. Figure 11-1 shows the most common types of structures of this kind. The term wharf is confined in practice to the T-type and U-type marginal wharves. The other structures shown are all called piers, with the exception of the quay. A quay is a constructed landing place made toward the sea or at the side of a harbor for convenience of loading and unloading. All the structures shown in figure 11-1 may consist of fill supported by bulkheads. A marginal wharf or a pier usually consists of a timber, steel, or superstructure, supported by a series of timber, steel, or concrete pile bents.

11-3. Construction Features

To be sure that a wharf can absorb the normal wear and tear, three types of piles are used for wharf construction: bearing pile, fender pile, and mooring pile.

a. Bearing piles support the wharf or pier framework and decking. The piles should be straight and measure at least 6 inches across the top, 18 inches across the butt (bottom), and from 60 to 80 feet in length. The length varies according to the depth of the water and condition of the bottom. These bearing piles should be spaced from 6 to 10 feet apart, center to center, in one direction and 5 feet apart, center to center, in the other direction.

b. The force of a moving ship coming in direct contact with bearing piles is enough to collapse a wharf if the pilings are not protected. To furnish this protection and absorb the initial shock, fender piles are placed about 2 1/4 feet out from the centerline of the outside row of bearing piles. These piles are placed about 18 feet apart and along the sides where the ships dock.

c. The third type of piles, mooring, is placed in line with the outside row of bearing piles, spaced approximately 30 feet apart, and braced along the outside row of bearing piles. These piles usually extend about 4 feet above the floor, or deck, of the platform. The 4-foot extension provides ample space to secure mooring lines.

d. Timber piling must be treated with creosote or some other preservative compound to protect it from fungi and marine borer attacks.

11-4. Special Tools

Since all of the heavy timbers used to build waterfront structures cannot be manhandled, special tools are used to move and place these timbers. They are known as logger's tools and consist of peavys, cant hooks, timber carriers, and pike poles (fig. 11-2). The peavy and cant hook are lever type tools and are primarily used to roll timbers. Timber carriers are considered two-man tools; they are primarily used to pick up and/or carry timbers. Pike poles are used to hold or steady timbers while they are being placed. Although the crane cannot be considered a special tool, it is included here because it is used to raise and lower heavy timbers. Normally, two men are assigned to the crane: the operator and the helper. The helper drives the crane carrier (truck), hooks and unhooks loads, and signals the operator when to lift and lower the load and where to position the load. Standard signals are used for these purposes. After the heavy timbers have been moved and placed, the carpenter's level is used to level them properly.

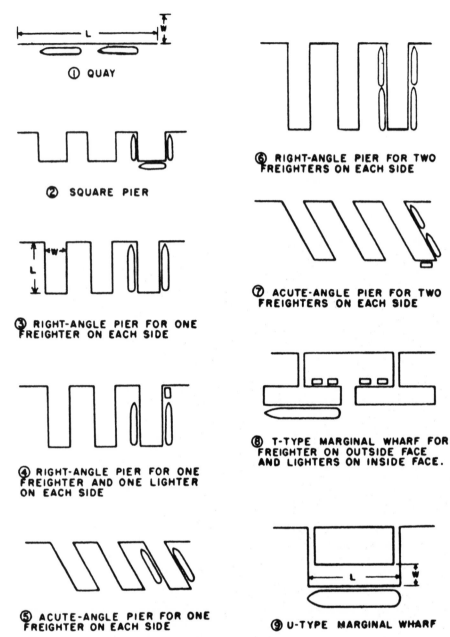

W = WHARF WIDTH   L = WHARF LENGTH

NOTE: NOT TO SCALE. FOR EXPLANATION OF
LAYOUT TERMINOLOGY ONLY

Figure 11–1. Common types of wharfage structures.

11–5. Straightening, Cutting, Capping, and Bracing Piles

Pile-driving equipment and the methods of driving and pulling piles are covered in TM 5–258. The equipment is operated by a special crew, but the carpenter is present during the pile-driving to direct the alinement of the piles.

a. Straightening Piles. Piles should be straightened as soon as any misalinement is noticed during the driving. The accuracy of alinement to be sought for the finished job depends on various factors, but if a pile is more than a few inches out of its plumb line, an effort should be made to true it up. The greater the penetration along the wrong line the more difficult to get the pile back into plumb. The following are ways to realine a pile:

(1) By the use of pull from block and tackle

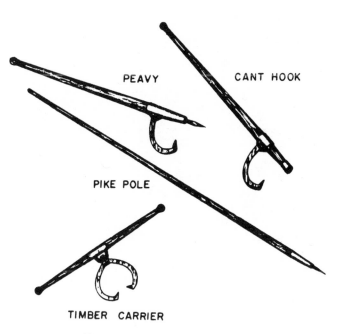

Figure 11-2. Logger's tools.

(fig. 11–3) with the impact of the hammer jarring the pile back into line.

(2) By the use of a jet (fig. 11–4), either alone or in conjunction with the above.

(3) When all the piles in a bent have been driven they may be pulled into proper spacing and alinement by using a block and tackle and an alining frame as shown in figure 11–5.

b. Templates. When a floating piledriver is used, a frame (template) for positioning piles may be fastened to the hull. A floating template (fig. 11–6) is sometimes used for positioning the piles in each bent. The spacing of battens is such that the center line between them is along the line desired for each pile, and the battens are placed far enough apart so that as the pile is driven the larger-diameter butt end will not bind on the template and carry it under water. A chain or collar permits the template to rise and fall with the tide. If the ends of the battens are hinged and brought up vertically, the template may be withdrawn from between

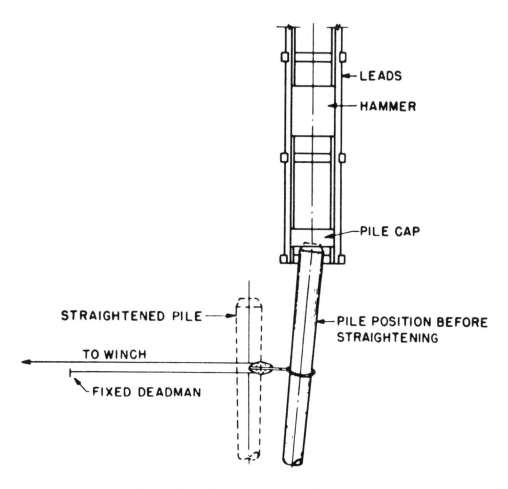

Figure 11-3. Realining pile by pull from block
and tackle.

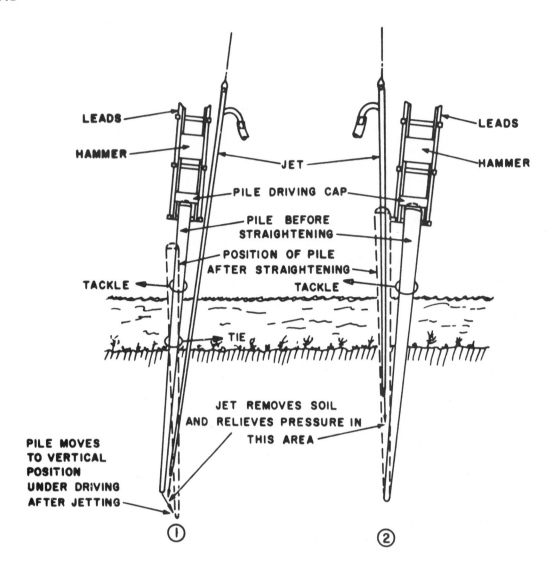

Figure 11–4. Realining pile by jetting.

the bents and floated into position for the next bent. Several templates may be used for a bent, or a single template is moved for use with the next group if the pile spacing is uniform. The position of the piles is controlled as follows:

(1) After each bent has been driven, a line is run back from each pile in the outer bent to the corresponding pile several bents shoreward.

(2) The alinement and longitudinal spacing of the outshore bent is verified.

(3) Any deviation in position by previously driven piles is made up when the template is positioned for the next bent. Piles which are slightly out of position may later be pulled into place as described in *a* above.

11–6. Cutting Piles

The lengths of pile selected for a structure should be such that after driving to the desired pene-

tration the butts are 2 or 3 feet higher than the desired finished elevation. Since the pile capping should bear evenly on every pile in the bent, the cutting-off should be carried out accurately. The best way is to nail sawing guides across all piles in the bent (fig. 11–7).

11–7. Capping Timber Piles

Caps are large timbers which are placed on top of the timber bearing piles to support the superstructure. The following are ways of fastening pile capping:

a. After the piles have been cut, the cap is put in place, a hole for a driftpin is bored through the cap into the top of each pile, and the driftpins driven into it.

b. At a joint between pile cap timbers, a splice scab (fig. 11–8) is bolted across the joint to each side of the pile cap.

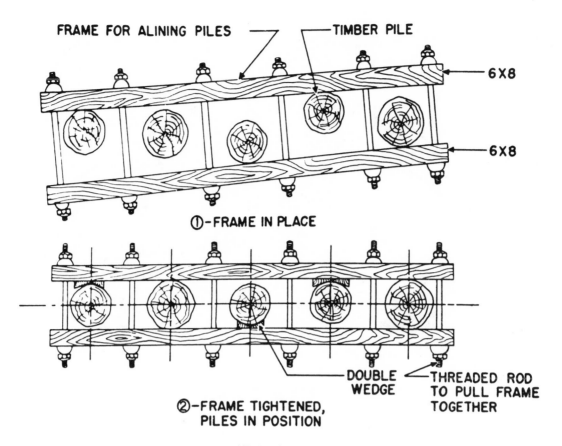

FRAME FOR ALINING PILES — TIMBER PILE

— 6X8

— 6X8

①-FRAME IN PLACE

DOUBLE WEDGE — THREADED ROD TO PULL FRAME TOGETHER

②-FRAME TIGHTENED, PILES IN POSITION

Figure 11-5. Alining frame for pile bent.

c. The working platform, the alining cables, or the spacing frame may then be removed, since the driftpins will hold the piles in the proper relative positions.

11-8. Bracing Piles
Bents are braced as follows:

a. Diagonal timbers are bolted to each pile with the bracing running in one direction on one side of the bent and the opposite direction of the other side (fig. 11-8).

b. If the piles in a bent differ considerable in diameter at the point of bracing, the large ones may be flattened down with an adze (dapped), or the smaller ones blocked out with filler pieces, or the flexibility of the braces made use of to pull them tight against each of the piles (fig. 11-9).

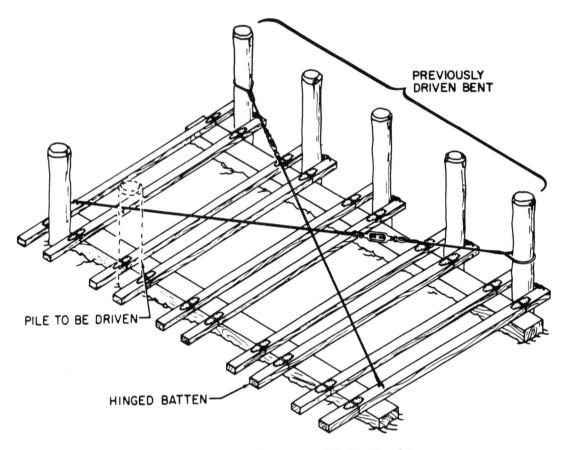

PREVIOUSLY
DRIVEN BENT

PILE TO BE DRIVEN

HINGED BATTEN

Figure 11-6. Floating template.

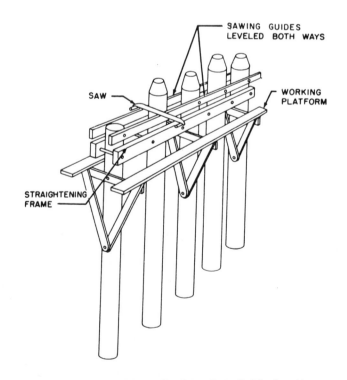

SAWING GUIDES
LEVELED BOTH WAYS

SAW

WORKING
PLATFORM

STRAIGHTENING
FRAME

Figure 11-7. Cutting pile to finish elevation.

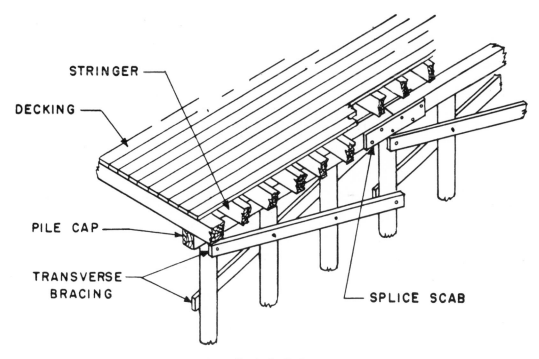

Figure 11–8. Typical pile bent.

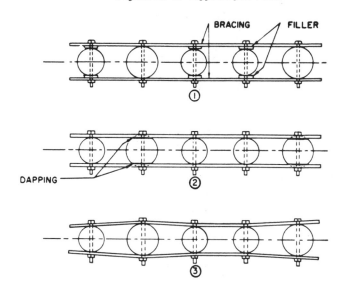

Figure 11–9. Transverse bracing for piles of differing sizes.

Section II. WHARF SUPERSTRUCTURE

11–9. General

After the timber pile bents have been alined, braced, and capped, the construction of the wharf superstructure is begun. The building of the superstructure consists of the installation of stringers, the decking, the curb or stringpiece, the erection of the fender systems, and the installation and bracing of dock hardware.

11–10. Erection of Stringers

The positions of the stringers are measured off from the centerline of the wharf. The stringers are toenailed to the pile caps with two 3/8- by 10-inch spikes at each bearing point. The ends of the stringers have overlap to provide complete bearing on the pile caps. Spacer blocks (fig. 11–10) between stringers are toenailed with two 60d nails.

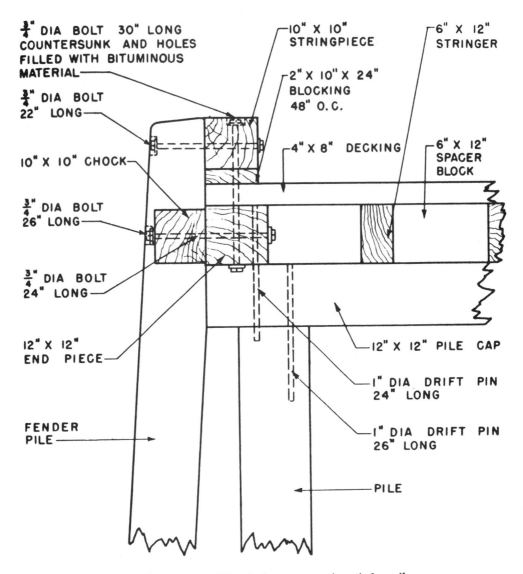

$\frac{3}{4}$" DIA BOLT 30" LONG COUNTERSUNK AND HOLES FILLED WITH BITUMINOUS MATERIAL

$\frac{3}{4}$" DIA BOLT 22" LONG

10" X 10" CHOCK

$\frac{3}{4}$" DIA BOLT 26" LONG

$\frac{3}{4}$" DIA BOLT 24" LONG

12" X 12" END PIECE

FENDER PILE

10" X 10" STRINGPIECE

2" X 10" X 24" BLOCKING 48" O.C.

4" X 8" DECKING

6" X 12" STRINGER

6" X 12" SPACER BLOCK

12" X 12" PILE CAP

1" DIA DRIFT PIN 24" LONG

1" DIA DRIFT PIN 26" LONG

PILE

Figure 11-10. Wharf-edge cross-section, timber-pile wharf.

11-11. Decking

Standard decking consists of 4- by 8-inch planks (fig. 11-10) which are spiked to each stringer with two 5/16- by 7-inch spikes, and set with 1/4-inch spacing. Openings between planks greater than 1/4 inch may be used in areas which are subject to heavy rains.

11-12. Stringpiece

The stringpiece, or curb, is placed on 2- by 10-inch blocking, 24 inches in length spaced on 48-inch centers along the edge of the deck (fig. 11-10). Stringpiece bolts are countersunk and the hole sealed with bituminous material.

a. When the stringpiece is parallel to the direction of the wharf stringers, the stringpiece is

bolted through the blocking, the decking, and the stringer end piece (fig. 11-10).

b. When the stringpiece is perpendicular to the direction of the stringer, it is bolted through the blocking, the decking, alternate stringers, and pile cap.

11-13. Fender Piles and Chocks

a. Use of Timber. For theater of operations construction, timber is the most suitable material for use as wharf fenders. Fender piles serve the following purposes:

(1) They cushion a wharf from impact of ships and protect the outer row of bearing piles from damage.

(2) They protect the hulls of craft from undue abrasion.

(3) The 3- or 4-foot extension of a fender pile above the deck level of a wharf supplements wharf mooring hardware but is not used for warping a ship into or out of the berth.

b. *Ease of Replacement.* Since fender piles are not part of the structural support of the wharf, they are easier to replace than bearing piles.

c. *Methods of Protecting Fender Piles.* To lengthen the life of fender piles, various protective devices are used.

(1) A heavy timber wearing ribbon which may easily be replaced is sometimes installed along a line of fender piles at the elevation which receives the heaviest abrasion.

(2) Floating logs or camels are used.

(3) Rope wrappings, particularly on corner fenders, are used.

d. *Fender Piles for Quays.* Structures which are almost completely rigid, such as solid-fill quays, sometimes have their fender piles backed up with heavy springs to provide a combination of yielding and resistance.

e. *Installation.* Fender piles are driven at a slight batter, usually 1 to 12 along the outside edge of all rows of bearing piles, except on the extreme inshore wharf sections. Every third fender pile may extend 3 to 4 feet above the curb. The others are cut off flush with the top of the curb.

f. *Chocks and Wales.*

(1) Chocks are timber braces placed between fender piles, at the level of the stringpiece or pile cap, to hold them in position and give them lateral stability. The ends of the chocks should be firmly seated against the piles.

(a) *Timber pile wharves.* Each chock is fastened with two bolts through the stringer endpiece or pile cap.

(b) *Steel pile wharves.* Each chock is bolted to 12- by 12-inch blocks driftpinned to the ends of the stringers or bolted to the ends of the wharf pile cap.

(2) Wales (horizontal beams) are used at mean low water elevation when tidal currents are swift or tidal variations are great to add rigidity to the line of fender piles. A 12- by 12-inch continuous longitudinal timber wale is fastened to the back fender of each pile with bolts. Timber chocks are placed between fender piles and bolted to the line wales.

11–14. Pile Clusters and Corner Fenders

Pile clusters, whether at the faces or corners of wharves or acting as isolated dolphins (para 11–16), must combine beam strength, rigidity, and stability against horizontal stresses of the component piles. Therefore, the individual piles which make up the cluster must be joined so that the cluster acts as a unit.

a. *Mooring Piles.*

(1) Mooring piles are clusters of three or more piles used to supplement or replace wharf mooring hardware. The top of the cluster is lashed together as described in paragraph 11–16b.

(2) They are placed at intervals along the face of a wharf when bollards and other items of mooring hardware are not available. A maximum of three piles of each cluster extend 3 feet or more above the wharf deck (fig. 11–11).

b. *Corner Fenders.* Corner fenders are provided so that a ship may use the corner to pivot in warping in and out of the berth. Corner fenders are piles driven in clusters at the exposed corners, bolted and lashed together. The wharf structure at the corners is strongly reinforced with layers of diagonal planking laid one across the other, and this reinforcing is backed up with diagonal batter piles. The standard corner-fender cluster is made up of 10 piles battered for adequate spacing at the points. Timber connectors may be used in conjunction with the bolts to tie the piles more firmly into a single rigid member. To avoid undue abrasion to the hulls of ships, and to the outside pile surfaces, heavy rope mats may be lashed to the clusters at the level of contact. To supplement mooring hardware, the corner piles extend 3 to 4 feet above deck level.

Figure 11–11. Pile cluster at face of timber pile wharf.

(1) *Deck reinforcing on wood pile wharves.* Before setting stringers, wooden piles battered inward are driven to support a cap set diagonally across each corner and bolted to the bottom face of the other caps. Another piece of cap timber is set to act as a strut between the fender cluster and the diagonal cap. The space between the cluster and the diagonal cap is then floored over with two layers of plank each 6 inches thick, laid diagonally (and transversely to each other) to fill the thickness between the cap timbers. To complete the reinforcing, stringers are set close and spiked together over the outer half of each corner panel.

(2) *Steel pile wharves.* In steel pile marginal wharves and piers with corner fenders the deck in each corner panel is similarly reinforced with timber. Wood piles battered inward carry a diagonal cap timber bolted to the bottom flanges of the steel pile caps. The diagonal cap is strutted against the fender cluster, the diagonal layers of plank are applied, and the stringers are set close and spiked together, as described above for wood pile wharves.

11-15. Floating Log Fenders (Camels)

a. Floating logs are used to absorb part of the impact shock when a ship is berthed and protect the surface of fender piles while the ship is tied up. The simplest type of fender logs is a single line of floating logs. Each log is secured by two or more lengths of 1/2-inch galvanized chain fastened to 3/4-inch eyebolts in the fender log and the wharf pile. Some arrangement such as loose steel collars around the wharf piles is provided to permit the floating logs to rise and fall with the tide.

b. Floating clusters or logs or strongly constructed rafts are called camels. In addition to absorbing impact shock, and protecting fender piles from the sliding friction of a ship moving in the berth, camels may be required to breast a ship off the face of the wharf into deeper water than exists at the face of the wharf.

11-16. Construction of Pile Mooring Dolphins

a. Dolphins are isolated clusters of piles to which a ship may be moored. The center of the cluster called a king pile may be a single pile or a cluster driven vertically and wrapped as to act as a unit. The other piles are driven in one or more concentric rings around the king pile, each battered towards the center. The king pile normally is left somewhat longer than the others for use as a mooring post (fig. 11-12).

b. The king pile when composed of a cluster is wrapped with at least six turns of 1-inch diameter galvanized wire rope stapled to each pile at every turn.

c. Two wrappings of the same type as described above are used for the pile cluster. One wrapping is located near the top of the cluster. The second wrapping is located about 2/3 the distance above mean low water.

d. To further assure that the cluster will act as a unit, the piles are chocked and bolted together approximately 2 feet above mean low water.

11-17. Mooring Hardware

Ships tie up to wharves with lines fastened to mooring fittings such as bollards, corner mooring posts, and cleats.

a. *Bollards.* Bollards, single or double-bitt, are steel or cast iron posts (fig. 11-13) to which large ships tie up. The prevent ships' lines from riding up off the post, they may have waist diameters smaller than top diameters, caps, or projecting, rounded horns. Double-bitt bollards are also known as double steamship bitts or simply as double bitts. Bollard bodies may be hollow for filling with concrete after installation. They are usually designed to take line pulls of about 35 tons.

b. *Corner Mooring Posts.* Corner mooring posts (fig. 11-14), which are larger than bollards, are sometimes located at the outshore corners of a pier, wharf, or quay. They are used to bring the ship into the pier or to warp the ship around the corner of the pier or around a turning dolphin as well as for securing lines. Corner mooring posts usually are designed to take line pulls of up to 50 tons.

c. *Cleats.* Cleats (fig. 11-15) are generally cast iron, shaped with arms extending horizontally from a relatively low body. The base may be open or closed. They are used for securing smaller ships, tugs, and workboats.

d. *Chocks.* Open or closed chocks (fig. 11-16), generally made of cast iron, are used for directing lines and for snubbing lines when working a ship into or out of her berth. The closed chock must be used when there is a change in the vertical as well as the horizontal direction of the line.

e. *Pad Eyes.* Pad eyes (fig. 11-17) are metal rings mounted vertically on a plate and intended to receive a ship's line spliced with thimble and shackle. They are used for securing only small craft.

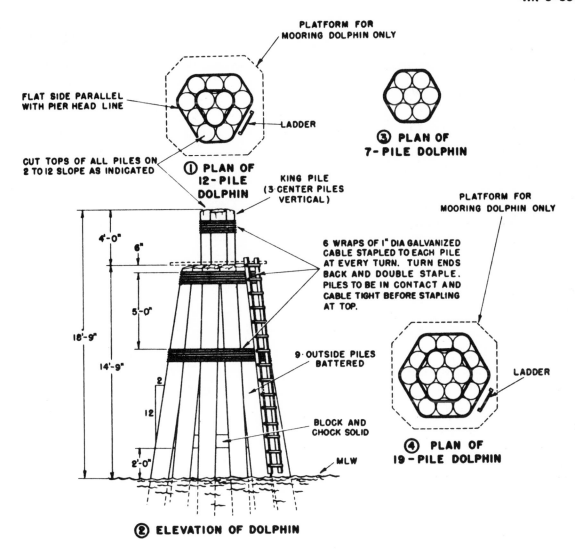

PLATFORM FOR
MOORING DOLPHIN ONLY

FLAT SIDE PARALLEL
WITH PIER HEAD LINE

LADDER

③ PLAN OF
7-PILE DOLPHIN

CUT TOPS OF ALL PILES ON
2 TO 12 SLOPE AS INDICATED

① PLAN OF
12-PILE
DOLPHIN

KING PILE
(3 CENTER PILES
VERTICAL)

PLATFORM FOR
MOORING DOLPHIN ONLY

6 WRAPS OF 1" DIA GALVANIZED
CABLE STAPLED TO EACH PILE
AT EVERY TURN. TURN ENDS
BACK AND DOUBLE STAPLE.
PILES TO BE IN CONTACT AND
CABLE TIGHT BEFORE STAPLING
AT TOP.

4'-0"

6"

5'-0"

18'-9"

14'-9"

2

12

2'-0"

9 OUTSIDE PILES
BATTERED

BLOCK AND
CHOCK SOLID

LADDER

④ PLAN OF
19-PILE DOLPHIN

MLW

② ELEVATION OF DOLPHIN

Figure 11-12. Timber pile dolphins.

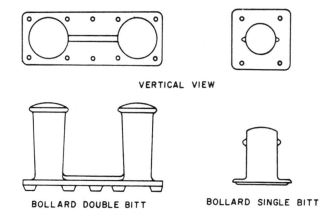

VERTICAL VIEW

BOLLARD DOUBLE BITT

BOLLARD SINGLE BITT

Figure 11-13. Bollards.

11-18. Installation of Wharf Hardware

a. Stringer Reinforcement. Proper installation requires that the vertical and horizontal stress on any structural unit on which mooring hardware is attached be transferred to a considerable extent to the wharf structure. This is done by increasing the number and size of stringers under the hardware installation and by providing an anchorage for mooring hardware bolts that will transfer the stress through the pile cap of one or more bents to several piles. The number and size of stringers are increased at the location of major items of hardware. When base widths of hardware are less than 24 inches, but greater than 12 inches, at least two 12- by 12-inch stringers are needed; for base widths less than 36 inches, but greater than 24 inches, three 12-inch stringers; and so forth. Stringers are laid close together and spiked to each other and at each bearing point. Mooring hardware bolts pass through stringers, filler blocks, and anchorage timbers.

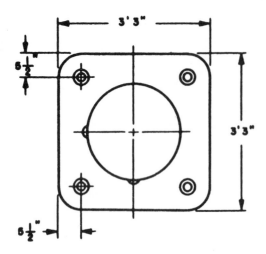

VERTICAL VIEW

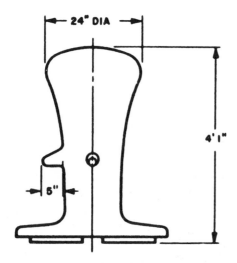

Figure 11–14. Corner mooring post.

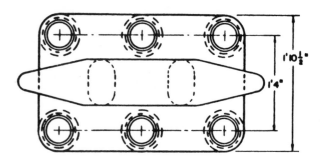

VERTICAL VIEW

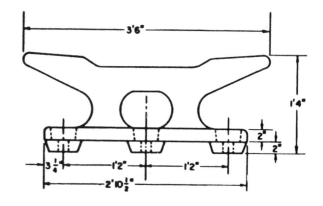

Figure 11–15. Open wide-base cleat.

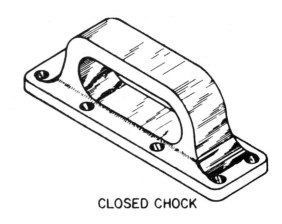

CLOSED CHOCK

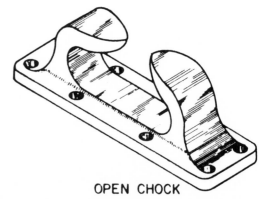

OPEN CHOCK

Figure 11–16. Chocks.

b. *Standard Installations.* The standard wharf structures have mooring hardware as follows:

(1) Pier, 90 x 500 feet—six, large double-bitt bollards on each side on 100-foot centers and five 42-inch cleats on each side centered between bollards.

(2) Offshore marginal wharf, 60 x 500 feet —six large, double-bitt bollards and five 42-inch cleats spaced as above on the outshore side only.

(3) Lighterage quay, 35 x 500 feet—eleven 42-inch cleats on 50-foot centers.

c. *Nonstandard Installations.*

(1) For nonstandard wharf structures, mooring hardware should be installed in numbers, types, and spacing approximating that of standard wharves.

(2) When cleats and pad eyes are not available, every third fender pile must be installed to

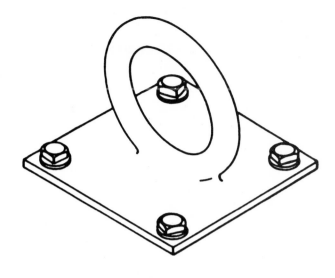

Figure 11–17. Pad eye.

extend 3 to 4 feet above the wharf deck. Fender pile extensions may be used to steady a ship in the berth, but not to winch a ship into position.

(3) On berths located near enough to the shore, bollards or mooring posts may be located on shore.

d. Location. Bollards and other mooring hard-

ware are placed clear of cranes and traffic, and as close to the curb as possible. Where onshore mooring anchors are used, they should be located so the lines will not have to be moved for traffic.

11–19. Anchorages for Hardware

a. Location Between Pile Bents. The provide an anchorage for heavy items of mooring hardware located between pile bents, a timber grillwork of 12- by 12-inch timbers is bolted underneath the pile cap (fig. 11–18). Each of the four piles directly affected by the upward pull on the grillwork is strapped to the pile cap with 3- by 3/8-inch steel strapping. The straps are spiked to piles and pile caps. Filler blocks of 12- by 12-inch timbers are centered to receive the mooring hardward bolts.

b. Location at Pile Bent. Mooring hardware is also located directly over the outside bearing pile of a bent (fig. 11–19). Mooring hardware with 22- to 26-inch bolt centers is anchored as follows:

(1) Two 12- by 12-inch by approximately 20-foot long timbers are bolted to both sides of three piles of the bent and under the pile cap over which the hardware is located. The batter

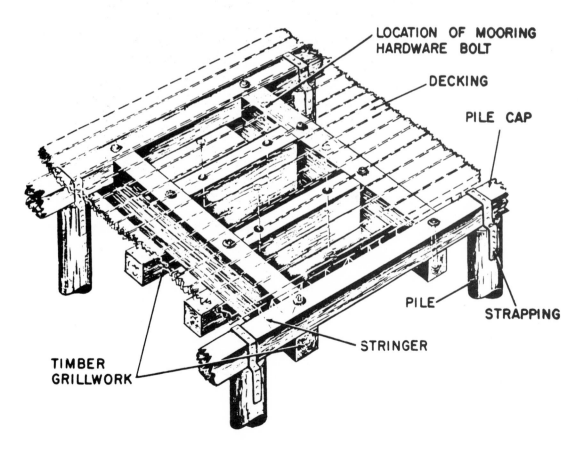

Figure 11–18. Timber grillwork for hardware anchorage.

pile and batter pile cap shown in figure 11–19 may be omitted when the wharf design does not need additional lateral stability.

(2) Twelve- by twelve-inch filler timbers approximately 4 feet long are bolted to the wharf pile cap under the hardware bolt location.

(3) Each of the three piles which is directly affected by the upward pull on the grillwork is strapped to the pile cap with steel strapping as described in *a* above.

(4) Items of mooring hardware with bolt centers greater than 26 inches require timber wider than 12 inches, doubling the number of timbers, or locating the hardware between bents

using timber grillwork anchorage described in *a* above.

c. Bracing. The wharf structure is longitudinally braced at the location of bollard installations. Diagonal bracing is done from just below the pile caps to approximately low water level at the location of each bollard. The cross bracing is bolted to each pile.

d. Installation of Light Items. Light items of mooring hardware, with bolt centers less than 8 inches, such as cleats, chocks, and pad eyes, are bolted through the stringpiece, blocking, decking, and stringer end piece.

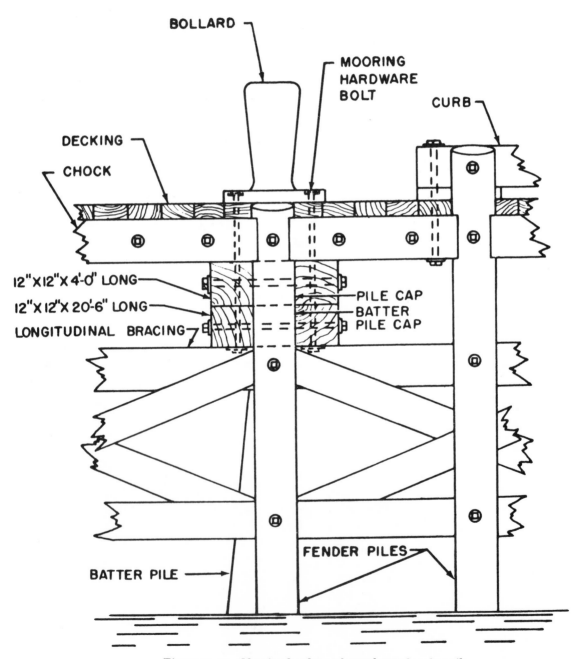

Figure 11–19. Mooring hardware located over bearing pile.

APPENDIX A
REFERENCES

A–1. Field Manuals

FM 5–34   Engineer Field Data

A–2. Technical Manuals

TM 5–232	Elements of Surveying
TM 5–233	Construction Surveying
TM 5–258	Pile Construction
TM 5–302	Construction in the Theater of Operations
TM 5–312	Military Fixed Bridges
TM 5–330	Planning and Design of Roads, Air Bases, and Heliports in the Theater of Operations
TM 5–333–1	Planner's and Estimator's Handbook
TM 5–360	Port Construction and Rehabilitation
TM 5–461	Engineer Handtools
TM 5–617	Roofing; Repairs and Utilities
TM 5–621	Repairs and Utilities; Buildings and Structures; Lathing and Plastering
TM 5–622	Wharves, Shore Structures, and Dredging; Repairs and Utilities
TM 5–704	Construction Print Reading in the Field
TM 5–725	Rigging
TM 5–742	Concrete and Masonry
TM 5–805–8	Building Construction Materials and Practices: Building Hardware

APPENDIX B
ABBREVIATIONS AND SYMBOLS

B-1. Abbreviations

The following abbreviations in connection with lumber are used by the carpenter:

AD .... air-dried
al .... all length
av .... average
avw .... average width
avl .... average length
bd .... board
bd ft .... board foot
bdl .... bundle
bev .... beveled
bm .... board (foot) measure
btr .... better
clg .... ceiling
clr .... clear
CM .... center matched; that is, tongue-and-groove joints are made along the center of the edge of the piece
Com .... common
Csg .... casing
Ctg .... crating
cu ft .... cubic foot
D & CM .... dressed (one or two sides) and center matched
D & M .... dressed and matched; that is, dressed one or two sides and tongue and grooved on the edges. The match may be center or standard
DS .... drop siding
D & SM .... dressed (one or two sides) and standard matched
D 2S & CM .... dressed two sides and center matched
D 2S & M .... dressed two sides and (center of standard) matched
D 2S & SM .... dressed two sides and standard matched
Dim .... dimension
E .... edge
FAS .... firsts and seconds, a combined grade of the two upper grades of hardwoods
fbk .... flat back
fcty .... factory (lumber)
FG .... flat grain
Flg .... flooring
fok .... free of knots
Frm .... framing
ft .... foot or feet
Hdl .... handle (stock)
Hdwd .... hardwood
Hrt .... heart
Hrtwd .... heartwood
in .... inch or inches
KD .... kiln-dried
kd .... knocked down
lbr .... lumber
lgr .... longer
lgth .... length
linft .... linear foot, that is, 12 inches
LR .... log run
Lr MCO .... log run, mill culls out
M .... thousand

MFBM ....thousand (feet) board measure
MCO ....mill culls out
Merch ....merchantable
MR ....mill run
msm ....thousand (feet) surface measure
mw ....mixed width
No ....number
1s & 2s ....ones and twos, a combined grade of the hardwood grades of firsts and seconds
Ord ....order
P ....planed
Pat ....pattern
Pky ....picky
Pln ....plain, as in plain sawed
Pn ....partition
Qtd ....quartered (with reference to hardwoods)
rd ....round
rdm ....random
res ....resawed
rfg ....roofing
Rfrs ....roofers
rip ....ripped
rl ....random length
rw ....random width
S & E ....surfaced one side and one edge
S2S & M ....surfaced two sides and standard or center matched
S2S & SM ....surfaced two sides and standard matched
Sap ....sapwood
S1E ....surfaced one edge
S1S1E ....surfaced one side and one edge
S1S2E ....surfaced one side and two edges
S2E ....surfaced two edges
S4S ....surfaced four sides
S & CM ....surfaced one or two sides and center matched
S & M ....surfaced and matched; that is, surfaced one or two sides and tongued and grooved on the edges. The match may be center or standard.
S & SM ....surfaced one or two sides and standard matched
S2S & CM ....surfaced two sides and center matched
Sap ....sapwood
SB ....standard bead
Sd ....seasoned
Sdg ....siding
Sel ....select
SESd ....square-edge siding
sf ....surface foot; that is, an area of 1 square foot
Stfwd ....softwood
ShD ....shipping dry
Ship ....shiplap
Sm ....standard matched
sm ....surface measure
snd ....sap no defect
snd ....sound
sq ....square
sq E ....square edge
sq E & S ....square edge and sound
sqrs ....squares
Std ....standard
stk ....stock
SW ....sound wormy
T & G ....tongued and grooved
TB & S ....top, bottom, and sides
tbrs ....timbers
VG ....vertical grain
wal ....wider, all length
wdr ....wider
wt ....weight
wth ....width

B-2. Symbols

Symbols commonly used in carpentry are given below. For additional information on the various symbols used in construction plans and blueprints, refer to TM 5–704.

a. Architectural

Tile	
Earth	
Plaster	
Sheet metal	
Built-in cabinet	
Outside door: Brick wall	
Frame wall	
Inside door: Frame wall	
Brick	
Firebrick	
Concrete	
Cast concrete block	
Insulation: Loose fill	
Board or quilts	
Cut stone	
Ashlar	
Shingles (siding)	
Wood, rough	
Wood, finished	
Cased or arched openings	
Single casement window	
Double-hung windows	
Double casement window	

b. Plumbing.

Bathtubs:

Corner ------------

Free standing --------

Floor drain ------------

Shower drain -----------

Hot-water tank --------- ○ H.W.T.

Grease trap -------------

Hose bibb or sill cock ----

Lavatories:

Pedestal ------------

Wall-hung -----------

Corner -------------

Toilets:

Tank ------------

Flush valve --------

Urinals:

Stall-type ----------

Wall-hung ---------

Laundry trays ---------

Built-in shower --------

Shower ---------------

Sinks:

Single drain board.

Double drain board.

c. Electrical

Pull switch ----------------

Single-pole switch ---------- S₁

Double-pole switch -------- S₂

Triple-pole switch ---------- S₃

Buzzer -----------------

Floor outlet -------------

Bell -------------------

Drop cord ---------------

Ceiling outlet -----------

Wall bracket -----------

Single convenience outlet ------------------

Double convenience outlet ------------------

Ceiling outlet. gas & electric ------------------

Motor -----------------

Light outlet with wiring and switches indicated ---------------

APPENDIX C

CONVERSION TABLES

Length

Metric to English

1 millimeter (mm)	= 0.04 inch (0.03937 inch)
1 centimeter (cm)	= 0.3937 inch
1 meter (m)	= 3.281 feet
1 m	= 1.094 yards
1 kilometer (km)	= 0.621 statute mile
1 km	= 0.5396 nautical mile

English to Metric

1 yard	= 91.44 centimeters (cm)
1 foot	= 30.48 cm
1 inch	= 2.54 cm
⅞ inch	= 2.22 cm (22.22 millimeters (mm))
¾ inch	= 1.90 cm (19.05 mm)
⅝ inch	= 1.59 cm (15.88 mm)
½ inch	= 1.27 cm (12.70 mm)
⅜ inch	= 0.98 cm (9.84 mm)
¼ inch	= 0.64 cm (6.35 mm)
⅛ inch	= 0.32 cm (3.18 mm)

Area

1 sq centimeter	= 0.155 sq inch
1 sq meter	= 10.76 sq ft
1 sq meter	= 1.196 sq yards
1 hectare	= 2.47 acres
1 sq kilometer	= 0.386 sq miles

1 sq inch	= 6.45 sq centimeters
1 sq foot	= 0.0929 sq meter
1 sq yard	= 0.836 sq meter
1 acre	= 0.405 hectare
1 sq mile	= 2.59 sq kilometers

APPENDIX D

MANPOWER ESTIMATES—CARPENTRY

This appendix contains tables which may be used in preparing manpower estimates for carpentry work. The tables do not include provision for loading and hauling materials to the jobsite. All tables presume average working conditions in terms of weather, skill, crew size, accessibility, and the availability of equipment.

Table D-1. Rough Framing [1]

Description	Unit	Man-hr/unit		
Beams (3-2″ x 8″)	MFBM [2]	40		
Blocking	MFBM	32		
Bridging	100 pairs	5		
Ceiling joists	MFBM	32		
Door bucks	ea.	3		
Floor joists, sills	MFBM	32		
Furring including plugging	1000 linft	32		
Grounds for plaster	1000 linft	48		
Rafters	MFBM	48		
Trusses	ea.	Man-hr assembly	Man-hr placement	Hours hoist time
Span ft 20		2.5	4	8
30		5	8	12
40		12	8	16
50		20	6 [3]	8 [3]
60		24	6 [3]	9 [3]
80		32	6 [3]	11 [3]
Wall frames, plates	MFBM	56		

[1] Typical crew: 1 leader, 8 men.
Minimal crew: 1 leader, 2 men.
[2] Thousand board feet measure.
[3] Assumes use of organizational crane.

Table D–2. Sheathing and Siding [1]

Description	Unit	Man-hr/unit
Roof decking	1000 sq ft	
plywood		24
tongue & groove		32
Siding	1000 sq ft	
corrugated asbestos		32
drop siding		32
narrow bevel		48
plywood		24
shingles		40
Wall sheathing	1000 sq ft	
Bldg paper		16
fiber board		24
tongue & groove		24
plywood		16

[1] Typical crew: 1 leader, 4 men.

Table D–3. Flooring [1]

Description	Unit	Man-hr/unit
Linoleum	1000 sq ft	32
Soft tile	1000 sq ft	
cemented		24
nailed		32
Wood floors	1000 sq ft	
Finish floor		
hardwood		32
softwood		24
Subfloor		
plywood		16
tongue & groove		24

[1] Typical crew: 1 leader, 4 men.

Table D–4. Insulation [1]

Description	Unit	Man-hr/unit
Acoustic	1000 sq ft	
Quilt		8
Strip		24
Thermal	1000 sq ft	
Board		
ceiling		24
floor		8
roof		16
wall		32
Foil alone		16
Rigid foam		32
Rock wool		
batts		24
loose		16

[1] Typical crew: 1 leader, 8 men.

Table D–5. Finish Carpentry [1]

Description	Unit	Man-hr/unit
Baseboard (2 member)	1000 linft	72
Ceilings	1000 sq ft	
cemented tile		32
panel w/suspension		72
plasterboard (including tape)[2]		64
wood		48
Door frame, trim	ea.	2.5
Installing prefab. closets	ea.	16
Molding (chair)	1000 linft	48
Plasterboard (complete)	1000 sq ft	110
Setting kitchen cabinets	ea.	1.5
Sliding door w/pocket	ea.	8
Shelving	1000 sq ft	64
Stairs		
closed stringer, built on job	story	16
closed stringer, prefab.	story	8
open stringer	story	24
Walls	1000 sq ft	
plasterboard (including tape)		48
plywood		80
Wood frame, trim	ea.	3

[1] Typical crew: 1 leader, 8 men.
[2] Includes installation of furring strips when necessary.

Table D–6. Wood Door Installation [1]

Description	Unit	Man-hr/unit
Caulking (w/gun)	1000 linft	16
Doors w/hardware	ea.	
exterior [2]		2
interior [2]		1.5
manual sliding (including tracks)		8
motorized sliding [3]		56
overhead (including machinery)		16
screendoors		1.5
Weatherstripping	ea. opening	1.5

[1] Typical crew: 1 leader, 4 men.
[2] For double doors add 50% to labor estimates.
[3] Includes tracks and all necessary machinery, with control equipment.

Table D-7. Wood Window Installation [1]

Description	Unit	Man-hr/unit
Caulking (w/gun)	1000 linft	16
Screens	ea.	1.5
Weatherstripping	ea. opening	1.5
Windows (avg 20 sq ft)	ea.	
casement		1.5
double hung		2.5
jalousie		2.5
louvers		4
skylight		8
sliding		2.5
Venetian blinds	ea.	1

[1] Typical crew: 1 leader, 4 men.

Table D-8. Built-Up Roofing, Insulation and Flashing [1] (pitch 1/2"—3"/ft)

Description	Unit	Man-hr/unit
Flashing	1000 linft	60
Insulation	1000 sq ft	25
Roofing	1000 sq ft	
2 ply		12
3 ply		20
4 ply		25
5 ply		30

[1] Typical crew: 1 leader, 6 men.
Table includes melting asphalt, laying felt, mopping, and laying gravel.

Table D-9. Roll Roofing [1] (pitch at least 2"/ft)

Description	Unit	Man-hr/unit
Asphaltic aluminum (including primer)	1000 sq ft	18
Canvas (including 2 coats paint)	1000 sq ft	25
Paper (plain) & felt	1000 sq ft	7

[1] Typical crew: 1 leader, 6 men.
Table includes cleaning deck, applying prime coat, and laying rolls.

Table D-10. Shingle Roofing [1] (pitch at least 3"/ft)

Description	Unit	Man-hr/unit
Asbestos	1000 sq ft	45
Asphalt	1000 sq ft	30
Metal	1000 sq ft	50
Slate	1000 sq ft	55
Wood	1000 sq ft	35

[1] Typical crew: 1 leader, 4 men.
Table includes placing and nailing.

Table D-11. Metal, Asbestos-Cement and Tile Roofing [1] (pitch at least 3"/ft)

Description	Unit	Man-hr/unit
Asbestos-cement	1000 sq ft	
metal purlins		45
wood purlins		35
Metal —	1000 sq ft	
corrugated & V-crimp		
metal purlins		36
wood purlins		18
Tile	1000 sq ft	
clay		55
metal		60

[1] Typical crew: 1 leader, 5 men.
Table includes placing, caulking, drilling, and fastening materials.

Table D-12. Pile Bracing and Capping [1]

Description	Unit	Man-hr/unit
Bracing [2]	ea.	
diagonal		0.8
horizontal		1
Capping	1000 linft	
wood		100

[1] Typical crew: 1 leader, 6 men.
[2] Table based on 4 in x 10 in x 4 ft bracing members.
Pile bracing includes catting, drilling, handling, and fastening materials.

Table D-13. Pier Framing [1]

Description	Unit	Man-hr/unit
Bridging	1000 linft	40
Bull rail	1000 linft	60
Bumper	1000 linft	36
4" deck	1000 sq ft	20
Stringers	MFBM [2]	200
2" wearing surface	1000 sq ft	16

[1] Typical crew: 1 leader, 10 men.
[2] 1000 board-foot measure.
Installation of pier framing includes the cutting, drilling, handling, and fastening of stringers, bridging, all decking, rails, and bumpers.

Table D-14. Deck Hardware [1]

Description	Unit	Man-hr/unit
Bits	ea.	3
Bollards	ea.	4
Chocks	ea.	3
Cleats	ea.	2
Pad eyes	ea.	1

[1] Typical crew: 1 leader, 4 men.
Installation of deck hardware includes required drilling, handling, and fastening of bits, bollards, chocks, cleats, and pad eyes.

GLOSSARY

Anchor—Irons of special form used to fasten together timbers or masonry.

Anchor bolts—Bolt which fastens columns, girders, or other members to concrete or masonry.

Backing—The bevel on the top edge of a hip rafter that allows the roofing board to fit the top of the rafter without leaving a triangular space between it and the lower side of the roof covering.

Balloon frame—The lightest and most economical form of construction, in which the studding and corner posts are set up in continuous lengths from first-floor line or sill to the roof plate.

Baluster—A small pillar or column used to support a rail.

Balustrade—A series of balusters connected by a rail, generally used for porches, balconies, and the like.

Band—A low, flat molding.

Base—The bottom of a column; the finish of a room at the junction of the walls and floor.

Batten (cleat)—A narrow strip of board used to fasten several pieces together.

Batter board—A temporary framework used to assist in locating the corners when laying a foundation.

Batter pile—Pile driven at an angle to brace a structure against lateral thrust.

Beam—An inclusive term for joists, girders, rafters, and purlins.

Bedding—A filling of mortar, putty, or other substance in order to secure a firm bearing.

Belt course—A horizontal board across or around a building, usually made of a flat member and a molding.

Bent—A single vertical framework consisting of horizontal and vertical members supporting the deck of a bridge or pier.

Bevel board (pitch board)—A board used in framing a roof or stairway to lay out bevels.

Board—Lumber less than 2 inches thick.

Board foot—The equivalent of a board 1 foot square and 1 inch thick.

Boarding in—The process of nailing boards on the outside studding of a house.

Bollard—Steel or cast iron post to which large ships are tied.

Braces—Pieces fitted and firmly fastened to two others at any angle in order to strengthen the angle thus treated.

Bracket—A projecting support for a shelf or other structure.

Break joints—To arrange joints so that they do not come directly under or over the joints of adjoining pieces, as in shingling, siding, etc.

Bridging—Pieces fitted in pairs from the bottom of one floor joist to the top of adjacent joists, and crossed to distribute the floor load; sometimes pieces of width equal to the joists and fitted neatly between them.

Building paper—Cheap, thick paper, used to insulate a building before the siding or roofing is put on; sometimes placed between double floors.

Built-up member—A single structural component made from several pieces fastened together.

Built-up timber—A timber made of several pieces fastened together, and forming one of larger dimension.

Carriages—The supports or the steps and risers of a flight of stairs.

Casement—A window in which the sash opens upon hinges.

Casing—The trimming around a door or window opening, either outside or inside, or the finished lumber around a post or beam, etc.

Ceiling—Narrow, matched boards; sheathing of the surfaces that inclose the upper side of a room.

Center-hung sash—A sash hung on its centers so that it swings on a horizontal axis.

Chamfer—A beveled surface cut upon the corner of a piece of wood.

Checks—Splits or cracks in a board, ordinarily caused by seasoning.

Chock—Heavy timber fitted between fender piles along wheel guard of a pier or wharf.

Chord—The principal member of a truss on either the top or bottom.

Clamp—A mechanical device used to hold two or more pieces together.

Clapboards—A special form of outside covering of a house; siding.

Cleats—Metal arms extending horizontally from a relatively low base used for securing small ships, tugs, and work boats.

Column—A square, rectangular, or cylindrical support for roofs, ceilings, and so forth, composed of base, shaft, and capital.

Combination frame—A combination of the principal features of the full and balloon frames.

Concrete—An artificial building material made by mixing cement and sand with gravel, broken stone, or other aggregate, and sufficient water to cause the cement to set and bind the entire mass.

Conductors—Pipes for conducting water from a roof to the ground or to a receptacle or drain; downspout.

Cornice—The molded projection which finishes the top of the wall of a building.

Counterflashings—Strips of metal used to prevent water from entering the top edge of the vertical side of a roof flashing; they also allow expansion and contraction without danger of breaking the flashing.

Cross brace—Bracing with two intersecting diagonals.

Deadening—Construction intended to prevent the passage of sound.

Decking—Heavy plank floor of a pier or bridge.

Diagonal—Inclined member of a truss or bracing system used for stiffening and wind bracing.

Drip—The projection of a window sill or water table to allow the water to drain clear of the side of the house below it.

Fascia—A flat member of a cornice or other finish, generally the board of the cornice to which the gutter is fastened.

Fender pile—Outside row of piles that protects a pier or wharf from damage by ships.

Filler—Piece used to fill space between two surfaces.

Flashing—The material used and the process of making watertight the roof intersections and other exposed places on the outside of the house.

Flue—The opening in a chimney through which smoke passes.

Flush—Adjacent surfaces even, or in same plane (with reference to two structural pieces).

Footing—An enlargement at the lower end of a wall, pier, or column, to distribute the load.

Footing form—A wooden or steel structure, placed around the footing that will hold the concrete to the desired shape and size.

Foundation—That part of a building or wall which supports the superstructure.

Frame—The surrounding or inclosing woodwork of windows, doors, etc., and the timber skeleton of a building.

Framing—The rough timber structure of a building, including interior and exterior walls, floor, roof, and ceilings.

Full frame—The old fashioned mortised-and-tenoned frame, in which every joint was mortised and tenoned. Rarely used at the present time.

Furring—Narrow strips of board nailed upon the walls and ceilings to form a straight surface upon which to lay the laths or other finish.

Gable—The vertical triangular end of a building from the eaves to the apex of the roof.

Gage—A tool used by carpenters to strike a line parallel to the edge of a board.

Gambrel—A symmetrical roof with two different pitches or slopes on each side.

Girder—A timber used to support wall beams or joists.

Girt (*ribband*)—The horizontal member of the walls of a full or combination frame house which supports the floor joists or is flush with the top of the joists.

Grade—The horizontal ground level of a building or structure.

Groove—A long hollow channel cut by a tool, into which a piece fits or in which it works. Two special types of grooves are the *dado*, a rectangular groove cut across the full width of a piece, and the *housing*, a groove cut at any angle with the grain and part way across a piece. Dados are used in sliding doors, window frames, etc.; housings are used for framing stair risers and threads in a string.

Ground—A strip of wood assisting the plasterer in making a straight wall and in giving a place to which the finish of the room may be nailed.

Hanger—Vertical-tension member supporting a load.

Header—A short joist into which the common joists are framed around or over an opening.

Headroom—The clear space between floor line and ceiling, as in a stairway.

Heel of a rafter—The end or foot that rests on the wall plate.

Hip roof—A roof which slopes up toward the center from all sides, necessitating a hip rafter at each corner.

Jack rafter—A short rafter framing between the wall plate; a hip rafter.

Jamb—The side piece or post of an opening; sometimes applied to the door frame.

Joint-butt—Squared ends or ends and edges adjoining each other:

> *Dovetail*—Joint made by cutting pins the shape of dovetails which fit between dovetails upon another piece.
>
> *Drawboard*—A mortise-and-tenon joint with holes so bored that when a pin is driven through, the joint becomes tighter.
>
> *Fished*—An end butt splice strengthened by pieces nailed on the sides.
>
> *Glue*—A joint held together with glue.
>
> *Halved*—A joint made by cutting half the wood away from each piece so as to bring the sides flush.
>
> *Housed*—A joint in which a piece is grooved to receive the piece which is to form the other part of the joint.
>
> *Lap*—A joint of two pieces lapping over each other.
>
> *Mortised*—A joint made by cutting a hole or mortise, in one piece, and a tenon, or piece to fit the hole, upon the other.
>
> *Rub*—A flue joint made by carefully fitting the edges together, spreading glue between them, and rubbing the pieces back and forth until the pieces are well rubbed together.
>
> *Scarfed*—A timber spliced by cutting various shapes of shoulders, or jogs, which fit each other.

Joists—Timbers supporting the floorboards.

Kerf—The cut made by a saw.

Knee brace—A corner brace, fastened at an angle from wall stud to rafter, stiffening a wood or steel frame to prevent angular movement.

Laths—Narrow strips to support plastering.

Lattice—Crossed wood, iron plate, or bars.

Ledgerboard—The support for the second-floor joists of a balloon-frame house, or for similar uses; ribband.

Level—A term describing the position of a line or plane when parallel to the surface of still water; an instrument or tool used in testing for horizontal and vertical surfaces, and in determining differences of elevation.

Lintel (cap)—A horizontal structural member spanning an opening, and supporting a wall load.

Lookout—The end of a rafter, or the construction which projects beyond the sides of a house to support the eaves; also the projecting timbers at the gables which support the verge boards.

Louver—A kind of window, generally in peaks of gables and the tops of towers, provided with horizontal slots which exclude rain and snow and allow ventilation.

Lumber—Sawed parts of a log such as boards, planks, scantling, and timber.

Matching, or tonguing and grooving—The method used in cutting the edges of a board to make a tongue on one edge and a groove on the other.

Meeting rail—The bottom rail of the upper sash of a double-hung window. Sometimes called the check-rail.

Member—A single piece in a structure, complete in itself.

Miter—The joint formed by two abutting pieces meeting at an angle.

Molding Base—The molding on the top of a baseboard.

> *Bed*—A molding used to cover the joint between the plancier and frieze (horizontal decorative

band around the wall of a room); also used as a base molding upon heavy work, and sometimes as a member of a cornice.

Lip—A molding with a lip which overlaps the piece against which the back of the molding rests.

Picture—A molding shaped to form a support for picture hooks, often placed at some distance from the ceiling upon the wall to form the lower edge of the frieze.

Rake—The cornice upon the gable edge of a pitch roof, the members of which are made to fit those of the molding of the horizontal eaves.

Mortise—The hole which is to receive a tenon, or any hole cut into or through a piece by a chisel; generally of rectangular shape.

Mullion—The construction between the openings of a window frame to accommodate two or more windows.

Muntin—The vertical member between two panels of the same piece of panel work. The vertical sash-bars separating the different panels of glass.

Newel—The principal post of the foot of a staircase; also the central support of a winding flight of stairs.

Nosing—The part of a stair tread which projects over the riser, or any similar projection; a term applied to the rounded edge of a board.

Pad eyes—Metal rings mounted vertically on a plate for tying small vessels.

Partition—A permanent interior wall which serves to divide a building into rooms.

Pier—(*a*) Timber, concrete, or masonry supports for girders, posts, or arches. (*b*) Intermediate supports for adjacent ends of two bridge spans. (*c*) Structure extending outward from shore into water used as a dock for ships.

Piers—Masonry supports, set independently of the main foundation.

Pilaster—A portion of a square column, usually set within or against a wall.

Piles—Long posts driven into the soil in swampy locations or whenever it is difficult to secure a firm foundation, upon which the footing course of masonry or other timbers are laid.

Piling—Large timbers or poles driven into the ground or the bed of a stream to make a firm foundation.

Pitch—Inclination or slope, as for roofs or stairs, or the rise divided by the span.

Pitch board—A board sawed to the exact shape formed by the stair tread, riser, and slope of the stairs and used to lay out the carriage and stringers.

Plan—A horizontal geometrical section of a building, showing the walls, doors, windows, stairs, chimneys, columns, etc.

Plank—A wide piece of sawed timber, usually 1½ to 4½ inches thick and 6 inches or more wide.

Plaster—A mixture of lime, hair, and sand, or of lime, cement, and sand, used to cover outside and inside wall surfaces.

Plate—The top horizontal piece of the walls of a frame building upon which the roof rests.

Plate cut—The cut in a rafter which rests upon the plate; sometimes called the seat cut.

Plow—To cut a groove running in the same direction as the grain of the wood.

Plumb cut—Any cut made in a vertical plane; the vertical cut at the top end of a rafter.

Ply—A term used to denote a layer or thickness of building or roofing paper as two-ply, three-ply, etc.

Porch—An ornamental entrance way.

Post—A timber set on end to support a wall, girder, or other member of the structure.

Pulley stile—The member of a window frame which contains the pulleys and between which the edges of the sash slide.

Purlin—A timber supporting several rafters at one or more points, or the roof sheeting directly.

Rabbet or rebate—A corner cut out of an edge of a piece of wood.

Rafter—The beams that slope from the ridge of a roof to the eaves and make up the main body of the roof's framework.

Rafters, common—Those which run square with the plate and extend to the ridge.

Cripple—Those which cut between valley and hip rafters.

Hip—Those extending from the outside angle of the plates toward the apex of the roof.

Jacks—Those square with the plate and intersecting the hip rafter.

Valley—Those extending from an inside angle of the plates toward the ridge or center line of the house.

Rail—The horizontal members of a balustrade or panel work.

Rake—The trim of a building extending in an oblique line, as rake dado or molding.

Return—The continuation of a molding or finish of any kind in a different direction.

Ribband—(See Ledgerboard.)

Ridge—The top edge or corner formed by the intersection of two roof surfaces.

Ridge cut—(See Plumb cut.)

Rise—The vertical distance through which anything rises, as the rise of a roof or stair.

Riser—The vertical board between two treads of a flight of stairs.

Roofing—The material put on a roof to make it wind and waterproof.

Rubble—Roughly broken quarry stone.

Rubble masonry—Uncut stone, used for rough work, foundations, backing, and the like.

Run—The length of the horizontal projection of a piece such as a rafter when in position.

Saddle board—The finish of the ridge of a pitch-roof house. Sometimes called comb board.

Sash—The framework which holds the glass in a window.

Sawing, plain—Lumber sawed regardless of the grain, the log simply squared and sawed to the desired thickness; sometimes called slash or bastard sawed.

Scab—A short piece of lumber used to splice, or to prevent movement of two other pieces.

Scaffold or staging—A temporary structure or platform enabling workmen to reach high places.

Scale—A short measurement used as a proportionate part of a larger dimension. The scale of a drawing is expressed as $\frac{1}{4}$ inch = 1 foot.

Scantling—Lumber with a cross-section ranging from 2 by 4 inches to 4 by 4 inches.

Scarfing—A joint between two pieces of wood which allows them to be spliced lengthwise.

Scotia—A hollow molding used as a part of a cornice, and often under the nosing of a stair tread.

Scribing—The marking of a piece of wood to provide for the fitting of one of its surfaces to the irregular surface of another.

Seat cut or plate cut—The cut at the bottom end of a rafter to allow it to fit upon the plate.

Seat of a rafter—The horizontal cut upon the bottom end of a rafter which rests upon the top of the plate.

Section—A drawing showing the kind, arrangement, and proportions of the various parts of a structure. It is assumed that the structure is cut by a plane, and the section is the view gained by looking in one direction.

Shakes—Imperfections in timber caused during the growth of the timber by high winds or imperfect conditions of growth.

Sheathing—Wall boards, roofing boards; generally applied to narrow boards laid with a space between them, according to the length of a shingle exposed to weather.

Sheathing paper—The paper used under siding or shingles to insulate in the house; building papers.

Siding—The outside finish between the casings.

Sills—The horizontal timbers of a house which either rest upon the masonry foundations or, in the absence of such, form the foundations.

Sizing—Working material to the desired size; a coating of glue, shellac, or other substance applied to a surface to prepare it for painting or other method of finish.

Sleeper—A timber laid on the ground to support a floor joist.

Span—The distance between the bearings of a timber or arch.

Specifications—The written or printed directions regarding the details of a building or other construction.

Splice—Joining of two similar members in a straight line.

Square—A tool used by mechanics to obtain accuracy; a term applied to a surface including 100 square feet.

Stairs, box—Those built between walls, and usually with no support except the wall.

Standing finish—Term applied to the finish of the openings and the base, and all other finish work necessary for the inside.

Stringer—A long horizontal timber in a structure supporting a floor.

Stucco—A fine plaster used for interior decoration and fine work; also for rough outside wall coverings.

Stud—An upright beam in the framework of a building.

Studding—The framework of a partition or the wall of a house; usually referred to as 2 by 4's.

Subfloor—A wood floor which is laid over the floor joists and on which the finished floor is laid.

Threshold—The beveled piece over which the door swings; sometimes called a carpet strip.

Tie beam (collar beam)—A beam so situated that it ties the principal rafters of a roof together and prevents them from thrusting the plate out of line.

Timber—Lumber with cross-section over 4 by 6 inches, such as posts, sills, and girders.

Tin shingle—A small piece of tin used in flashing and repairing a shingle roof.

Top plate—Piece of lumber supporting ends of rafters.

To the weather—A term applied to the projecting of shingles or siding beyond the course above.

Tread—The horizontal part of a step.

Trim—A term sometimes applied to outside or interior finished woodwork and the finish around openings.

Trimmer—The beam or floor joist into which a header is framed.

Trimming—Putting the inside and outside finish and hardware upon a building.

Truss—Structural framework of triangular units for supporting loads over long spans.

Valleys—The internal angle formed by the two slopes of a roof.

Verge boards—The boards which serve as the eaves finish on the gable end of a building.

Vestibule—An entrance to a house; usually inclosed.

Wainscoting—Matched boarding or panel work covering the lower portion of a wall.

Wale—A horizontal beam.

Wash—The slant upon a sill, capping, etc., to allow the water to run off easily.

Water table—The finish at the bottom of a house which carries water away from the foundation.

Wharf—A structure that provides berthing space for vessels, to facilitate loading and discharge of cargo.

Wind ("i" pronounced as in "kind")—A term used to describe the surface of a board when twisted (winding) or when resting upon two diagonally opposite corners, if laid upon a perfectly flat surface.

Wooden brick—Piece of seasoned wood, made the size of a brick, and laid where it is necessary to provide a nailing space in masonry walls.

INDEX